Human Behaviour
in the
Concentration Camp

Human Behaviour
in the
Concentration Camp

Elie A. Cohen
Translated from the Dutch
by M.H. Braaksma

With a new Preface by the author and a
Foreword by Dinora Pines

'an association in which the free development of each is the condition
of the free development of all'

Free Association Books / London / 1988

Published 1988 by
Free Association Books
26 Freegrove Road
London N7 9RQ

First published by Jonathan Cape 1954
Copyright © 1988 Dinora Pines for the Foreword
Copyright © 1988 Elie A. Cohen for the Preface

British Library Cataloguing in Publication Data
Cohen, Elie A. (Elie Aron)
    Human behaviour in the concentration camp.
    1. Europe. German concentration camps.
    Prisoners. Psychology
    I. Title
    155.9′62

ISBN 1-85343-047-1

Printed and bound in Great Britain by
Short Run Press Ltd, Exeter

A MEMORIAL
*to my beloved ones,
who were killed in Auschwitz*

On the basis of this book, the author received
the degree of Doctor of Medical Science from the
University of Utrecht. The degree was conferred
under the sponsorship of Dr H. C. Rümke,
professor of psychiatry.

Contents

Foreword (1988) by Dinora Pines   ix

Preface (1988) by Elie A. Cohen   xvii

Introduction   xxi

CHAPTER ONE

Some General Aspects of German Concentration
Camps   3

     THE TERM   3

     THE AIM   7

     ORGANIZATION   18

     THE LAYOUT   25

     THE PRISONERS   26

     EXTERMINATION OF HUMAN BEINGS   28
         Gas Chambers · Selection · Death Marches

CHAPTER TWO

Medical Aspects of the Concentration Camps   46

     MORTALITY   46

     NUTRITION   51

     THE SICK, THEIR ATTENDANTS, AND THEIR
     CARE   58

     THE DISEASES   63
         Infections · Frostbite · Diseases of the Respira-
         tory Organs · Diarrhoea · Acute Infectious Dis-
         eases · General Physical Weakness: Chronic Mal-
         nutrition · Injuries

     MEDICAL EXPERIMENTS ON PRISONERS   81
         High-Altitude Experiments · Freezing Experi-

ments · Malaria Experiments · Mustard and Phosgene Gas Experiments · Sulfanilamide Experiments · Bone, Muscle, and Nerve Regeneration and Bone Transplantation Experiments · Sea-Water Experiments · Typhus Experiments · Sterilization Experiments

JEWISH PRISONERS AS OBJECTS OF ȘTUDY ON BEHALF OF MEDICO-ANTHROPOLOGICAL SCIENCE   102

EUTHANASIA IN THE CONCENTRATION CAMPS   106

CHAPTER THREE

The Psychology of the Concentration-Camp Prisoner 115

THE STAGE OF INITIAL REACTION   115
THE STAGE OF ADAPTATION · *Hunger*   125
THE STAGE OF RESIGNATION   179
THE PRISONER AND GROUP PSYCHOLOGY   203

CHAPTER FOUR

The Psychology of the SS   211

THE ORIGIN OF THE SS   211
THE ORGANIZATION OF THE SS   212
THE IDEOLOGY OF THE SS   215
QUALIFICATIONS REQUIRED OF THE SS   223
THE SS A CRIMINAL ORGANIZATION   227
GERMAN EDUCATION   242
THE CAMP SS   246
THE SS AND GROUP PSYCHOLOGY   269

CHAPTER FIVE

Conclusions   277

Bibliography   285

Foreword (1988)

Eight years after his liberation from Ebensee concentration camp, Dr Elie Cohen published his medical thesis, 'Human behaviour in the concentration camp', which is now reissued as a book. Dr Cohen's thesis, written, as he himself states, out of an inner necessity, is one of the earliest detailed accounts of the general organization of these camps and their medical procedures, together with an account of the terrifying and grotesque 'pseudo-medical' experiments practised there. Detailed descriptions of the behaviour both of the prisoners and their SS guards whilst in the camps make this a most important document.

In attempting to understand human behaviour in this most gruesome of settings Dr Cohen, who is a general physician and not a psychoanalyst, has not only relied upon his study of Sigmund Freud's writings, but also on extensive reading of survivors' accounts and studies of the Holocaust, as the bibliography at the end of his book strikingly shows us. The inner necessity that impelled Dr Cohen to write his thesis is thus not only an attempt to observe, understand and master intellectually what was unthinkable before his Holocaust experience. It also represents a pressing attempt to mourn the destruction of his entire personal world, and thus to be freer to resume his life.

In my view such a tragic past can never be lost. Working with women survivors of the Holocaust has led me to believe that victims of massive psychic traumatization, where the real terror of annihilation was constantly present, could not avail themselves of normal human defences such as denial. The psychotic world of the camps, where progressive dehumanization of both aggressors and victims occurred, led to unintegrated terror, hopeless despair and, for the survivors, a traumatic loss of basic trust. Many continue to live in a double reality, the reality of their present life and the haunting reality of the camps where so many others perished. Psychoanalysis can help to alleviate the guilt of the survivor, but cannot entirely cure it.

In his original introduction Dr Cohen stresses his wish to remain objective in his book, and in order to achieve this he has given priority to the accounts of others rather than to his own. Yet the reader cannot remain objective. Despite the fact that so much has been written in the last thirty years describing the world of darkness that pervaded the camps, the impact of Dr Cohen's book, his thoughtful observations of prisoners, their guards and their behaviour arouse shock, horror and anger at man's senseless inhumanity to man. In *Civilization and its Discontents*, Sigmund Freud, a man of wide European culture educated in 19th-century Vienna, expressed his doubts about the solidity of cultural development in the face of human nature. He wrote: 'The existence of this inclination to aggression which we can detect in ourselves and justly assume to be present in others is the factor which disturbs our relations with our neighbours. In consequence of this primary mutual hostility of human beings civilized society is perpetually threatened with disintegration.' Dr Cohen's book about his Holocaust experiences and suffering bears eloquent witness to the profound truth of Freud's pessimistic statement. For European culture, which had seemed to be so rich and fruitful, disintegrated under the impact of human barbarism that the Nazi regime unleashed.

The ideals of the 18th-century European Age of Enlightenment – faith and reason, love of humanity, belief in progress – had brought a new freedom of thought to Europe. Jews who had been confined to ghettos, both physically and intellectually, by the peoples amongst whom they lived embraced this new philosophy with fervour, since it enabled them to struggle for emancipation from the oppression in which they had lived. The Jewish tradition of honouring scholarship and learning integrated well with the new ideals, the belief in the power of rational thought and culture. Cultured Europeans such as Freud, Thomas Mann and their contemporaries believed that education would bring about man's inner liberation from prejudice and ignorance, transcending all differences of nationality, faith and religion through the unfolding of the individual personality. Thus Freud's work on the psychopathology of man, with its focus upon the individual, was in keeping with the cultural climate in which Freud lived.

Yet educated man's pursuit of the idea of rational thought and understanding could not prevail against the more powerful forces of irrationality, violence and narcissistic rage that followed the defeat of Germany and Austria in the First World War. Psychoanalysis, which is based on the careful observation of human behaviour, inevitably acknowledges the presence of powerful and primitive conscious and unconscious instinctive forces in every human being. The pursuit of the good and of the ideal, the powerful life forces of Eros, are paralleled by destructive and self-destructive impulses in each individual and in each nation. The outcome of this human conflict will depend upon our capacity to integrate our own destructive impulses, and to maintain the positive aspects of human ambivalence. It is all the more impressive that Dr Cohen, despite the senseless tragedy that shattered his life and despite the dehumanizing experience of the concentration camp, returns to his earlier stance of an educated European eight years later.

Thus the inner necessity that impelled Dr Cohen to write his book is not only an attempt to bring rational thought to bear on all that is irrational in his experience, but is also an opportunity for the reader to seek answers. For, as I have suggested, the author writing his thesis was not only to observe, understand, and by working through master what was unthinkable before his Holocaust experience, but also to mourn the destruction of his entire personal world. The reader is also moved to mourn the disintegration of European culture, which ended in genocide, the glorification of a barbarous ideology which culminated in the destruction of millions of dehumanized human beings, and the triumph of human evil over goodness.

Dr Cohen's life experience has its antecedents in the treatment of European Jews following their emancipation from ghetto life. Jews, educated in the humanistic traditions of European culture, became identified with the intellectual's revived faith in the power of rational thought and learning, and strove to maintain it throughout their life. Yet at the same time they were made to be aware of their dual identity by the people amongst whom they continued to live. Kafka reflected this predicament in his books: it was the predicament of an educated Czech with an identity forced upon him by his fellow citizens – that of the Jew, the perpetual outsider on trial for a crime that he has committed by the accident of birth. Sigmund Freud, to whom Dr Cohen turns in order to reach an intellectual understanding of the Holocaust experience, struggled with this dual identity throughout his own life. As an assimilated Jew he internalized and identified with German culture and learning; on the other hand, as the son of a Jewish family he was forced to accept the identity that his Austrian compatriots gave him, that of a second-class citizen, from which neither intellectual ability nor faith in his own professional merit could ever free him. What followed in the next generation of Europeans was the murderous acting out of the antisemitism that had always existed and been written about in the previous generation. Its antecedents had lain in the persecution of European Jews throughout the centuries. In our own century 6,000,000 European Jewish adults and children were sadistically destroyed.

Rational enquiry and analysis, together with his great discovery of the force of unconscious wishes, drives and fears, enabled Freud to attempt to expose them and oppose rational understanding to the maturational forces that led to prejudice and dehumanization of the outsider. For these had not yet been fully acted out in such a way in his lifetime. Despite this, Dr Cohen, when faced with the disintegration of his world, turns to his profound reading of Freud in an attempt to bring education, rational thought, and understanding to bear upon it. He rightly focuses upon the transmission of parental views and values that forms the German character; in particular, submission to a tyrannical father and his views. Nevertheless, I think he fails to appreciate the depth and importance of Teutonic myth and fantasy, which is also transmitted. These are myths concerning the mighty task attributed to the blond Aryan people, whose heroic struggle must culminate in the destruction of the satanic outsider, to whom all evil is attributed. Thus the Nazi ideology, through which blond Aryans were commanded to overcome their humanity in order to destroy the dark Jewish outsider, was also part of the fantasy life of children. Yet in my view each individual normally has some freedom to choose good or evil in his life: a point to which I shall return.

Dr Cohen rightly focuses upon the question of the quality of the superego in his camp guards. It enabled them to dehumanize and destroy fellow human beings in the course of their duties and still remain fond fathers and husbands. What enabled medical professors to conduct senseless pseudo-medical experiments, or distinguished visitors to an extermination camp to watch their fellow men's death throes in a gas chamber as if it were an entertainment, and then enjoy wine and a good dinner afterwards without conflict or guilt? Dr Cohen thus asks the question that remains in the mind of the reader. What was it that unconsciously contributed to the fact that thousands of normal human beings throughout Europe colluded with a government that attacked freedom of thought; who could observe humanity in their family relations and yet, unchecked by morality, dehumanize those whom it degraded, imprisoned and murdered? Dr Cohen does not exempt himself, and rightly expresses his own submission to a system in which the individual becomes dulled and loses his own capacity to choose good or evil in an effort to remain alive himself. He destroys our omnipotent and idealized wish to believe that human goodness can survive in himself or others when human beings are treated in this way.

It is impressive to read his account, which he writes objectively, without anger. Yet the reader is inevitably moved to pain, depression and despair at man's inhumanity to man, as if he must express these powerful feelings for the writer. In this way Dr Cohen's writing reflects many survivors' difficulty in expressing powerful feelings for themselves. My clinical experience in working with survivors of the Holocaust leads me to believe that the survivor's anger is deeply repressed and expressed through others, such as the analyst in the analytical situation – since anger would have led to death in the camps.

In my view true mourning cannot be achieved if anger is repressed. For anger with the beloved lost object, or anger with its murderer, must be experienced and worked through before mourning can be achieved. Dr Cohen's new preface, written over thirty years later, shows us that something has changed. Time has allowed him to express his anger, his outrage at what had happened to European Jewry, and his own guilt at his participation in the selection of the victims. Yet there is a vast difference between the actions of the prisoner doctors who had no choice between good and evil if they wished to survive, and the actions of the German SS doctors who chose to participate in cruel and senseless experiments. In his study of these doctors many years later, Lifton concluded that their actions were connected to some kind of perversion. The perverse aspects of their own psychopathology enabled these men to destroy the boundary between healing and killing. The Nazi ideological justification for their actions shielded them from a conflict of guilt, since Jews were regarded as a gangrene that must be destroyed. The SS doctors obviously frightened their own people by their actions; Dr Cohen remarks that the SS personnel always turned to prisoner physicians for medical help, since they recognized that their own doctors were killers!

Finally, Dr Cohen's new preface strikingly illustrates the central task of all victims of massive psychic trauma now facing old age and death. Henry Krystal, himself a survivor, suggests that accepting one's final task – of coming to terms with one's life – is particularly difficult for the survivor. He suggests that acceptance of the Nazi brutality calls to mind submission to Nazi persecution, with all its helplessness, shame and pain. Self-healing contributing to personal integration becomes equated with giving Hitler a final victory. My clinical experience in working with survivors of the Holocaust has made me aware of their difficulties in expressing the affects appropriate to their tragic plight, in particular the rage and protest at the loss of the beloved person that are necessary for the completion of mourning. Psychotherapy where the analyst can attempt to alleviate and share the patient's burden may enable some of these affects to be expressed.

Dr Cohen's enraged protest at his future Queen marrying a German and the subsequent lifting of the repression of affects which would have led to death in the camps led to a coronary thrombosis two weeks later. It affected the victim rather than the persecutors, many of whom are living a guiltless, healthy and vigorous old age. However, his struggle to survive and remember, despite his despair, can only lead us to identify with him and his human feelings, and to share his outraged protest against the disintegration of European culture. Dr Cohen is an eyewitness to the evil that is inherent in human nature and which cost him and millions of others so dear. We must learn from his book not only to remember what has happened in the recent past, but to remain aware and vigilant in order to fight against its re-emergence in the future.

DINORA PINES
Member of the British Psycho-Analytical Society

References

Freud, S. (1930) *Civilization and its Discontents*, in James Strachey, ed. *The Standard Edition of the Complete Psychological Works of Sigmund Freud*, 24 vols. London: Hogarth, 1953-73. vol. 21, pp. 57-46.

Krystal, H. (1984) 'Interpretation and self-healing in post-traumatic states', in S. Luel and P. Marcus, eds *Psychoanalytic Reflections on the Holocaust*. New York: Ktav Publishing House, pp. 113-33.

Lifton, R.J. (1984) 'Medicalized killing in Auschwitz', in S. Luel and P. Marcus, eds *Psychoanalytic Reflections on the Holocaust*. New York: Ktav Publishing House, pp. 11-33.

Pines, D. (1986) 'Working with women survivors of the Holocaust'. *Int. J. Psycho-Anal.* 67: 295-307.

Preface (1988)

When I wrote my doctor's thesis in 1952, published in book form as *Human Behaviour in the Concentration Camp*, everything I had suffered from in the concentration camps was still vivid in my mind. But in spite of that I tried very hard to readapt myself to normal life in The Netherlands: I remarried, had two children, and was very active in rebuilding a practice as a general practitioner. I judged most things from the point of view of the concentration camp mentality: it meant that very few events gave me a shock. As time went by I got the feeling that I had adapted myself pretty well to normal life, and was living in a rather normal way, but there were still some remnants: I did not pay a visit to Germany, nor did I buy German goods; and I still judged people according to their behaviour during the war. I began to think that the time of war had been only an incident in my life.

Until lightning struck me: the marriage of our Crown Princess to a German, in March 1966. I felt this as a personal offence, as if my own daughter were to marry a German. I was active in protest committees, and initially had the feeling that a large part of the Dutch people shared my opinion.

Until the wedding day, that is: then I drove through the town of Arnhem, a sea of flags. I had to admit that I stood alone, with only a little minority of the Dutch people on my side. I had to accept my defeat; the psychological shock was very hard, and a fortnight later I had a coronary. The connection between the two facts was very clear to me, and from that moment on I became interested in the consequences of the sufferings in the German concentration camps. I called this disease post-concentration camp syndrome, having myself experienced the way in which the symptoms could be repressed for many years by leading a busy, normal life.

I had not realized that the humiliations which the Germans had inflicted on me as a Jew, and the suffering in different German camps, would have lifelong consequences. A smell, a photograph, a remark would cause violent reactions recalling the past. And though many memories have faded in the course of the years, and many sharp edges worn off, the aftermath of the war still exists. In short: time does not alleviate all grief.

The Jews who lived in the countries occupied by Nazi Germany were subjected to the measures of the *Endlösung der Judenfrage* ('the final solution of the Jewish question'). In my opinion we must use the German expressions for the greatest murder in the history of mankind, the murder of six million Jews. That's why I don't speak about Holocaust, final solution, Shoah, genocide. Germans planned and carried out the murder of the Jews. The correspondence and the orders were written in the German language. In every other language they lose their aim and sharpness.

To camouflage their criminal purpose the Germans even used a special terminology. They spoke about *Umsiedlung* (resettlement) and *Arbeitseinsatz* (mobilization of labour), but meant deportation. *SB* or *Sonderbehandlung* (special treatment) and *GU* or *Gesonderte Unterbringung* (separate accommodation) stood for gassing. The specially constructed gassing vans were called *Entlausungswagen* (delousing wagons) or *Sonderwagen* (special wagons), or simply *S-Wagen*.

Over the years I have had a number of explanations about why I managed to survive the concentration camps. The most important of them, as I see it now, was my egoism. Let me say what I mean by this. In my function as a transport doctor in Westerbork, a Jewish transit camp in The Netherlands, I saw the departure of a train packed with Jews on their way to the 'East' every week for eight months; we called it that as we did not know its destination. For example, 19 trains containing 34,313 Jews (of whom 19 survived) departed for Sobibor without the name of Sobibor being mentioned. I am sure of this, as I was present at the departure of all 19 trains.

Being a transport doctor in Westerbork I had the power to hold back individuals who were designated for transport. On medical grounds I could give them a certificate that they were 'unfit for transport', so that they could stay in Westerbork for at least another week.

In the beginning I was very liberal with these certificates, and declared that many people had a high fever, or were suffering from fainting fits or other serious diseases. Thus I could save many people – until I was unmasked. A controller proved that most of the cases were fakes, and the chief doctor, who was a Jew, told me, 'If you do it again, you and your family will have to go on transport.' From that moment on I worked honestly, though now and then I made some 'mistakes'; it was my egoism that led me to this decision, because I wanted to stay in The Netherlands.

At that time I did not know anything about the *Endlösung der Judenfrage*. I did not know that in Auschwitz about 85 percent, and in Sobibor more than 90 percent, of the transports went directly to the gas chambers. Furthermore, it is important for me to say: I was not corrupt; I did not give certificates for money, gold, diamonds, women.

As a rule the transports were an emotional affair because relatives, friends and acquaintances would be leaving and we did not know what was in store for them. But after their departure I took a shower, went to bed for a rest, and in the evening went to a cabaret performance and amused myself. I admit that I had forgotten the train with the Jews on their way to an unknown destination. I was glad that it had not been my turn, and for some days I forgot the next deportation train. I trusted entirely to my function in Westerbork, thinking that I was absolutely safe. This feeling of safety lulled me to sleep; I did my work as a doctor and transports were for others, not for me.

Until the moment came that I too had to get into the train with my family, calmly. Yes, calmly indeed, because (and I have to emphasize this fact) I did not know what lay beyond Westerbork.

When I learned the truth in Auschwitz, and knew that my wife and my little son of four had been gassed, my reaction was not one of grief, or despair, or there being no reason for me to carry on any more. No, on the contrary, I fought for my life. I wanted to survive, and I went as far as assisting the German camp doctor with the selections. It is an experience I described in a book I later wrote,

The Abyss: A Confession. I know that it was a choice between life and death, and I chose life.

But now, many years later, free from danger, I realize that I did dirty work for the SS. The price was too high, I besmeared my conscience: I should have drawn the line at my willingness to collaborate. I think that I went across that line. On the other hand, I should not forget that I was able to help many inmates because of my position, and I did so. But knowing all this now, I am not sure if I would act differently in the same circumstances.

It is curious that I suffer from feelings of guilt about things I have done under unimaginable conditions, while the perpetrators, the criminal SS, the murderers of the Jews, don't have these feelings of guilt. They explain their misdeeds by saying that *they only did their duty*; they had to carry out their superiors' orders and show unconditional obedience. Responsibility lay with the men who gave the orders, not with them. And therefore they were not guilty.

From The Netherlands about 60,000 Jews were deported to Auschwitz; 1,052 survived and I am one of them. In Groningen, my place of birth, there lived 2,842 Jews at the beginning of the war; 2,550 of them were deported to Poland. Only ten returned and I was one of them.

The number of survivors of the *Endlösung der Judenfrage* is small and getting smaller and smaller. We are irreplaceable eyewitnesses, passing away. When we are gone, nobody can tell the truth from his or her experience any more. I feel and consider it to be my duty to do so as long as I can.

That's why I welcome the many publications about the *Endlösung der Judenfrage*, in order that the complete truth will be known, and the world warned of 'the depths of misery, madness and criminality to which man is capable of descending'. This is how I put it in *The Abyss* fifteen years ago, and it remains true today.

ELIE A. COHEN
Arnhem, 1988

References

Cohen, E. (1973) *The Abyss: A Confession.* New York: Norton.
— (1981) 'The post-concentration camp syndrome: a disaster syndrome', *Science and Public Policy*, June, pp. 239–46.

Introduction

ANY WRITER of a book on German concentration camps is under no delusion that nowadays there is a great deal of general interest in the subject. Though it is only a very few years since the survivors left these camps, thanks to the military defeat of Germany, and the world learned of the horrors that had occurred, interest in them is very much on the wane. This was already noted by Federn in 1946, when he wondered: "Will my work be accorded the same interest as it would have been immediately after the fall of Hitler?" (42, p. 80).

There are many publications on concentration camps, but only in a small number of these has any attempt been made to explain them. Particularly in the Netherlands there is a notable paucity of scientific works whose aim is explanation rather than statement. To write the present book was felt by me as an inner necessity; this is one of the reasons why I am grateful for the opportunity to have it published in the form of a medical thesis. I experienced in my own person what a concentration camp was,[1] and I am of the opinion that every-

---

[1] August 13, 1942: Arrested (through betrayal) for an unsuccessful attempt to escape to Sweden.
August 14, 1942–October 23, 1942: Confined in prison at Amsterdam.
October 23, 1942–December 8, 1942: "Polizeiliches Durchgangslager Amersfoort" (concentration camp Amersfoort, Netherlands). Abbreviation: P.D.A.
December 8, 1942–September 14, 1943: "Judendurchgangslager Westerbork" (Transit Camp for Jews Westerbork, Netherlands).
September 16, 1943–January 18, 1945: Concentration camp Auschwitz I.[a]
January 18, 1945: Beginning of the death march.[a]
End of January 1945: Arrival in Mauthausen.
Early February–early April, 1945: Melk, "Outside camp"[a] of the concentration camp Mauthausen.
End of April, 1945: Transport to Ebensee, "Outside camp"[a] of the concentration camp Mauthausen.
May 6, 1945: Liberated by Americans at Ebensee.
[a] These terms will be described later in the text.

one who is in a position to do so should add his contribution to our knowledge of the German concentration camps.

The aim of this book is not a warning to humanity, nor the publication of any scientific discovery, but rather to provide an explanation for what happened in the concentration camps to the best of my ability; as I have as a rule taken my experiences of Auschwitz as my starting point, my considerations will often bear reference to this camp. This is not necessarily a disadvantage, as Auschwitz had all the general characteristics of a concentration camp, differing only from others—and each concentration camp differed in some way from another—in the wholesale gassing of human beings that took place there.

After giving a general impression, without an attempt at exhaustiveness, of what a concentration camp was like, I propose to deal with some of its medical aspects. After that I will go on to my real aim: to find a psychological explanation for the behaviour of the camp prisoners and an answer to the question, How did the SS come to be capable of the inhuman acts they committed? These explanations will be based on Freud's theory of psychoanalysis.

I realize that I am under certain disadvantages for the fulfilment of so difficult a task; in the first place because as a general practitioner I lack the special psychiatric training which would have made it so much easier. This disadvantage I hope to have overcome by thorough study.

It might be further objected that I have restricted myself to studying the literature relative to my subject and have refrained from interviewing groups of individuals. As far as my statements on the prisoners are concerned, this does not seem to me a serious drawback, because of the regular contact I have maintained with my former fellow sufferers; as to the SS, my statements have been based on authoritative written sources. With this, I admit, the defects have not been made good.

The next difficulty is of far greater import: since Nazi Germany, to be more specific the SS, murdered all those who were dear to me, thus inflicting a sorrow upon me from which I have not yet recovered, and because of what I went through in German concentration camps, there is still the danger that lack of objectivity may prevent me from viewing the problems I have set myself to solve in their true proportions. In order to avoid this danger as much as possible—in furtherance, therefore, of objectivity—I have often given priority to the accounts of others rather than to my own; this procedure, however, is likely to be little more than a shifting of the difficulty, as none of the one-time prisoners can have succeeded in ridding themselves entirely of the subjective view. In spite of earnest endeavors on my part to avoid being subjective, it still remains possible that personal rancour may cause an occasional resurgence of the subjective view. Still, I think, there cannot be any insuperable objection to my attempting to form an opinion; for the very reason that no one who has not had any personal experience of a German concentration camp can possibly have any conception of concentration-camp life, an attempt attempt on my part at an analysis of this life appears expedient. Once again I experienced the indignities that were inflicted on me, and again I was bowed down by the violence of grief. This was a burden not to be lightly taken up once more, a burden to which Vrijhof, who was never in a concentration camp, refers in these words: "There may perhaps be people able and willing to muster sufficient strength and courage, to live through again and reflect on these circumstances" (150, p. 83).

Thus I have experienced mentally my imprisonment, and all that it entailed once more, so that much that had been repressed emerged again into my conscious mind. Because this effected the emotional relief of a catharsis, I did derive personal benefit from it. In many ex-prisoners this black period in their lives remains repressed, with all its after effects. This period during which they were hurt, insulted, humiliated, and tortured cannot be expunged from their minds. They feel misunderstood, and it is their daily experience that society refuses to make allowances for their sufferings in the concentration camps. If with this book I should, though without premeditation, effect a better understanding of my fellow sufferers, I should regard this as a considerable gain.

I am aware that this work is not perfect. As I was naturally restricted to the field of medical psychology, the sociological, criminological, historical, and political aspects have not, or only too briefly, been considered. It appears most important to me that light will have been thrown on these aspects by those who are qualified to do so. Apart from these imperfections I am aware of the incompleteness of my work. This, however, was inevitable: concentration-camp life revealed all the affects of the soul in unprecedented rawness. It goes without saying that it would have been impossible to deal with every affect within the scope of a single book; therefore I have confined myself to those which I deem to be the most significant.

Human Behaviour
in the
Concentration Camp

Some General Aspects of German Concentration Camps

The Term

To THE term concentration camp (contractions: K.L. and K.Z.) [1] various individuals have attached various degrees of significance. Three categories of individuals must be distinguished:

(a) *People who never were inmates of any camp;* according to my estimate, this group numbers at least 95 per cent of the people of the Netherlands.

De Wind has pointed out how comparatively soon the desire of this group to read about concentration camps was dulled, and he is amazed at "how little is known to the people of the Netherlands of what actually took place, especially in Polish camps, such as Auschwitz" (155, p. 1).

On the one hand he accounts for this by the fact that it is far from pleasant "to be constantly reminded of the sufferings of other people and thus often experiencing the feeling that one has failed, either in actual fact, or only in the imagination, in one's duty toward those who have perished or have suffered much" (156, p. 1). On the other hand, he suggests this explanation: "whoever shortly after their liberation wrote about their

---

[1] K.L. was the official contraction of "Konzentrationslager" (concentration camp); K.Z. was the contraction used by the prisoners.

own experiences did so in the first place to unburden their own troubled minds. By writing about the camps one overcame one's pent-up feelings." Therefore it is understandable, according to De Wind, "that the reader, who thus had to take the author's burden upon his own shoulders, very soon felt he had had enough" (156, p. 1).

This is undoubtedly true, but also Minkowski's opinion on this subject appears to me to be of great significance. Minkowski seeks to conceive the state of mind of those who came back from the concentration camps. The only effective method, according to him, is the "diagnostic par pénétration" (diagnosis by penetration). Thus he states that "we ourselves, the one more, the other less, have been affected by the events, and our own personalities have as a result, in various degrees, been changed"; and he goes on to say that "ourselves to a certain extent victims, we lack in ourselves the vibrations essential for a true and deep penetration" (108, pp. 281 f.).

Minkowski therefore admits that, owing to the sufferings he had himself experienced, it was impossible for him to conceive completely what the victims in the concentration camps had gone through. Here we are already confronted by the idea which is common to many ex-prisoners, viz. that their experiences in concentration camps can never be fully appreciated.

Vroom (149, p. 94) has come to much the same conclusion. Referring to the air raids he witnessed, he notes that those who have never had personal experience of such raids always fail to appreciate the emotions of those who have.

Even the various groups that have come back from Germany fail to understand one another. As Minkowski points out: "In our days, apart from geographical boundaries, *psychological boundaries* between man and man have sprung up. They are the result of experiences that have been lived through. Repatriated prisoners, deportees on political or racial grounds who afterwards escaped, those who were forced to work in Germany, those who have known occupation and persecution on the spot, have constituted groups who do not always understand each other" (108, p. 282).

It is surely asking too much that those who have never known what it is to be an inmate in a camp should realize to the full what a concentration camp actually was. For this large group the word "concentration camp" means something that might aptly be compared to the significance that the word "death" conveys to many people. I deliberately except those who, as a result of their religious belief, have formed a well-defined image of death. To others death is often something terrifying, a dark hole, into which they do not care to look, because they are afraid.

In fact, there is a very close resemblance between death and the concentration camp, because for many people being in a concentration camp literally meant death. It is not, however, this resemblance I meant to stress, but the fact that many people face the conception of a concentration camp with fear, refusing to think of it, repressing the very thought of it. For these people, therefore, the word "concentration camp" signifies something mysterious, from which they mentally shrink. This is the group of people who say to the victims: "You should stop thinking of it now. You have got to live on."

(b) *Those who were placed in other than concentration camps:* as, for example, prisoner-of-war camps, camps for hostages, and so-called "Vorzugslager" (preference camps). These people have had actual experience of camp life and can to a certain degree picture what a concentration camp was like. They generally realize that they have been spared the worst, especially if their camp adjoined a concentration camp. Herzberg, who kept a diary in Bergen Belsen, notes this in the following entry: "It is clear that one should avoid any accusation of sabotage, for sabotage means at least K.Z. And concentration camp means being tortured to death" (67, p. 54).

(c) *The group of ex-inmates of concentration camps: the prisoners.* For these people the word "concentration camp" is pregnant with the personal memories which it continually recalls to their minds. They are convinced that it will always remain extraordinarily difficult to bring home to the two other groups what the reality of life in a concentration camp was and how it has affected them. Frankl quotes a most touching remark made by an ex-prisoner: "To those others we shall never be able to make it clear what happened inside our minds —and what is still happening there" (46, p. 13).

And this from Rousset: "Normal people do not know that anything is possible. Even if the accounts of eyewitnesses force their minds to accept, their bodies refuse to believe. The prisoners from the concentration camp know. . . . They are divided from others by an experience which it is impossible to transmit" (127, pp. 181 f.).

There are statements to the same effect by Miss Adelsberger (2, p. 125), Hunsche (75, p. 6), and Mrs. Lingens-Reiner (102, p. 15 f.). The existence of a gulf between ex-concentration-camp prisoners and the rest of mankind is also admitted by those who, though not themselves prisoners, have been willing to make a thorough study of the conditions that prevailed in concentration camps. Thus Minkowski, relating the arrival of transports in Auschwitz: "And here we are on the threshold of the camp. We dare not enter, so terribly does life in the camp appear to surpass our power of imagination" (108, p. 288).

And Gilbert, who, in his function of prison psychologist attended the Nuremberg trials of Göring and the rest, remarks: "Certainly life in that world cannot be conceived of by those who have never lived in it. The mute evidence of what transpired in those camps was incredible even to those who saw it in the last months of the war" (61, p. 240). The word "concentration camp" has, for this group, an extraordinary significance, and it should be noted that the ex-prisoners will always designate the camp of which they once were inmates by the name of the place where the camp was situated. If asked where they spent the war years, they will not reply, "In a concentration camp" but "In Amersfoort, Vught, Buchenwald, Auschwitz," etc. It is the name of the place where they often spent years of their lives and to which they are bound by ties of memory. The name of the place has grown into a conception with an even stronger emotional effect than the word "concentration camp."

The Aim

After Hitler's assumption of power, the concentration camps were established by Göring in 1933. In an interview with Gilbert on February 2, 1946, Göring stated: "as police chief of Prussia I arrested thousands of Communists. That is why I set up the concentration camps in the first place—to keep the Communists under control" (60, p. 131).

Bettelheim's statement is more comprehensive: "When the concentration camps were first established the Nazis detained in them their more prominent foes" (17, p. 441). And when the supply of these began to give out, because they had either fled or died: "Still an institution was needed to threaten the opponents of the system" (17, p. 441).

Kogon is of the same opinion, and states as the main object: "*To eliminate every real or supposed opponent* of National Socialist domination. To isolate, to defame, to humiliate, to crush, and to annihilate. This had at the same time another desired effect: The intimidation of 90 per cent of the population. Thus it was expected to nip any form of opposition in the bud" (87, pp. 25 f.).

Also in *German Crimes in Poland* the aim of concentration camps is stated as being "the extermination of resisting elements and as a means of terrorizing the whole population" (32, p. 15).

The population was the more easily terrorized as the camps were established in secluded regions and sealed off. Only sporadically did facts about conditions in the camps penetrate into the outside world. Neither did the letters which prisoners wrote to their families contain any information on this subject, for "it was forbidden to give information about the camp itself, labour, or living conditions" (75, pp. 51 f.). And those who left the concentration camps alive told but little. Before their release they had to sign a statement to the effect that they had been treated well, and to pledge themselves not to tell any outsider about the actual conditions in the camps; any breach of this pledge would have resulted in their being taken back to the K.Z. (see also 75, p. 155); this last threat especially must have been very effective in sealing the lips of many ex-prisoners.

The lack of official statements, together with the news that filtered through occasionally, prepared a soil from which rumour easily arose. Most people refused to believe what they were told, considering it impossible. On the other hand, they could not simply ignore it. This very uncertainty helped considerably to inspire the population with the fear of concentration camps and to keep this fear alive.

Only the death notices could be checked. They were not long in coming after the first victims had been taken to the camps. The causes of death as officially stated were often impossible to believe if they related to physically sound young men. Distrust became intense when the cause of death that was mentioned was manifestly false, such as death from appendicitis of a person whose appendix was known to have been removed years ago.

A single instance of the rate at which men were slaughtered should be mentioned here.

On March 4, 1941 (116), Rauter reported to Himmler and to the "Reich Commissioner" Seyss-Inquart: In consequence of Jewish provocation culminating in Jewish resistance to a raid by the Security Police on an ice-cream shop in Amsterdam, after reference to Himmler and the Reich Commissioner, 425 Jewish hostages were arrested, on February 22 and 23, 1941, of ages ranging from twenty to thirty-five. On Thursday, February 27, 420 of these men were transported to the concentration camp Buchenwald. Shortly afterwards they were retransported to the concentration camp Mauthausen. From a photostat of a "Survey of prisoners detained as of today (account-day December 28, 1941) added as an appendix to the secret weekly report of the German Security Service and Security Police, information from the Netherlands" (115, p. 13), it appears that of the 420 healthy young Jewish men only 8 were still alive on that date.[2] The Netherlands State Institute of War Docu-

---

[2] This conclusion by the Netherlands State Institute for War Documentation is wrong, as in 1941 more raids on Jews had been made: in June, 1941, at Amsterdam, in October, 1941, in the east of the Netherlands. Of all these per-

mentation comments that of the whole group only one came back alive (116, p. 6). This man happened to be ill at the moment when those of the group who were then still alive were retransported to Mauthausen, and was left behind in Buchenwald. He relates his experiences in *Nederland in Oorlogstijd* (February, 1947). Like Kogon (87, p. 157), he relates that he owed his life to the courage of German fellow prisoners.

That the Germans deliberately used the threat of concentration camps as a means of intimidation appears from the following German announcement in an extra edition of *The Jewish Weekly* published by the Jewish Council for Amsterdam, on August 7, 1942:

(1) All Jews who do not instantly obey the order to go to Germany to ease the labour situation there, will be . . . sent to the concentration camp Mauthausen.

(2) All Jews who do not wear the Jews' star, . . . to the concentration camp Mauthausen. . . .

(3) All Jews who . . . move to another town or into another house . . . to the concentration camp Mauthausen (153, p. 152).

As a result of the mystery that shrouded everything that took place inside the camps, the threat of being sent there became even more potent. Consequently the population lived in constant terror of the concentration camps. Whether this terror could have been intensified if the population had known what actually took place can be disregarded for the simple reason that the Germans did not want it known.

Apart from eliminating opponents and intimidating possible opponents, the concentration camp served as a training ground for the SS, who were here made to shed every human response to the sufferings of their victims. The result was that "after having been guards in the camp for some time, they got accustomed to inhuman behaviour, they became 'conditioned' to it; it then became part of their 'real' life" (17, p. 432).

Alexander confirms this: "The peculiar process of indoctrination in crime and cruelty which young men went through

---

sons, whose number is estimated at about 900 by Herzberg (68, p. 97), only eight were alive on December 28, 1941.

in concentration camps after they had joined the SS constituted the 'hardening process,' the 'brutalization course' which the SS organization regarded as essential for transforming its personnel into willing and reliable tools for its criminal purposes" (7, p. 301).

By starving the prisoners and giving them little or no pay an enormous quantity of very cheap labour became available. After the introduction of the total "Arbeitseinsatz" (employment of labour) in 1942 this cheap labour became a matter of outstanding importance for the economic system of Germany. In order to use it to the greatest possible advantage the "Arbeitseinsatz" in 1942 appointed a representative in the concentration camps, the "Arbeitseinsatzführer" (Manpower Utilization Officer).

During the war the concentration camps served another aim: *the extermination of the Jews in the countries under German domination.* The extermination of large numbers was undertaken in a few camps only, such as Auschwitz, Maidanek. The number of Jews that were murdered in Nazi Germany can only be estimated. There is one man, according to Rudolf Hoess, commander of the Auschwitz concentration camp from May 1, 1940, to December, 1943, who could give exact information (142, Vol. XI, p. 397); this is one Eichmann, chief of sub-office IV B-4 of the RSHA (Reich Security Main Office),[3] where all Jewish affairs were handled. It is now known that by the end of August, 1944, Eichmann declared: "In the various extermination camps about four million Jews must have been killed, another two millions having died from other causes, of which number the greater part were shot by the 'Einsatzkommandos' (Special Task Force) of the Security Police[4] during the Russian campaign."[5]

[3] "The 'Reich Security Main Office' dealt with all organizational, personal, economic, and technical affairs of the Security Police and the Security Service. It is also the central office of the state police and criminal police executive, as well as the central management of Intelligence Service of the Security Service" (142, Vol. XXXI, p. 45).
[4] Sicherheitspolizei (Security Police) is Sipo; there were two subdivisions; Kriminalpolizei (Criminal Police), or Kripo, and Geheime Staatspolizei (Secret State Police), or Gestapo.
[5] Affidavit by W. Höttl, speaker and deputy chief in Office VI of the RSHA— 142, Vol. XXXI, p. 86. ("The Office VI of the RSHA was the so-called Aus-

From this statement it is clear that as early as August, 1944, Eichmann put the number of Jews murdered at six millions. Eichmann himself has disappeared, and it is doubtful whether his statistics, from which the exact numbers might be ascertained, will ever be found. Consequently the only conclusion that is justified at this moment is that at least six million European Jews were murdered by Nazi Germany. The number of Netherlands Jews killed can be computed with a reasonable degree of accuracy. According to the report of the "Pakkettencommissie" [6] "Of approximately 140,000 Jews in the Netherlands 110,000 were deported, of which number only 6,000 have returned" (122, p. 12). It is further known that of more than 60,000 Netherlands Jews sent to Auschwitz, about 500 returned (11, p. 8); 34,313 were sent to Sobibor, of whom 19 returned (134, p. 3).

Statistical Data on Jews in the Netherlands issued by the Jewish Council of Amsterdam in 1942 shows that on August 22 of the previous year, 140,552 people had registered themselves as "pure Jews" (11, p. 4). At the May 31, 1947, census 14,346 people were registered members of the Netherlands Israelitic Church; [7] this number is no exact reflection of the actual number of Netherlands Jews who have survived the war, as some would not register as Jews or had emigrated. It is not known whether there were many of these or few, but the figures as stated show unmistakably how enormous was the massacre of Jews in the Netherlands.

Investigation by Blokker and Broekman on behalf of the Netherlands Red Cross (12) and based on the available remains of the accounts of camp Westerbork,[8] a photostat of the accounts of Block 12 of the men's camp at Birkenau [9] (the so-

landsamt [Foreign Office] of the Security Service and dealt with the intelligence service in every country of the world" [142, Vol. XXXI, p. 85]).

[6] The "Pakkettencommissie" was a committee established to investigate the charge that, if more Red Cross parcels had been sent to Netherlands prisoners in Germany, many lives would probably have been saved.

[7] A. Pais, "De Joden in Nederland" in *De Joodse Wachter*, 43rd year of publication, no. 3, p. 17.

[8] Westerbork, in the northeast of the Netherlands, was a camp where Netherlands Jews were collected before being transported to Germany.

[9] The concentration camp Auschwitz was administratively subdivided into: Auschwitz I—Stammlager; Auschwitz II—Birkenau (this camp contained the

called "Krankenbau" or sick bay of the camp) from January, 1942, to August 19, 1942, and of the Auschwitz Death Book,[10] into the fate of the first 13 transports from Westerbork to Auschwitz reveal the following facts:

Altogether from June 15, 1942 to August 24, 1942 11,172 people were transported from Westerbork to Auschwitz; of these, 27 men and 2 women returned alive, In those days the Germans had at their disposal only a crudely built gas chamber, so that the majority of the victims must have died in the camps of hunger, exhaustion, torture, and illness. The report also states that "The accounts of Block 12 are . . . representative of the whole of the men's camp. Not only deaths in the sick bay but also deaths elsewhere in the men's camp Birkenau have been recorded in the accounts of Block 12" (12, p. 8). The final conclusion is that "the camp population present on a certain date (during the period under consideration) must have become extinct in just over sixteen weeks. The picture this presents, however, is far from being a reflection of the actual facts . . . as the death rate varied a great deal in the different categories of prisoners. As a rule the percentage of deaths was by far the highest in the category of Jewish prisoners." The investigators add, "We are driven to the assumption that of the persons who left Westerbork in July, 1942, all but a very few were dead about eight weeks after departure" (12, p. 15).

Working out the data they had collected on Block 12 at Birkenau, Blokker and Broekman arrived at the following figures:

Present on Wednesday evening, June 10, 1942	13,803
New arrivals from June 11, 1942 to August 19, 1942 . . .	21,262
	35,065
Present on Wednesday evening, August 19, 1942	22,925
Absent	12,140

gas chambers); Auschwitz III, the camps around I and II (these were called Nebenlager or Aussenlager or Aussenkommandos—outside camps). Auschwitz III numbered 31 outside camps. As of November 25, 1944, these camps were called respectively K.L. Auschwitz (the original camps Auschwitz I and II) and K.L. Monowitz (the original Auschwitz III) (32, pp. 36 f.).

[10] In 11, pp. 8 ff. By "Auschwitz Death Book" is meant: *Standesamt Auschwitz. Sterbebuch (Erstbuch) 1942. Band 22, Nr. 31501–33000.*

Of these prisoners:

Released 158
Removed to other camps 824
"Escaped" 27   1,009
Died .... 11,131 [1]

[1] The weekly totals are given in the following table, which shows the number of prisoners present at roll call on Wednesday evening and the deaths, arrivals, etc., during the week following (adapted from 12, p. 14):

Date of roll call (1942)	Prisoners present at roll call	Deaths	Moved to other camps	Released	"Escaped"	New arrivals
June 10	13,803	882	18	67	12	707
" 17	13,531	1,177	21	59	4	1,868
" 24	14,138	854	57	1	3	2,783
July 1	16,006	850	719	26	1	2,128
" 8	16,538	862	9	3	3	603
" 15	16,264	935	—	1	—	3,519
" 22	18,847	1,190	—	1	3	3,441
" 29	21,094	871	—	—	—	2,558
Aug. 5	22,781	1,467	—	—	1	1,697
" 12	23,010	2,043	—	—	—	1,958
" 19	22,925					
		11,131	824	158	27	21,262

In the period from June 11 to August 19, 1942—i.e., in ten weeks—of the 35,065 registered Jews 11,131 had died; it is not, therefore, surprising that from Auschwitz only about 500 Netherlands Jews, male and female, have returned alive.

As early as January 30, 1939, Hitler in a speech to the Reichstag threatened the extermination of European Jews: "Today I am going to prophesy again: If the international Jewish financiers within or without Europe succeed in plunging the nations once more into a world war the result will not be the Bolshevization of the world, and the victory of Jewry, but the *obliteration of the Jewish race in Europe*" (142, Vol. III, p. 527).

The extermination of the greater number of European Jews was accomplished in various stages. For our present purpose a simplified division into three phases will suffice.

The first phase began with a letter from Heydrich, chief of the Sipo (Security Police) and the SD (Security Service) and head of the RSHA (Reich Security Main Office), dated September 21, 1939, addressed to the chiefs of all "Einsatzgruppen" [11] (Special Task Units) of the Security Police. It dealt with the Jewish question in the occupied territory (Poland): "With reference to the conference which took place today in Berlin, I would like to point out once more that the *total measures planned* (i.e., the final aim) are to be kept *strictly secret.* A distinction is to be made between (1) the final aim (which will take some time), and (2) sections of the carrying out of this aim (which can be carried out within a short space of time). The measures planned require the most thorough preparation both from the technical and the economic point of view. It goes without saying that the tasks in this connection cannot be laid down in detail. . . . *The first necessity for the attaining of the final aim is the concentrating of the country Jews in the large cities* . . . as few 'concentration' points as possible are to be established in order to facilitate later measures. Care must be taken that only such towns be chosen as concentration points as are either railroad junctions or at least lie on a railway . . ." (144, pp. 119 f.). It is now known what Heydrich meant by "the final aim," viz. the gassing of all Polish Jews. It is not certain at what time the Germans started gassing people, but Hoess made a statement to the effect that in the early part of 1941 Jews were being gassed in three extermination camps: Treblinka, Belzec, and Wolzek. Hoess, who for "studying purposes," to be mentioned below,[12] visited Treblinka in 1941, also stated, "The camp commandant at Treblinka told me that he had liquidated 80,000 in the course of one half-year. He was principally concerned with liquidating all the Jews from the Warsaw Ghetto" (142, Vol. XI, p. 416).

The second phase began in May, 1941, when Hitler issued a "Führerbefehl" with a view to the invasion of the Soviet Union fixed for June 22, 1941, "directing that the Security Police and the Security Service be called in to assist the army

[11] These "Einsatzgruppen" are not the same as those in the second phase.
[12] Page 32 of this book.

in breaking every means of resistance behind the fighting front" (144, p. 36). Heydrich, who had been detailed by Himmler to carry out this instruction, established four "Einsatzgruppen," designated by the letters A, B, C, and D. He instructed them to safeguard security in the territories to be conquered in Russia "and as part of this function they were directed to exterminate all Jews, gypsies, government officials, Communist party leaders, and other so-called 'undesirable elements' in their assigned territories" (144, p. 370). The effect of this instruction will be found in the "Opening Statement of the Prosecution" of the trial held at Nuremberg against many prominent figures of these "Einsatzgruppen," [13] which states that "four of these small forces totaling not more than 3,000 men killed at least 1,000,000 human beings in approximately two years' time" (144, p. 39).

The following record (144, p. 166 f.) is from the summary report by "Einsatzgruppe A" covering the period from June 23, 1941, to October 15, 1941.

ENCLOSURE 8—Survey of the number of executed persons

	Jews	Communists	Total
Lithuania	80,311	860	81,171
Latvia	30,025	1,843	31,868
Esthonia	474	684	1,158
White-Ruthenia	7,620	—	7,620
	118,430	3,387	121,817

To be added to these figures:

In Lithuania and Latvia, Jews annihilated by pogroms	5,500
Jews, Communists, and partisans executed in old Russian area	2,000
Lunatics executed	748
	122,455 [1]

Communists and Jews liquidated by State Police and Security Service Tilsit during search actions	5,502
	135,567

[1] The correct total is 130,065.

[13] This trial was officially called "United States of America vs. Otto Ohlendorf, et al. (Case No. 9)." It is known as "the Einsatzgruppen Case."

The third phase, that of "the final solution of the Jewish question" was worded by Hoess: "The 'final solution' of the Jewish question meant the complete extermination of all Jews in Europe" (142, Vol. XI, p. 416). Orders to this effect were issued in the summer of 1941, as appears from:

(1) A statement by Hoess: "In the summer of 1941 I was summoned to Berlin to Reichsführer SS Himmler to receive personal orders. He told me something to the effect—I do not remember the exact words—that the Führer had given the order for a final solution of the Jewish question. We, the SS, must carry out that order. If it is not carried out now, then the Jews will later on destroy the German people" (142, Vol. XI, p. 398).

Himmler pointed out to Hoess that he was to regard this order as a "top secret" and that he was to receive further instructions from Eichmann, which he did four weeks later at Auschwitz (142, Vol. XI, p. 399).

(2) A letter from Göring (written July 31, 1941) to Heydrich: "Complementing the task that was assigned to you on January 24, 1939, which dealt with arriving—through furtherance of emigration and evacuation—at a solution of the Jewish problem, as advantageously as possible, I hereby charge you with making all necessary preparations. . . . for bringing about a complete solution of the Jewish question in the German sphere of influence in Europe. . . ." (144, pp. 132 f.).

It may seem strange that both Himmler and Heydrich should have been in possession of the order concerning the "final solution." The most likely explanation seems to me that Heydrich as Head of the Security Police and the Security Service was to round up the Jews. The methods to be applied, and by what standard it was to be decided who were Jews and who were not, were discussed at a conference held in Berlin on January 20, 1942 (144, p. 669). On the subject discussed on this occasion, my opinion differs from that of Herzberg, who has said, "There is no doubt that at the conference of January 20, 1942, it was decided at Heydrich's suggestion to exterminate completely all Jews in Europe by means of gas chambers and forced labour and also that the plan was worked out in every detail" (68, p. 40). I cannot believe this is true, as from Hoess's statement as well as from Göring's letter to Heydrich it is evident that the decision was made as early as the summer of 1941.

It seems far more plausible that the conference of January 20, 1942, was held to plan the organized extermination of the European Jews, up to the extermination camps. Since Heydrich had no control over these camps, because they fell under the WVHA,[14] Himmler as Reich leader of the SS was to make possible the liquidation of the Jews rounded up by Heydrich in these camps; hence Himmler's instruction to Hoess.

And what about the part played by Eichmann? Because he was charged with the task by Heydrich, originally assigned to the latter, he must have been detailed to organize the rounding up of Jews and their transport to the extermination camps. Moreover, it appears to me, he was the connecting link between the RSHA and the WVHA, in the present instance the extermination camps, so that the "final solution of the Jewish question" might go as smoothly as possible. (See also 121, p. 162; this book, as well as 122a, contains a detailed account of the liquidation of the Jews in Nazi Germany.)

At this point one may wonder why Poland should have been chosen as the most suitable country for the liquidation of all Jews. According to a statement by Hoess, Himmler chose Auschwitz "on account of its easy access by rail and also because the extensive site offered space for measures ensuring isolation" (142, Vol. XI, p. 398).

Alexander looks for another motive, particularly because he wonders why the Germans should have dragged Netherlands Jews, for example, all the way to Auschwitz, thus putting a heavy burden of traffic on their railroad system. His explanation is based on the implications of Rosenberg and Darre's "Blut und Boden" theory. This theory of "Blood and Soil" postulates "that the soil in which people of Germanic race

14 "Wirtschaftsverwaltungshauptamt" (Economic and Administrative Main Office). "The 'SS-Wirtschaftsverwaltungshauptamt' dealt with all instructions given to it by the Reich Leader SS and the Chief of the German police, Heinrich Himmler, in the fields of economy and administration" (142, Vol. XXXI, p. 45).

were buried itself became German and in turn could also give German characteristics to people who nourished themselves from the products of that soil and that thus German people could be progressively Germanized by feeding from soil in which Germans were buried. Conversely the dead were also to make the soil increasingly German" (8, p. 554).

This, according to Alexander, may possibly account for the fact that the Germans chose Poland, being non-German soil, as the slaughterhouse of Jews. Were Germany to be used for this purpose, the corpses of Jews would poison German soil, with, of course, unimaginably disastrous effect.

This explanation seems open to various objections. After the conquest of Poland, that part of Poland in which Auschwitz lay was added to the German "Reich," and became German soil. Moreover, the possibility that the Germans had chosen Poland for the extermination of all the Jews because more than three millions lived there, is worthy of consideration. For thus they could begin close to the source, especially if the Russian Jews are taken into account. And once they had established Auschwitz, the Germans did not mind the trouble of transporting thither all West European Jews. Yet another consideration may have been that Auschwitz was very far from the densely populated West European regions, which would help to secure secrecy.

Organization [15]

Originally the concentration camps were under the control of the SA; after some time the SS assumed the management of the camps. The guards were drafted from the "Allgemeine SS" (General SS) and now formed a separate unit, the SS "Death-Head" units,[16] of which SS Lieutenant General Theodor Eicke was the chief. As such he was appointed "Inspector of Concentration Camps"; later this function was transferred to Office I of the "SS Führungshauptamt" (SS Leadership Main Office)—contraction: SS-FHA.[17] Eicke and his staff were

[15] Many data derived from 130, pp. 62 f.
[16] See p. 213 of this book.
[17] "The Reich Leader SS uses the SS-Führungshauptamt as a command centre of the Armed SS and for the pre- and post-military training and education of

charged with the control and administration of all concentration camps. In 1940, when Eicke was appointed commander of the "Waffen SS Panzerdivision Totenkopf," [18] Richard Glücks was his successor. Still the complete organization of the concentration camps had not reached its final stage. At Himmler's order, "Office VI (Inspection of Concentration Camps) and all its sub-offices shall be withdrawn from the SS Führungshauptamt as of March 16, 1942, and shall be controlled by the SS Economic and Administrative Office." [19]

The SS-FHA remained answerable only for armament, military regulations, military training of the camp guards. Until the end of the war the organization of the concentration camps remained a subdivision of the SS Economic and Administrative Main Office, and that as "Amtsgruppe D" under the direction of Glücks. Chief of the whole SS Economic and Administrative Main Office was SS Major General Pohl, who was directly subordinate to Himmler. Many concentration camps consisted of one central camp with subsidiary camps, which administratively formed one whole. Often the subsidiary camps had a different name from the central camp.

Although life in all concentration camps was bad, there was officially a classification into three grades: Grade I—"Arbeitslager" (labour camps); here conditions were least intolerable (e.g., Dachau; cf. 142, Vol. XXX, p. 16). Grade II meant an aggravation of conditions as compared with Grade I (e.g., Flossenbürg; 142, Vol. XXX, pp. 20 f.).[20] Grade III was the worst; in these camps very many people lost their lives.

The "Vernichtungslager" (extermination camps) fell into an entirely separate category. They may be subdivided into:

(a) Camps in which the majority of prisoners were liqui-

---

the General SS. The "Führungshauptamt" comprises the following offices: Command Office of the Armed SS, SS-Administrative Office, SS-Arms Office, Office for Führer-education, SS-Health Office, Inspection SS Group (142, Vol. XXXI, p. 46).

[18] Eicke was killed in action in 1943.

[19] Translated from a photostat of a document from the Himmler archives in the Netherlands State Institute of War Documentation (No. H. 779/3287). It should be observed that Office VI is mentioned in this document. A change must have been made here which I have not been able to trace.

[20] The concentration camp Buchenwald belonged to both Grade I and Grade II (cf. 142, Vol. XXX, pp. 35 f.).

dated immediately upon or shortly after their arrival, while the remainder were allowed to live until their working power had been completely used up (e.g., Auschwitz, Maidanek).

(b) Camps where practically everybody was gassed immediately upon arrival. Only a small party of the people who arrived were left alive, and these "were occupied in burying the bodies of the victims and sorting the belongings they left" (32, p. 16). In this category were Chelmno, Belzec, Sobibor, and Treblinka.

In Treblinka the Jews herded into the Warsaw Ghetto were murdered. A description of this camp is to be found in *German Crimes in Poland* (32, pp. 95 ff.). The facts put on record in this book are largely derived from a party of 13 Jews who, during a revolt on August 2, 1943, managed to escape. The first transport arrived on July 23, 1942; the camp was closed down in November, 1943. From the number of trains that arrived at Treblinka it has been concluded that "the number of victims murdered at Treblinka amounts to at least 731,600" (32, p. 104).

Four Jews who successfully escaped from the camp Chelmno have also given us detailed information about this camp.[21] The classification made above applied only to concentration camps and therefore is not valid for other camps, such as "Durchgangslager" (transit camps), e.g. Amersfoort, Westerbork, or "Vorzugslager" (preference camps), e.g. Bergen Belsen.

THE SS

The personnel of the camps was organized as follows: [22]

---

[21] 32, p. 109. A letter written by Rabbi J. Silman of Grabow, dated January 19, 1942, and dealing with Chelmno, is extant: ". . . Today there was a witness here who has been through all hell. There is a village named Chelmno, near Dombie, and all the people are buried in a wood, called Luchow. This has already happened to Kwil, Dombie, Klodve, Izbitz-Kviasky. Also thousands of Gypsies from Lodz have been taken there, and suffered the same fate. Since last week thousands of Jews from Lodz have also been brought in. All are murdered by means of poison gas or by shooting. . . . Do not think that an idiot is writing you this. But it is a hard, cruel truth. . . ." (*I. Tabaksblatt:* "Choerban Lodz" ["The Destruction of Lodz"], Buenos Aires, 1946, p. 124. A French translation may be found in *Les Temps Modernes,* January, 1949, p. 114.)

[22] Most of these data are from 84, pp. 55–63.

LAGERKOMMANDANT (CAMP COMMANDER) [1]

↓

ADJUTANT

(He passed on the orders issued by the commander and was charged with the official intercourse with superior and inferior authorities.)

VERWALTUNGSFÜHRER
(He directed all the "economic affairs" of the camp, such as food, clothing, etc.)

LAGERFÜHRER
(He was charged with the routine management of the prisoners' camp and took all necessary decisions under the direction of the commander. In fact, he was the absolute ruler over the prisoners. There usually were several "Lagerführer.")

↓

ARBEITSEINSATZFÜHRER
(From 1942 on, the representative of the total employment of labour inside the camp and as such the chief of the "Arbeitsdienstführer.")

RAPPORTFÜHRER
(The principal link between the "Lagerführer" and the camp; through him the "Lagerführer" was kept abreast of everything concerning the prisoners.)

ARBEITSDIENSTFÜHRER
(Organized, recorded, and directed all the work done by the prisoners.)

KOMMANDOFÜHRER
(Supervisor of the labour groups)

BLOCKFÜHRER
(Inspector of the blocks in the camp)

LAGERARZT (CAMP PHYSICIAN)—Director of H.K.B. (Häftlingskrankenbau = Prisoners' hospital) and polyclinic.

S.D.G.—Sanitätsdienstgefreiter (medical service orderly) (Charged with routine inspection of the H.K.B.)

[1] A dotted line indicates that the relation between the commander and these other members of the personnel was purely military, hence one of superior to inferior in rank. This was no hard-and-fast rule, as in some camps the "commander" had an inferior rank to the camp physician.

In the exercise of his function the camp physician was independent of the camp commander; he was accountable to the "Standortarzt," who, as regards concentration camps, was subordinate to the "Leitender Arzt K.L." (chief of the medical services of all concentration camps). Occasionally the functions of Standortarzt and camp physician were held by the same person.

Likewise independent of the camp commander were the representatives of the Gestapo in the camp, the "political department." They controlled independently all the business in their own province, such as the release, examination, and trial of the prisoners; they also had the authority to decide which persons should be sent to the gas chambers, and which not. The political department, where prisoners also were set to work, was under direct control of the RHSA (Reich Security Main Office); as regards the camps this department was only concerned with condemning people to imprisonment in the concentration camps, the grade of camp (I, II, etc.) to which a prisoner was to be sent, and the infliction of punishment.

The soldiers who manned the watch towers, those who formed the "sentry chain" round the camp and the men who guarded the labour groups, likewise received their orders not from the camp commander but from the "Waffen SS" (Armed SS).

THE PRISONERS

It was impossible for the SS to regulate all the business of the camp. Hence they had to allow the prisoners a certain measure of self-management, the system of which might vary in different camps. In Auschwitz I—to which the following description applies—the camp was, as it were, organizationally subdivided into two smaller camps:

(1) "Lager" (Camp)—i.e., prisoners able to work.
(2) "Häftlingskrankenbau" (Prison hospital)—i.e., the medical service. In many other camps this distinction was not made, but the medical service formed, as a labour group supervised by a Kapo, part of the camp itself.

In Auschwitz the block physician of Block 28 found himself in a peculiar position. There were only a few wards in this block, which were rather frequently placed at the disposal of SS physicians for medical experiments on prisoners. It also contained a few specialists' consulting rooms (eye and ear and X-ray laboratory). The principal duty of the block physician was to introduce patients whose admission to the prison hospital he judged necessary or whom he wanted to have exempted

LAGER (CAMP)

L.Ä.: LAGERÄLTESTE (SENIOR CAMP PRISONER)

This person formed the link between the camp and the SS; he was appointed by the SS. Often prisoners succeeded in having appointed to this position a person whom they thought the most suitable. Sometimes there were two or more L.Ä's, according to the size of the camp.

B.Ä.: BLOCKÄLTESTE (SENIOR BLOCK PRISONER)
Manager of a block, under the control of the "Blockführer."

ST. Ä.: STUBENÄLTESTE (ROOM SENIOR)
Each Block was subdivided into various "Stuben" (rooms). The St. Ä. were in charge of these rooms; for the "rough" work they had at their disposal a number of "Stubendienste" (room servants)

→ BLOCKSCHREIBER (BLOCK CLERK)
In charge of the block accounts.

SCHREIBSTUBE (ADMINISTRATIVE ROOM)
The administrative centre, also housing the prison card catalogue. Here it was decided which of the blocks was to house the newly arrived prisoners, and here was recorded every removal of prisoners to other blocks or camps, as well as the release of prisoners. The exact number of prisoners at any given time was recorded here, and the lists for roll call were made out; lastly the "Verpflegungszuteiling" (rationing of food) was taken care of.

→ LAGERPOLIZEI (CAMP POLICE)
Assisted in maintaining order in the camp, so that, to a certain extent, the SS dropped into the background.

→ FEUERWEHR (CAMP FIRE BRIGADE)

HÄFTLINGSKRANKENBAU (PRISONERS' HOSPITAL)

LAGERÄLTESTE

Senior camp prisoner, responsible to the camp physician; he might be a physician himself.

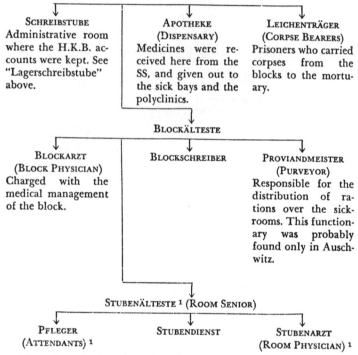

SCHREIBSTUBE	APOTHEKE (DISPENSARY)	LEICHENTRÄGER (CORPSE BEARERS)
Administrative room where the H.K.B. accounts were kept. See "Lagerschreibstube" above.	Medicines were received here from the SS, and given out to the sick bays and the polyclinics.	Prisoners who carried corpses from the blocks to the mortuary.

BLOCKÄLTESTE

BLOCKARZT (BLOCK PHYSICIAN)	BLOCKSCHREIBER	PROVIANDMEISTER (PURVEYOR)
Charged with the medical management of the block.		Responsible for the distribution of rations over the sick-rooms. This functionary was probably found only in Auschwitz.

STUBENÄLTESTE [1] (ROOM SENIOR)

PFLEGER (ATTENDANTS) [1]	STUBENDIENST	STUBENARZT (ROOM PHYSICIAN) [1]

[1] Sometimes the functions of Stubenälteste and attendant, or those of Stubenälteste and room physician, were combined in one person.

from labour for some days, to the camp physician, with whom the final decision rested.

LABOUR

In the field of camp labour the link between the "Arbeitsdienstführer" (later: "Arbeitseinsatzführer"—chief of labour employment) and the prisoners was constituted by the "Arbeitsstatistik" (bureau of labour statistics): "It recorded the manpower available in each camp in a card index which showed the occupations of the prisoners and settled the numbers of hours worked" (87, p. 62).

A very important duty of the "Arbeitseinsatzführer" was the composition of prisoner transports to other camps. When, as a result of the large number of transports, he was unable to carry out this task without assistance, those prisoners who were employed in his bureau secured considerable influence on the composition of these transports, and consequently were often in a position to keep back certain fellow prisoners and to get rid of others. Prisoners who held a position of authority in the labour groups were the *Oberkapo,* the chief of the Kapos; *Kapo,* the chief overseer, entrusted with the command over a labour group and, in the absence of the "Oberkapo," responsible to the "Kommandoführer"; *Vorarbeiter,* foreman subordinate to the Kapo and in command of a part of the labour group.

The Layout

Most of the camps were laid out on the same plan. A large entrance gate gave on to a space fenced off with barbed wire. In Auschwitz and a few other camps a large inscription over the gate read "Arbeit macht frei" (Labour gives freedom). The barbed-wire fence, charged with electric current, was tall and the wires were strung close together. At the four corners and halfway between them stood watch towers, each manned by an SS man equipped with a machine gun and a searchlight.

Inside the fence stood the "Wohnblöcke" (dwelling blocks). These blocks were spaced at regular distances on either side of the camp street in which the prisoners could walk up and down in their spare time. Also inside the fence were the camp hospital, the kitchen, the administrative room, clothing depot, the lavatory and the space where the prisoners had to line up for roll call.

Most camps presented a desolate appearance. The prisoners saw hardly anything but sand, stone, and wood. There was not a blade of grass, not a single tree. I have seen a few exceptions, however. In Auschwitz there was grass; one of the birch-lined streets was given the sonorous name of "Birkenallee" (Birch Avenue). In Ebensee also the view was far from dreary, as the blocks stood among pine trees.

The Prisoners

The prisoners were clothed in striped suits which before long were in tatters. These suits were made of thin shoddy or cotton stuff and were worn in summer as well as in winter. Occasionally, in winter, prisoners would be given an overcoat of the same material. They wore small caps, and on their feet pieces of cloth (for socks) and boots or so-called "Holzpantinen," narrow lengths of wood with a strip of cotton as a covering for their toes. Some prisoners might be given worn civilian clothes with red-paint stripes across the back and down the trouser legs or with a zebra patch sewn on to the back of the coat and the trousers. On the left side of the breast and the right of trousers there was a ribbon with the prison number. In Auschwitz the prison number was tattooed on the skin of the left forearm, because, as Spritzer has stated, many mistakes were made in the card index (137, p. 43). *German Crimes in Poland* records that this practice was begun in the early part of 1942 (32, p. 45). The Jews had an inverted triangle tattooed below the number, a practice which was later abandoned. The prisoners' heads were either completely shaved or only partly, so that a shaved strip ran across their skulls from front to back. A few, chiefly German prisoners, did not have their skulls shaved. These were the so-called "Vorzugshäftlinge," which belonged to the group of "prominents"—privileged prisoners, who were considered the camp aristocracy. Their numbers were small, but their power was considerable, as they held positions of authority; they were well dressed and well fed and enjoyed such advantages as the camps could present. In Auschwitz some of these privileged prisoners even wore gloves lined with Persian lamb.

The SS classified the prisoners in various categories. For the sake of distinction they had to wear above their number an inverted triangle of varying colours on which, in the case of foreigners, a letter showing their nationality was printed— e.g., N.L. for the Netherlands, F. for France. The category to which the prisoner belonged was shown by a distinctive colour, which distinction, however, was not the least proof that the bearer actually belonged in this category.

The system of classification was as follows:

1. *Green: German prisoners* exclusively. This group comprised:
   a. *B.V.*—*Befristete Vorbeugungshäftlinge* (Prisoners in limited-term preventive custody): All these had served many terms of imprisonment. The other prisoners used the German initials to designate this category as "Berufsverbrecher" (professional criminals).
   b. *S.V.*—*Sicherungsverwahrte* (prisoners in security custody): These were still serving sentence; they were soon called "Schwerverbrecher" (dangerous criminals). The letter S was printed on the green triangle.
   c. *K.V.*—*Kriegsverbrecher* (war criminals): people who gravely violated laws of war (looting, sabotage, etc.). The green triangle showed the letter K.
2. *Red: Political opponents,* but also National Socialists who had committed offences against the party, and soldiers who had refused to carry out orders or had deserted.
3. *Purple: Opponents of National Socialism on religious grounds.* This group consisted of ministers of various religions, who from 1942 on were chiefly imprisoned in Dachau. Also the members of the "Internationale Bibelforscher Vereinigung," more generally known as "Jehovah's Witnesses." (87, p. 41). These refused to swear allegiance to Hitler and to join the "Wehrmacht."
4. *Pink: Homosexuals.* In this group were found many people arrested on the charge of homosexuality merely because the Gestapo wanted to be rid of them.
5. *Black: "A-social elements"*—i.e., vagrants, drunkards, pickpockets, persons unwilling to work, also workers who had

repeatedly arrived late at their work, had taken a holiday without permission, or had taken on other work. Gypsies were also included in this category.

6. *Yellow: Jews.* On the triangle worn by this group was superimposed another triangle in the colour of the category to which the Jewish prisoners belonged, generally red, occasionally black. The two triangles together formed a Star of David.

Those prisoners who were assigned to the penal drill company had a large black dot below their number; those suspected of attempts to escape wore a red disk on the front and back of their prison uniform; many of these were under sentence of death.

In the H.K.B. (prisoners' hospital) at Auschwitz another distinction was made. The staff wore sleeve badges with the initials H.K.B.; these badges were blue for nurses, white for physicians, red for the technical staff. In Buchenwald the physicians and nurses who were sent to an outside camp wore armlets which read "Häftlingsarzt" or "Häftlingspfleger" (prisoners' physician or prisoners' attendant).

Extermination of Human Beings

The total number of human beings that have perished in the concentration camps is not known. Estimates vary considerably: Kogon (87, pp. 169 f.) says 7,500,000; De Wind (155, p. 6) says 9,500,000. But it is certain that there must have been many millions of victims, thanks to the various means to this end employed by the SS, such as starvation, torture, exhaustion, shooting fugitives, medical experiments, intravenous or intracardial injections of phenol, petrol or air, death marches, gas chambers, gas vans (in which the exhaust gases of the engine were discharged into the cabin).

Of this wide choice of means two will now be singled out for discussion, namely gas chambers and death marches. The others will be dealt with in the following chapter. It should be noted that gas chambers were constructed with the *deliberate* aim of killing people, whereas the death marches offered an unexpected opportunity, which was fully utilized, to attain the same object.

GAS CHAMBERS

Extermination camps differed from other concentration camps in that large numbers of people were killed there by means of poison gas. This is not to say that in other camps no people were gassed. Häfliger [23] was told by a prisoner who had worked in the crematory of the concentration camp Mauthausen: "In February (1945) people were first being gassed in a sham shower bath. On the very first day 66 prisoners were gassed. The SS gloated over the spectacle, peeping through Judas holes, as at a peep show. The number of people killed amounted to over one hundred a day, in March to more than one hundred and fifty" (58, p. 39).

The camp commander of Mauthausen, Ziereis, confirmed this statement, when on June 23 and 24, 1945, he dictated from his deathbed: "By command of Dr. Kresbach, SS-Hauptsturmführer, a gas chamber was built at Mauthausen concentration camp . . . a bathroom was being constructed. In that bathroom, inmates were gassed. . . ." (19, p. 337). Joseph Kramer, who, among other functions, had held that of commander of the concentration camp Natzweiler-Struthof, stated that in this camp, in the early part of August, 1943, about 80 prisoners from the K.L. Auschwitz were gassed in a gas chamber specially constructed for this purpose. (143, Vol. I, p. 740; 110, p. 167).

Also in the concentration camp Sachsenhausen people were gassed, as has been proved by information from an ex-prisoner of this K.Z., the Luxemburger Jean Chaussy (118, p. 22).

All this pales into insignificance before what happened in the extermination camps. In these camps people were murdered wholesale; here whole ethnic groups—Jews and Gypsies

---

[23] Häfliger is a Swiss citizen who, at the end of April, 1945, was assigned by the International Red Cross "to take nineteen trucks with food gift-parcels to one of the most notorious of all concentration camps, Mauthausen, the public hell of corruption, to distribute the gifts of humanity among the victims of inhumanity and to repatriate via Switzerland all non-German prisoners, to the best of his ability" (58, p. 6).

—were exterminated. This type of extermination is called "Genocide" (the term was first used by R. Lemkin) (18, p. 15).

Our knowledge of the extent of these murders is derived from the following data. It has been mentioned before that in Treblinka 80,000 Jews were gassed in six months (p. 11 of this book). Important data about the Auschwitz exterminations were given by Hoess, (60, pp. 249–253; 142, Vol. XI, pp. 396–422; 61, pp. 240–248), who told Gilbert that during the period that he was camp commander of Auschwitz (May, 1940–December, 1943) "approximately 2.5 million Jews had been exterminated under his direction" (60, p. 249). Information as to the period after Hoess had left the camp is to be found in the book by Mrs. Lengyel: "I have the figures only for the months of May, June and July, 1944. Dr. Pasche, a French doctor of the 'Sonderkommando,' [24] . . . provided me with these:

May, 1944	360,000
June, 1944	512,000
from the first to the 26th of July, 1944	442,000
	1,314,000

In less than three months the Germans had 'liquidated' more than 1,300,000 persons at Auschwitz-Birkenau" (99, p. 70).

At first Hoess had to manage with two provisional gas chambers, which he had set up in two farmhouses. According to Lettich, these crudely constructed gas chambers had a capacity of 400 to 500 a day, and the corpses were cremated in a large trench (101, pp. 28 f.). In order to kill as many Jews as possible, many of them were, during this period, murdered by means

[24] This Sonderkommando was made up of prisoners who were forced by the SS to assist in the gassings. According to Nyiszli, a Hungarian Jewish physician, who, thanks to the fact that he was a pathologist-anatomist and had been educated at a German university, looked after the pathologo-anatomical department of camp physician Dr. Mengele's "scientific" work—about which more in the next chapter—and who, in this function, lived among the members of the Sonderkommando, it consisted of about 820 prisoners (117, p. 1661). Nyiszli has further recorded that the members of the Sonderkommando were very well looked after; they were given good beds, good clothes, excellent food and medical care (117, p. 1855). But he has also put it on record that the whole Sonderkommando was murdered every four months, and that the first duty of the fresh Sonderkommando was to cremate the preceding one. Some escaped being killed as they were transferred to other camps (e.g., Lettich) or because of the revolt of October 7, 1944 (99, pp. 161–164) or owing to patronage (117, pp. 1883 f.; 155, p. 164).

of intravenous or intracardial injections.[25] In the meantime
the firm of J. A. Topf and Sons at Erfurt [26] were engaged in
constructing new gassing plants (135, p. 285; 32, p. 83) described by Lettich as "ultra-modern constructions, which only
German technicians could have conceived" (101, p. 29; see also
117, pp. 1661–1667). These refined plants for mass murder
were officially inaugurated, and on this occasion 8,000 Jews
from Cracow were gassed (55, p. 19; 152, p. 118).

Lettich has recorded this "ceremony": "At the end of January, 1943,[27] these plants were ceremoniously inaugurated. A
committee of exalted German authorities from Berlin had
come to watch the first gassing and subsequent cremation.
Through small Judas holes it was easy for them to watch the
progress of asphyxiation inside without running any personal
risk. These gentlemen expressed their great satisfaction. . . .
When it was all over cigarettes, tobacco, and drinks were
served" (101, p. 29; for a similar description see also 152, p.
118; 55, p. 19). But other people also would come to enjoy
the spectacle, among others Himmler, in the year 1942 (142,
Vol. XI, p. 401) of whom Hoess said, "He just watched it all
silently and showed no sign of emotion. All he said was, 'It is
a hard job, but we've got to do it' " (61, p. 253).

What poisons were used in gassing the Jews in Auschwitz?
In order to carry out the task which had been assigned to him by
Himmler, namely "the final solution of the Jewish question,"

25 Private eye-witness account by a Slovak Jew at Auschwitz.

26 On January 29, 1943, the chief of the SS central construction management
at Auschwitz informed Dr. Ing. Kammler, chief of office group C of the WHVA:
"The crematorium II has been completed . . . by the use of all the forces
available, in spite of unspeakable difficulties, the severe cold, and in 24-hour
shifts.
The fires were started in the ovens in the presence of Oberingenieur Pruefer,
representative of the contractors of the firm of Topf and Sons, Erfurt, and they
are working most satisfactorily. The planks from the concrete ceiling of the
cellar used as a mortuary . . . could not yet be removed on account of the
frost. This is, however, not very important, as the gas chamber can be used
for that purpose. The firm of Topf and Sons was not able to start deliveries
of the installations in time for aeration and ventilation . . . the complete in-
stallation may be expected to be ready for use 20 February 1943.
"We enclose a report (not attached to document) of the testing engineer of
the firm of Topf and Sons, Erfurt" (144a, pp. 619 f.).

27 According to information from two Jews who escaped from Birkenau, the
inauguration took place at the end of February or in the early part of March,
1943 (152, pp. 116, 118).

Hoess made a journey to Treblinka to make a study of the system of extermination prevailing there. He learned that the Jews were being gassed with carbon monoxide (exhaust gas from a Diesel engine was carried into the gas chamber). As he was of the opinion that this method was not sufficiently efficient, he decreed that another means should be used— Zyklon; [28] this, according to Hoess, is "crystalline Prussic acid which volatilized immediately, i.e. became effective immediately upon contact with oxygen" (61, p. 246; see also 117, p. 1664).

The next question to be answered is: What happened to the Jews from the moment they reached the gas chambers? On this subject Hoess is the best authority. He has left the following description, which, in my opinion, can only have applied to the first selection (this book, pp. 36 ff.):

"When they arrived, all had to undress completely in rooms which were made to look as if they were set up for delousing purposes.[29] The steady work detail which worked at these installations . . . helped in the undressing process and advised the sceptical ones to get ready so that the others would not have so long to wait. They were also told to note where they left their things, so that they could find them immediately after the bath. All this was done to dispel any suspicions that might arise. After the undressing they went into the next room, the gas chamber. This was set up like a bath, i.e., showers, pipes, drains, etc. had been installed. As soon as the entire transport was in the chamber, the door was closed and the gas thrown in through a special opening in the ceiling. . . . The people became stunned with the first breath of it, and the killing took three to fifteen minutes according to the weather and the number of those locked in. After this period there was no

[28] The SS was supplied with Zyklon B by the firm of Tesch and Stabenow at Hamburg (*Law Reports of Trials of War Criminals*, Vol. I, p. 94).

[29] As has been stated, Hoess considered the use of Zyklon B in place of carbon monoxide an improvement on the method employed in Treblinka. Other improvements applied by him were that people in Auschwitz thought they were going to be deloused, whereas in Treblinka they knew they would be gassed, and finally that he had at his disposal gas chambers with a capacity of 2,000 persons a day, while in Treblinka there were ten gas chambers, each for 200 persons (142, Vol. XXXIII, pp. 275–280: Affidavit of Rudolf Franz Ferdinand Hoess of April 5, 1946).

more movement. Thirty minutes after the gas had been thrown in, the chambers were opened and the removal of the corpses to the crematoria was begun. In all the years I knew of not a single case where any one came out of the chambers alive." [30] The hair was cut off the women's heads and any rings or gold teeth were removed by prisoner dentists employed in the detail (61, p. 246; see also 117, pp. 1661–1667).

It would be superfluous, I think, to add anything to this description. Unless, maybe, that there was a few minutes' delay before the gas was admitted, in order to allow the temperature in the gas chambers to rise, which, in the words of Mrs. Lengyel, "would facilitate the action of the gas." [31] Or to call attention to the fact that, when the victims had undressed, the SS no longer bothered about not arousing suspicion, but if necessary, forcibly drove the victims into the "bathroom" (99, p. 73). For the rest Hoess's description will do.

The Germans strove to exploit these mass-murders economically as much as possible. From a report by SS-Oberscharführer Reichenbach, which was found at Auschwitz after the German surrender, it appears that from December 1, 1944, to January 15, 1945, he had packed, to be forwarded to Germany, 99,922 children's garments and pieces of underwear, 192,652 women's garments and articles of underwear, and 222,269 articles of men's clothing and underwear (135, p. 299). Gold objects were melted down, and gold fillings removed from the victims' teeth [32] were sent to the "Deutsche Reichsbank" (German Reich Bank); finally the ashes of the burnt corpses were utilized as fertilizer; [33] the bones were made into superphosphate

[30] M. Nyiszli has recorded that one girl of about 15 survived gassing. The SS chief of the crematories, Mussfeld, was, however of the opinion that she could not be left alive, because she might tell everything she had seen. The girl was killed by a shot in the neck (117, pp. 1861–1866).

[31] In 99, p. 73; cf. Lettich: "After the doors of the gas chambers had been closed, there was a ten-minute delay before Zyklon B was let in, as only then the temperature inside the gas chambers 'had risen sufficiently to facilitate the volatilization of the hydrocyanic acid' " (101, p. 28).

[32] Detailed information received from my late friend, dental technician Berthold Krebs, who was actively employed in this work.

[33] See "United States of America vs. Ulrich Greifelt, et al. (Case No. 8)" (Trials of War Criminals, Vol. IV, p. 671). This utilizing as fertilizer of the ashes of cremated Jews is another argument against Alexander's theory (see this book, p. 17. According to Hoess, sometimes also "the ashes were pulverized

by the German firm of Strem, (55, p. 64; 135, p. 286) and "an attempt was made to manufacture soap from the fatty parts of the bodies."

To a question, put by Gilbert to Hoess, as to how many people could be killed in one day, the latter replied, "The killing itself took the least time. You could dispose of 2,000 head in a half hour, but it was the burning that took all the time" (60, p. 250).

The bodies were cremated in two large and two smaller crematories; each crematory, together with an undressing hall and a gas chamber, formed one unit. In addition to these, large trenches, in which the bodies were burned in the open, were also used.[34] Nyiszli gives the following eyewitness account of them: "The pyre is a ditch, 50 meters long by 6 meters wide, by 3 meters deep, filled with hundreds of corpses which are burning. Along the edges of the ditch, and on the side facing the road, SS soldiers awaiting their victims are placed, at five-meter distances. They carry small-calibre firearms—6 mm.—which are used in the K.Z. for shooting bullets into the prisoners' necks. At the end of the lane two members of the Sonderkommando catch the unfortunate victims by the arms, dragging them about 15 to 20 meters, to just before the firearms of the SS. Cries of terror drown the noise of the shots; nothing is heard but the pulling of triggers. Immediately afterward, even before life is extinct, the victims are hurled into the flames of the pyre. Fifty meters beyond, work is in full swing at another pyre entirely similar to the first" (117, p. 1857).

As has already been stated, the rate of extermination of the Jews was determined by the number of corpses which could be cremated in one day. How large was this number? Many statements are at our disposal, which, however, show considerable variations. To mention but a few: Mrs. Lengyel computes the capacity of the crematories at 17,280 corpses every twenty-four hours, and that of the trenches at 8,000 (99, p. 69); according to Friedman (55, p. 55) the crematories alone could con-

and thrown into the Weichsel River at secluded spots, and were then carried away by the stream" (61, p. 247).

[34] A photograph of this, secretly taken in August, 1944, by David Grek, who was a member of the "Sonderkommando," will be found in 32, p. 39.

sume 18,000 in twenty-four hours, whereas Lettich (101, p. 29) arrives at an estimate of 4,320. The best plan will probably be to assume that the numbers given by Hoess (61, p. 247) are, on the whole, correct. As regards the crematories, he states that they consumed 8,000 a day, and although he says that "the burning in open pits was virtually unlimited," he concludes: "It was therefore possible to exterminate and get rid of as many as 10,000 people in twenty-four hours" (61, p. 247). It is, however, almost certain that the number of 10,000 in twenty-four hours was considerably surpassed during the boom period. In the summer of 1944 (when Hoess was no longer in command), about 400,000 Hungarian Jews were murdered in Auschwitz (142, Vol. XI, p. 415). In *German Crimes in Poland* we find the following information: "When operations were in full swing in August 1944, the number of corpses burnt daily rose to 24,000" (32, pp. 88 f.; cf. also 144a, p. 663). Gassing ceased on November 2, 1944 (55, p. 20; 11, p. 8; Hoess gives the time as autumn, 1944 [142, Vol. XI, p. 415]; Nyiszli gives it as Nov. 17, 1944 [117, p. 1882]).

The next question to be gone into is whether the SS applied any criterion as to which people should be sent to their deaths, and, if so, what criterion. The predominant consideration was that the prisoner was a Jew, though it should not be lost sight of that neither Russians nor Poles were spared. According to Mrs. Lengyel (99, p. 68), after June, 1943 (Dr. Wenger [99, p. 169] says April, 1943), the "privilege" of being gassed was only granted to Jews and Gypsies, to which statement I should like to add that my experiences in Auschwitz-Stammlager from September, 1943, agree with hers. In the further treatment of this question the Gypsies will not be mentioned, because their number was very small as compared with Jews.

Once more, the predominant consideration was one's Jewish origin, and in the camps of category (b) of the extermination camps (this book p. 20) this was considered a criterion sufficient to gas every Jewish prisoner immediately upon arrival.[35] This rule was usually not observed in Auschwitz, which did nothing to alter the fact that, on arrival there, many truck loads were

[35] Sobibor may be named as an instance (134, p. 4).

consigned to the gas chamber in their entirety. An instance has been communicated by Nyiszli concerning a transport of women and children from Theresienstadt, who followed their husbands and fathers sent fourteen days before to a "labour camp." All were immediately gassed (117, p. 181).

In Auschwitz the method usually applied by the SS was that of

SELECTION

I would describe what is meant by selection as a decision by a member of the SS, often a physician, made in a fraction of a second, as to whether the human being who is standing before him is capable of heavy physical labour or not. In the latter case the decision meant that the person was consigned to the gas chamber. A clear distinction should be made between: (a) the selection on arrival, the *first* selection, and (b) the selections which took place frequently, though at irregular intervals, inside the camp.

The first selection. Immediately after the Jewish men and women had left the cattle cars that had carried them to Auschwitz, they had to march past a member of the SS, who sorted the arrivals by glancing at them or asking them a question. Condemned to death were: all mothers together with their children up to the age of about fourteen, the pregnant, the deformed, invalids, the sick, and all men and women over fifty. But also those who looked older or younger than their age, or who were very tired after the long and exhausting journey in the cattle cars, or who gave the impression of being ill, and those who failed to understand a question asked in German or made a stumbling reply, were often sent to the gas chamber. "Graciously" the SS man would consent to a daughter or son remaining with the mother or father; thus many more people entered the gas chamber. The SS knew only one standard: to liquidate as many Jewish men and women as possible, a very rare exception being made in the case of young people who could be assumed to be of some use as manpower for the German war industry. The result was that "the number of prisoners taken into the camp from Jewish transports amounted to an average of about 10% of all the people who were brought to Auschwitz" (32, p. 42). Of the transport of which I was a member, and which on arrival at Auschwitz consisted of over one thousand people, more than eight hundred were sent to gas chambers.

To Frankl we owe a striking description of the impression which the SS man made on the newly arrived prisoners: "Now he stands before me: tall, slender, smart, in his immaculate and brilliant uniform—an elegant, well-groomed man, very aloof toward us miserable creatures, who look very weary indeed and very shabby. There he stands, in a nonchalant posture, his right elbow cupped in his left hand, his right hand raised and motioning ever so slightly with the forefinger of this hand—now left, now right—far more often right" (46, pp. 19 f.; see also 144a, pp. 642 f. and p. 648).

Descriptions of these first selections are always the same, with only a few variations; sometimes the sick and infirm were driven away in Red Cross ambulances or trucks, or the SS man might first deliver an address, or during the selection a band composed of prisoners played popular tunes. I only mention this for the sake of completeness, although I have never personally known these things to happen. These variations are of no importance whatever, for whenever a transport arrived the SS did their utmost not to arouse in the victims any suspicion of their fate. In Treblinka the SS had even gone to the length of building "A sham railway station . . . with various inscriptions, such as 'refreshment room,' 'waiting room,' or 'booking office,' and signs showing the 'passengers' where to get in for Bialystok and elsewhere" (32, p. 99).

Selections which took place frequently, though at irregular intervals, inside the camp. During my stay at Auschwitz these selections, not mentioned by Hoess, took place almost exclusively in the H.K.B. Only twice did they take place in the "Lager" (camp), i.e., from among the workers, of whom, on one occasion, the prisoners selected, after being shut up in a hut for two full days, were released again, instead of being gassed. The other concurred with a selection in the H.K.B.; this selection, which was held at the end of September, 1944, and happened to be the last in the Stammlager-Auschwitz, took a heavy toll of victims, among whom was Professor Frijda of the University of Amsterdam. On the other hand, selections were very frequent in the "Lager" Auschwitz-Birkenau (99, pp. 40 ff.). According to Nyiszli, the persons selected from among the prisoners were not always gassed. The method applied by the SS in murdering these people depended on their numbers, Nyiszli states: "So long as their number does not exceed 500, they are killed by a shot through the neck, for the big plant of gas chambers is reserved for the liquidation of larger numbers. Killing 500 persons took as much gas as killing 3,000" (117, p. 1864).

As I witnessed many selections in Block IX of the H.K.B., I will give a brief account of the circumstances:

After the "H.K.B. administrative room" had given warning that the camp physician was about to make a selection, the whole block became a hive of activity, for everything had to be spick-and-span. Heavy demands were made on me in my function of room physician and lavatory inspector, for the W.C.'s had to look well cared for, and the medical service of the room had to be run smoothly, so as to cause no unnecessary delay to the German doctor. At last the great moment arrived —"The camp physician is coming"—and while everybody stood at attention, he made his entry with his retinue: S.D.G., Blockälteste and block clerk. The sick Jews were already lined up—as a matter of course, naked. Simultaneously with the presentation of the card with the personal notes concerning each prisoner, to the camp physician, the block physician, in whose ear the diagnosis was being whispered by the room physician, introduced the patient in question to him. The patient might or might not have to turn round, but in 90 per cent of the cases the card was handed to the S.D.G., which meant death by gassing for the patient, unless the political department gave orders to the contrary, which frequently occurred in the case of "Schutzhäftlinge." [36]

---

[36] A "Schutzhäftling" was a person who had been sent to a concentration camp for an infringement of German law. The Jews who had come along with the deportation transports were called "Aktions-Juden" (Raid Jews).

Not only emaciated prisoners, but also some who looked well fed were sometimes consigned to the gas chamber; and occasionally even members of the H.K.B. staff, who were officially exempt, had to suffer a similar fate. Therefore, especially when one considered the "medical style" of the camp physician, it was generally supposed that it was not only people incapable of work who were scheduled for killing, but that the decisive factor must be that a certain number of persons had to be gassed (102, p. 82).

It is thus more correct to substitute the word "commission" for selection as, in the end, became the general practice in Auschwitz. Since, however, in every publication on this subject the word "selection" is constantly used, I have preferred to employ this term throughout, the more so as the word is of less importance than the significance it bears.

Officially no one knew what the final object actually was, not even the staff of the administrative room, for after the names of the gassed the initials S.B., short for "Sonderbehandlung" (special treatment) were placed.

In spite of all this, more prisoners of the K.L. Auschwitz would have survived—and the same applies to other concentration camps—if it had not been for the

DEATH MARCHES

When the German armies were, at last, forced to retreat before the Allies, the SS had to evacuate several concentration camps. However, they did not go alone, but took the prisoners with them which had disastrous consequences for the prisoners. Through lack of exact figures, there is no absolute proof of this. Of the K.Z. Auschwitz it is known that when the complete roll was called for the last time, on January 17, 1945, there were present 48,342 male and about 16,000 female prisoners, while 96 Russian prisoners were specially mentioned (55, p. 78). Altogether there were, according to the records, 64,438 persons. It is further known that the Red Army, when it reached Auschwitz, found 2,819 prisoners alive. Taking into account those who died in the period between the last roll call and the liberation of Auschwitz, it may be safely assumed that about 60,000 prisoners set out on the death marches. Though we are in the dark as to the number who lived to see the liberation, it is certain that it was very small.

The question that automatically presents itself is: Was it impossible for the prisoners to escape this particular and fatal transfer? It was not exactly easy, though it is certain that many could have escaped by hiding in the camp. I do not know why only a few of the prisoners availed themselves of this opportunity, so I can only record my own considerations:

(1) My experiences in the camp had taught me that it was always the best policy to be one of the healthy. The sick were treated a great deal worse, as they were regarded as "rubbish." That the sick themselves were of the same opinion has been told by Mrs. Lengyel: "The sick were in panic. Those who had any strength left at all leaped from their beds to reclaim their clothing" (99, p. 195).

(2) I feared that the SS would destroy the whole camp (including the "livestock") before the Russians could liberate the prisoners. This fear, which was shared by many, caused even the medically unfit to join the transport. That the fear of an act on the part of the SS in which nothing and nobody would be spared was not unfounded, was proved by what happened at Fürstengrube, an "Aussenkommando" (outside camp) of Auschwitz, where "all the sick were burnt in their huts" (32, p. 92). The same atrocity was committed on the sick who were evacuated from the camp of which Frankl was a prisoner, on the last day before its liberation (46, p. 86).

Von Gagern has disclosed that during the night of May 2–3, 1945, the SS man Reiner handed to "his room-mate Häfliger all the documents concerning the destruction of the camps Mauthausen, Gusen I and II" (58, p. 21). These documents contained the order that the prisoners of concentration camps Gusen I and II should, on the approach of the Russians, be driven by a false air-raid warning into the "Stollen," [37] which

---

[37] "Stollen" were large caves, like horizontal mine shafts, cut in the mountainsides by the Germans, to serve as bombproof workshops. In the camp Melk I was employed in these "Stollen."

had been sapped beforehand and could be blown up at a moment's notice.[38] At the same time the prisoners of the camp Mauthausen were to be massacred (58, p. 22). According to Von Gagern, these orders were not carried out, thanks to Häfliger.

In this connection the attitude of the SS leaders toward concentration camps during the last stage of the war will be briefly reviewed. A statement to this effect was made by Hoess (142, Vol. XI, p. 407): First, Himmler had given the order that the camps were to be surrendered on the approach of the enemy. In the early part of 1945 this order was countermanded and the choice between evacuation and surrender was left to the SS management, who were responsible for the camps. When Buchenwald was about to be evacuated another order was issued by Himmler, namely, that only those prisoners who must on no account fall into Allied hands should be removed. Because of what had happened in the town of Weimar after the liberation of the K.L. Buchenwald ("internees had armed themselves and were carrying out plunderings in the town of Weimar" [142, Vol. XI, p. 407]), the Führer ordered that not a single camp with prisoners must fall into enemy hands. This is confirmed by Himmler's reply to a question dated April 14, 1945 by the commanders of the concentration camps Flossenbürg and Dachau, as to whether or not they were allowed to surrender their camps: "Surrender is out of the question. The camp must be evacuated at once. No prisoner must fall into enemy hands alive. The prisoners have committed atrocities on the civilian population at Buchenwald" (104, p. 21).

(3) A sense of fatalism had taken possession of me. A frequently heard expression in the camp was: "Wie es kommt, wird es gefressen" (as things come we'll eat them).

(4) The Jewish prisoners were persuaded that the SS would never allow them to leave the concentration camp alive and it fascinated me to find that this would happen after all.

These were the considerations which decided me to make

[38] In the camp Ebensee the SS, on the morning of May 6, 1945, tried in vain to order the prisoners into the "Stollen." A few hours later we were liberated by the Americans.

no attempt to escape. But though I thought it was the best thing I could do in the circumstances, it was not without misgivings that I set out with the transport. I knew that going to another camp meant for me starting again at the bottom of the ladder, and losing the comparatively privileged position I had been holding in Auschwitz. In my case the following statement by Bondy did not apply: "Often the prisoners are only too ready to go to some other place, even if it is still worse. Here the desire of men for change and new experiences plays a great role" (23; p. 465). Nor does what I have noticed in other people go to confirm Bondy's opinion. While still at the concentration camp Amersfoort I often knew prisoners to be glad to leave the camp; but merely because they thought it was impossible that things could be worse anywhere else, and certainly not from "the desire . . . for some other place."

Nor do descriptions given by other prisoners substantiate Bondy's point of view. As Utitz tells us of his experiences of Theresienstadt: "There was fear, nay panic, whenever a transport was about to leave" (145, p. 44). And Herzberg, in his Bergen Belsen diary, noted: "The departure of the transport tomorrow has caused great anxiety among the inmates of the camp. We are back again in the atmosphere of Westerbork on Tuesday. . . . Again we do not know where we are going, . . . once more a destiny unknown, a dark future" (67, p. 183).

Nor does Kaas [39] agree with Bondy. He holds that in Buchenwald only those prisoners tried to join a transport whose position in the camp was precarious, or who were afraid of somehow getting into trouble. Borst,[40] on the other hand, in the convict prison at Haarlem, knew of prisoners who applied voluntarily for a transport to the camp Erica at Ommen. Their argument was that they were about fed up with prison life, and that perhaps conditions at Ommen might be worse, but they would at any rate be different. Borst's observation may perhaps be explained by the appeal of the open air, which was denied them in the prison building. And on those who had

[39] Private information.
[40] Private information.

been placed in solitary confinement the fellowship of a concentration camp was bound to exercise a certain attraction.

So I was not looking forward to being transported to another camp; no more, I believe, were most of the other prisoners, for which various plausible explanations may be offered: the prisoners knew where they stood in the camp (and, as for Auschwitz, after the selections had ceased conditions were fairly tolerable); people were familiar with living conditions inside the camp, they had the sensation of being, to a certain extent "at home" there; and finally, through their prolonged residence they had made valuable contacts.

To return once more to the death marches. It looked as if Germany in her death struggle regarded the prisoners in the concentration camps as her most valuable possession; she would not let go of the prey she was holding in her claws. Thus the prisoners from the evacuated camps were dragged all over Germany: on foot, in cattle cars, without either food or drink, spending nights in the open in temperatures well below zero. The transports left an unmistakable trail of murdered prisoners, with bashed-in skulls, with half their craniums shot away, with faces mangled sometimes into one single clot of blood—for everyone who could no longer walk was beaten to death or shot by the SS (cf. 99, pp. 199 f.).

Von Gagern has recorded a description by Häfliger of such a transport on April 26, 1945: "An endless train of thousands of hollow spectres in rags. . . . Beside these march the SS, finger on trigger . . . Häfliger sees how a man who has collapsed from exhaustion . . . is dragged into the next field, and dispatched with two bursts of fire from a sub-machine gun. . . . Presently he is to see the same spectacle repeated a dozen times . . ." (58, pp. 8 f.).

A number of people decided, during these death marches, to escape, and thus save their lives (cf. 137, p. 132; 99, p. 20). I did not try to escape; my behaviour may be accounted for by the following circumstance: For years we had had it hammered into us by the SS that we only had to obey orders, that we must not think, that we must not take any initiative, that others thought for us, that we must not take our fate in our own hands—and consequently I was afraid to make an independent decision. Those who did venture an attempt to escape apparently had sufficient independence of spirit left to free themselves from this influence at this critical stage.

As a result of the death marches the number of victims jumped upward. In the camps to which these people were sent, the demand for lodging far exceeded the supply; added to this, the bad food, which became worse from day to day (during the last weeks we were given one thick slice of bread and one litre of potato-peel soup a day), the total lack of medical care, and the extraction of the last ounce of working power from the prisoners will sufficiently account for the fact that during the last months of the war the prisoners died like flies. Hoess has called the conditions prevailing in the camps catastrophic: "The number of the sick became immense. There were next to no medical supplies; epidemics raged everywhere. Internees who were capable of work were used over and over again. By order of the Reichsführer, even half-sick people had to be used wherever possible in industry. As a result every bit of space in the concentration camps which could possibly be used for lodging was overcrowded with sick and dying prisoners" (142, Vol. XI, p. 404).

Starvation reached such a level as I had never before experienced. I eked out my rations with grass, fresh shoots of pine trees, charcoal, brown coal, etc. There have been stories of prisoners eating human flesh. Cannibalism was observed by the Czech physician Blaha, when a transport arrived at Dachau in 1942: "On one transport which arrived in November 1942 I found evidence of cannibalism. The living persons had eaten the flesh from the dead bodies" (142, Vol. V, p. 172).

After what I have recorded, it will cause no surprise that of the 60,000 prisoners who left Auschwitz alive about the middle of January, 1945, only a very small proportion is still alive. Nor can there be any doubt that the same applies to the other concentration camps as well. The "Pakkettencommissie" relates of the concentration camp Sachsenhausen: "When the death march set out from Sachsenhausen on April 21, 1945, there were about 900 Netherlanders. The majority of these lost their lives on the way. From counts of political prisoners returning from Germany, taken at the frontier stations, it must be assumed that in the end not more than 236 of this group reached their native country" (122, p. 12).

I hope I have succeeded in giving an impression of what a German concentration camp was, and of what, as a manifestation of German National Socialism, took place in them. The next chapter will, I expect, strengthen this impression.

CHAPTER

TWO

Medical Aspects of the Concentration Camps

Mortality

MORTALITY in the German concentration camps was very high. Kogon (87, pp. 163 f.) gives figures derived from "Amtsgruppe D III" of the WVHA (Economic and Administrative Main Office), covering the period June through November, 1942. These figures relate to 16 "ordinary" concentration camps, for —as Kogon remarks—in this account there are no data on the extermination camps, such as Auschwitz and Maidanek.

TABULAR ACCOUNT [1]—JUNE–NOVEMBER, 1942

IN

Month	Admitted	Transferred	Total
June	10,322	2,575	12,897
July	25,716	6,254	31,970
August	25,407	2,742	28,149
September	16,763	6,438	23,201
October	13,873	5,345	19,218
November	17,780	4,565	22,345
Total	109,861	27,919	137,780

[1] 87, p. 163. The number of prisoners present in these 16 concentration camps on June 1, 1942, is not stated, so that percentages cannot be given.

46

OUT

Month	Released	Transferred	Died	Executed	Total
June	673	2,903	4,080	243	7,899
July	907	4,340	8,536	477	14,260
August	581	2,950	12,733	99	16,363
September	652	6,805	22,598	144	30,199
October	1,089	6,334	11,858	5,954	25,235
November	809	5,514	10,805	2,350	19,478
Total	4,711	28,846	70,610	9,267	113,434

The final account drawn up by Kogon (87, p. 164) shows:

In		Out	
109,861	arrivals	4,711	released
		9,267	executed
		70,610	died
109,861		84,588	
		25,273	net increase

Number of deaths: 79,877

About the concentration camp Buchenwald established on the Ettersberg in July, 1937, the following figures are known:

First roll call July 19, 1937: 149 prisoners.

The first death was registered on August 13, 1937; on August 15, 1937, there were two (86, p. 7). The following table (86, p. 10) gives a survey of the numbers of arrivals and deaths in Buchenwald:

Year	Arrived	Died
1937	2,912	48
1938	20,122 [1]	771
1939	9,553	1,235
1940	2,525	1,772
1941	5,890	1,522
1942	14,111	2,898
1943	42,177	3,516
1944	97,866	8,644
1945 (3 months)	43,823	13,056
Total	238,979	33,462

[1] Action against German Jews in November, 1938.

These returns do not include those prisoners who were sent on death transports, nor those who were removed to other camps in very poor health, nor those who were executed.

Referring to these returns, Kogon asserts: "The total number of deaths in the K.L. Buchenwald may surely, without exaggeration, be estimated at 55,000 in 7½ years, i.e., averaging 7,300 yearly. This implies that from 1937 until the end of 1941, every single year nearly the whole population of this camp, which until 1942 did not exceed 10,000, became extinct. Except for constant new arrivals brought in by the SS, the camp, viewed statistically, would in most years have become one enormous pile of corpses in eight months' time" (87, p. 165 f.).

Another instance is afforded by the returns of the "Hasag-Kommando Flöszberg" (86, p. 98), an outside camp of the concentration camp Buchenwald. The first transport consisted of 150 prisoners from Buchenwald.

"On February 20, 1945, 231 men were returned to Buchenwald as incapable of work, and 230 on March 4. In three months' time 168 of the prisoners that were brought in died" (86, p. 98).

Not included are the 461 prisoners who were taken to Buchenwald, of whom a large number undoubtedly died.

	Inventory	Deaths
December 28, 1944	150	—
January, 1945	393	18
February, 1945	1137	47
March, 1945	1163	84
April, 1945 [1]	1144	19

[1] On April 5, 1945.

Glyn Hughes (100, pp. 455–459), who entered the K.L. Belsen on the day of its liberation, April 15, 1945, has given the following description: "On our arrival we found 40,000 living, whilst on the ground were 10,000 corpses, and it was further reported that, in addition, 17,000 had died during the previous month of March. After a quick survey of the whole camp area an estimate was made that 25,000 required immediate hospitalization and of this number 10,000 would probably die, despite all efforts. These figures proved to be very near the mark, although the number of deaths after liberation was higher, approximately 13,000" (100, p. 456).

Mrs. Lingens-Reiner, an "Aryan" doctor, gives the following information as to the women's camp at Auschwitz-Birkenau: The camp was established in March, 1942. She arrived on February 20, 1943, and was given the number 36088. "At that time only about 13,000 women out of the 36,087 who had arrived before me were still alive" (102, p. 52). This shows a death rate, in less than one year, of about 64 per cent.

As has already been shown, of a total of 35,065 men, 11,131 died in ten weeks in Block 12, the men's hospital in Auschwitz-Birkenau (p. 13 of this book). "Assuming," to quote Blokker and Broekman, "that it is possible to compute a fairly accurate percentage of mortality, then, by basing our calculation on the difference between the average death figure per week and the average population figure per week, we arrive at a death percentage of 6.12. This would imply that the camp population present on any given day would have become extinct in just over 16 weeks" (12, p. 14 f.).

Another idea of the short time which elapsed between a prisoner's arrival in the K.Z. and his death is to be obtained from Richet: "Of my own comrades who came with me 75 per cent died in fifteen months. Out of 40,000, 13,000 died in three months" (100, p. 454).

The high mortality rate among prisoners in German concentration camps also becomes evident from a comparison with the mortality rates in a few Japanese internment camps.[1] Kouwenaar et al. give the following figures for some camps in north and central Sumatra (89, p. 9 f.):

[1] Likewise from what the *pakkettencommissie* has reported about Netherlands prisoners of war and about political prisoners: "The total number of Netherlands *prisoners of war* in Germany amounted to about 10,500, of whom 22 have been reported missing, and 244 registered as having died. The number of *political prisoners* transported into Germany amounted to 29,000, of whom 7,000 have been reported repatriated, 18,000 dead (so far as registrations have been found), and about 2,400 missing" (122, p. 12).

Camp	Total of Internees	Died	Period
Padang-Bangkinang (men)	± 850	124	1942–July 1945
Padang-Bangkinang (women)	2200	165	same
Soengei Sengkol	675	7	March '43–Sept. '44
Belawan Estate	675	20	July '43–Sept. '44
Si Rengo Rengo [1]	1850	115	Oct. '44–Aug. '45
Pakan Baroe	4800 [2]	696	14 months

[1] Si Rengo Rengo was a combination of the camps Soengei Sengkol and Belawan Estate, with the addition of a few hundred internees from other camps.

[2] Prisoners of war, who were forced to hard physical labour.

There was, indeed, a striking difference between the German concentration camps and the above-mentioned Japanese internment camps. As has been stated by Kouwenaar *et al.*: "During the first two years of internment mortality was not appreciably above normal" (89, p. 9). In the German camps, on the other hand, only a small number of the prisoners were still alive within a fraction of this time after arrival.

Many factors have been contributory to this difference in mortality. It was greatly influenced by the fact that the Japanese allowed the internees to keep their possessions, including any preserved food the latter had brought with them to the camps; also that for a long time they could buy extra food and that in some camps they were permitted to grow food for their own consumption.

Prisoners in German concentration camps, however, lived under terrible conditions, and these must, I am convinced, be primarily responsible for the high mortality rate: the food was bad, clothing was insufficient, climatic variations were severe, work was very hard, and the prisoners were seriously maltreated.

Of course, the difference may not apply to every Japanese camp. From all accounts it does not seem impossible that mortality in the camps for labourers forced to work at the Burma railway approached that in the German concentration camps.

Nutrition

The question of nutrition was of very great importance to the prisoners. With the exception of a small group of privileged prisoners (the so-called "prominents"), all were miserably fed. Borst has recorded that in the concentration camp Amersfoort (Netherlands) during the period January 30–April 20, 1942 "the calorie value of the diet . . . proved to lie between 1300 and 1400 a day" (75, p. 158).

Thanks to his efforts, "the calorie value of the diet was increased by 250 calories a day" afterwards (75, p. 158). Despite this Borst concludes: "If we had been forced to remain in Amersfoort a few months longer, the camp diet would have been responsible for many deaths from starvation" (75, p. 159). Whether a person was tall or short, had a high or low basal metabolism, performed heavy or light tasks, was young or old, had to work outdoors in the cold or indoors—none of these circumstances were taken into consideration. As to basal metabolism, Newburgh and Robinson are of the opinion that "fully active persons, other than those who support themselves by mechanical work, dissipate twice the basal metabolism in the twenty-four hours" (40, p. 512). Moreover, they are certain that there are great individual differences. Thus it is possible that for one person in ordinary circumstances only 1½ times the basal metabolism in his diet is essential, and for another 2¼ times, in order to keep up their "energy balance" (40, p. 512 f.).

De Langen has come to a similar conclusion. He had two undergraduates, with a basal metabolism of respectively +4 and +5, perform an equal amount of work, after which he determined the resting metabolism of both, finding respectively +24 and +12. Without attempting to draw any far-reaching conclusions, he states, "It seems justified to surmise that the first testee in doing the same, accurately measured amount of work, transmutes into heat and dissipates a considerably greater number of his calories, than the second. This might account for the difference in calorie need" (95, p. 3251).

In concentration camps, however, as already stated, this was not taken into account.

A fairly reliable check on a proper "energy balance" is the stability of body weight. Undernutrition will cause a decrease, overnutrition an increase. An idea of the nutritional state of a number of prisoners can be formed from two statistical returns by Kogon (87, p. 126), derived from autopsy reports of the K.L. Buchenwald:

90 Autopsies from February 13, 1940 through April 30, 1940:

Undernourished or badly undernourished	63 cases	70 %
Moderately or sufficiently nourished	14 cases	15.5%
Well nourished	13 cases	14.5%

For 75 autopsies from May 13, 1940 through November 1, 1940 the figures are:

	44 cases	59 %
	15 cases	20 %
	16 cases	21 %

There was a considerable difference between the food the prisoners were officially supposed to receive, and what they actually did receive, as there was a great deal of "leakage"; "to each 100 litres of soup four pounds of meat or, alternatively, two pounds of margarine were supposed to be added" (102, p. 51), according to a statement by Mrs. Lingens-Reiner. As, however, both the SS and the prominents "organized," [2] particularly in the provision stores and the kitchens, ordinary prisoners received far less than was intended for them.[3] Margarine was put in the soup under the inspection of an SS man; the cook, however, was not above fishing it out again, as soon as the SS man had turned his back. But also other people, Kapos, block seniors, room seniors, and room servants "organized" some of the food. And even without actually abstracting anything, one could stint others. Of this possibility I myself used to take advantage in Auschwitz-Stammlager. For about

[2] To organize meant to obtain unofficially; "organization" often became indistinguishable from outright theft.
[3] In the concentration camp Amersfoort this happened only sporadically in the spring of 1942 (private information supplied by Borst).

a year I was room physician of the neurologico-psychiatric department of Block 9. In this room were housed all mentally or otherwise deficient prisoners of the camp: the feeble-minded, imbeciles, psychotics, invalids, and prisoners too old to work. These people were not to be gassed, as they were "Aryans." There were also for a long time a number of old Jews, so-called "privilegierte Mischehen" (German married couples of whom one of the partners was Jewish and who had children; all the same they were eventually gassed). Because the portions of bread, sausage, cheese, and margarine were never equally large, I could always choose the largest. Before distributing the soup the room senior always stirred it horizontally, so that the "thick" stayed at the bottom. I always took care to have only of the "thick," and moreover, as room physician, I was entitled to an extra portion. The others were given the "thin." The argument that I was more valuable than the others, which I used to salve my conscience, was of course beside the point. If positions had been reversed I should not have acted differently.

That "organization" occasionally led to most disgusting results has been told by Rousset: in the concentration camp Neuengamme Robert Darnau, in November 1944, "found in his soup a human jaw" (126, p. 125). When this was reported to the commander, "investigation revealed that the kitchen Kapo and the crematory Kapo had agreed to sell the meat from the kitchen to civilians and feed the prisoners on corpses" (127, p. 126).

On the long way from distribution to consumption the portions were bound to shrink considerably, which did not exactly promote the prisoners' nutritive state. As to what their official allowance amounted to, we have at our disposal the following data:

In his appeal to the High Court at The Hague (on file in the [Netherlands] State Institute for War Documentation) Berg, the ex-commander of the concentration camp Amersfoort, stated that from March 8, 1943, to April 20, 1945, each prisoner in the camp was supplied with:

Daily:		*Calories*
1000 gr. potatoes	good quality [1]	920 [1]
350 gr. vegetables	turnips	136.5
350 gr. bread	rye bread	693
10 gr. butter in midday meal	margarine	76.6
10 gr. sugar in coffee	white sugar	39
9 gr. coffee-substitute	(not counted)	—
120 gr. Nährmittel (nutritious substance)	(not counted)	—
	Each prisoner, daily	1,865.1

Weekly:

3 × 25 gr. butter	margarine	574.5
2 × 75 gr. meat	beef (average quality)	304.5
2 × 75 gr. meat products	sausage (average quality)	483
2 × 75 gr. cheese	fresh (low fat content)	336
100 gr. marmalade	apple syrup	212
1 litre rye pap	flour pap	590
	Each prisoner, weekly	2,500
	This is, each prisoner, daily,	357.1

Total calorie value for each prisoner per day:

$$1,865.1 + 357.1 = 2,222.2 \text{ calories}$$

[1] These and subsequent calculations are based on the "Netherlands Food Products Tabulation" of the information office of the Food Council, published in May, 1946.

Investigations by the Central Commission for the Investigation of German Crimes in Poland have shown that the prisoners of the concentration camp Auschwitz officially received (32, pp. 63 ff.):

Breakfast: ½ litre coffee or tea made from herbs. To a 300-litre kettle 3 kilograms of sugar were added; ½ litre, therefore, contained 5 grams.

Midday meal: 1 litre soup. Four days a week with meat and on three days vegetarian. One litre of meat soup was supposed to contain:

　　150 gr. potatoes
　　150 gr. vegetables (cabbage, turnips, carrots)
　　20 gr. flour or A.V.O. (the nature of A.V.O. I have not been
　　　　able to ascertain)
　　5 gr. salt
　　20 gr. meat and bones

One litre of vegetarian soup contained:

　　500 gr. potatoes or 500 gr. turnips or 250 gr. mixed turnips,
　　　　potatoes, flour, and grits

40–50 gr. flour or A.V.O.

20–40 gr. margarine

5 gr. salt

Supper: ½ litre coffee or tea + 350 grammes bread +Sundays 40 grammes sausage; Mondays 40 grammes sausage; Tuesdays 40 grammes margarine and 50 grammes jam; Wednesdays 40 grammes sausage; Thursdays 40 grammes margarine; Fridays 50 grammes margarine and 50 grammes jam; Saturdays 50 grammes cheese.

Each prisoner, according to the above data, received *weekly*

		Calories
70 gr. sugar	white sugar	273
1350 gr. potatoes [1]	good quality	1,242
1350 gr. vegetables [1]	turnips	526.5
230 gr. flour [1]	semolina	784.3
80 gr. meat and bones	lean beef	94.4
250 gr. margarine [1]	margarine	1,915
2450 gr. bread	brown bread	5,733
120 gr. sausage	sausage (average quality)	386.4
50 gr. cheese	fresh (low fat content)	112
100 gr. jam	household jam	248
Total		11,314.6

[1] In this calculation the vegetable soup has been assumed to contain per litre: 250 grammes turnips, 250 grammes potatoes 50 grammes flour, and 40 grammes margarine.

The sick, and those who did no work at all, were given daily 1,616.3 calories.

The working prisoner was given an extra weekly allowance of 1400 grammes bread and 200 grammes sausage, making 3920 calories,[4] so that for this category the weekly number of calories was raised to 15,234.6 calories, which is 2,176.4 calories a day. Richet, who spent 15 months in Buchenwald, has recorded that "for a long time during 1944 we had only 1,750, and later only 1,050 calories" (100, p. 454).

Rosencher (125, p. 953) has stated that in the concentration camp Dachau the supply of calories per person became, in September, 1944, 1,017 daily, and in April, 1945, only 533. That towards the end of the war the prisoners must have been

[4] When I was in Auschwitz-Stammlager, the extra allowance for work was 1400 grammes bread, about 150 grammes sausage, about 40 grammes margarine and about 25 grams jam.

in the last stage of starvation is also evident from information given by Gsell, who, after examining various depositions by witnesses, calculated the number of calories supplied to each prisoner per day during the winter 1944–1945 at 800–900 in the K.L. Ravensbrück, 600–700 in the K. L. Bergen Belsen, and 500 in the K.L. Mauthausen (73, p. 123).

Before finally concluding that the prisoners were given too little nourishment to keep alive, we must go into the question: How many calories should a healthy, active person receive a day? According to Borst, "A man about 1 meter 70 cm. (5 feet 7 inches) tall doing regular work ought to receive about 2,500 calories a day" (75, p. 158).[5] Evans states: "A six-foot young man of normal weight (82 Kg., or 180 lbs.) doing hard labour in a cold climate may expend 4,000 to 5,000 calories daily" (40, p. 532). In *German Crimes in Poland* we read, "According to the standards of the Physiological Committee of the Section of Hygiene of the League of Nations a hard-working man ought to receive in 24 hours about 4,800 calories and an average working man more than 3,600 calories" (32, p. 69). Salzmann, basing his calculations on data supplied by Voit, Weber, Benedict, Rosenstein *et al.*, concludes that "a person weighing about 70 Kg. (154 lb.), in repose, needs in 24 hours, 1,680 calories, in order that his organism shall not prematurely exhaust itself" (73, p. 10).

These experiments, he adds, however, were partly made on trained people, fasting men, "who starved themselves under the very best conditions (rest, equable warmth, freedom from worry, no thirst)" (73, p. 10). De Langen points out that it is difficult to determine how many calories a normal person needs in twenty-four hours; the general estimate is 3,000. At any rate, in his function with the After-Care Service for Diabetics at Utrecht (Netherlands) he was struck by the fact "that diabetics in perfectly good condition live on a diet far lower in calorie value than is generally assumed to be the minimum for healthy persons in general" (95, p. 3251).

---

[5] The figure of 2,500 calories was meant as a minimum; it was mentioned in the campaign carried on to get nutrition in the concentration camps improved. This amount is almost certainly too little (personal information by Borst).

During the control period of the Minnesota experiment the testees did not appreciably lose weight. "On the average this control diet provided 3150 calories, 34 per cent of which were from fats, and included 110 grams of proteins.. . . . The weight change from the beginning to the end of this control period averaged —1.84 Kg., the extremes being —5.68 Kg. and +3.8 Kg." (84, p. 15).[6]

De Jongh says that it is now almost generally assumed "that for an adult, who does eight hours' light work daily, a daily ration of 80 grammes of protein, 70 grammes of fat, and 350 grammes of carbohydrate (2400 calories) is sufficient" (21, p.233)

Basing my conclusion on these statements, I believe that, when I put the daily need of calories for hard-working, healthy young men in a concentration camp at 3,000, I am not exaggerating. From this it follows that the official daily allocations (2,222.2 calories at Amersfoorst, 2,176.4 at Auschwitz) were already deficient in calories. Considering the additional fact that the prisoners were living in extraordinarily bad conditions, I think that these allocations fell considerably short of the required calorie value.

In reality things were, however, far worse. The potatoes were certainly not of good quality. And what prisoner ever received 1 kilogramme of potatoes a day, or 100 grammes of marmalade, or 150 grammes of cheese, or over 300 grammes of sausage a week? Owing to the "organizational" capacity of the SS and "prominents" the ordinary prisoner received so little food that he could not but rapidly emaciate with, as a result, the symptoms of chronic malnutrition, including such visible ones as sunken eyes, projecting cheekbones, thin skin, skin pigmen-,

[6] An experiment carried out by Keys, Brozek, Henschel, Mickelsen, and Taylor. It was an "experiment on starvation and nutritional rehabilitation in man" (85, p. 7) that took place in the University of Minnesota laboratory for "Physiological Hygiene." The control and starvation periods lasted from the autumn of 1944 to the end of July, 1945, followed by a period of three months for "controlled rehabilitation." First 36 young men of ages from 20 to 33 were carefully controlled as to their health condition. Next, 34 men (one had dropped out on account of a urinary infection, another for psychological reasons) were put on a drastically restricted diet: "the average individual daily intakes averaged for successive months, 1—1834, 2—1833, 3—1766, 4—1661, 5—1694, 6—1764 Calories." The testees therefore received over six months an average of 1,758 calories each per day.

tations, edema. All this, in addition to the close-cropped skulls and the identical clothing, led to a curious resemblance of the prisoners to one another. These very emaciated people were called "Mussulmen." They showed, according to Desoille and Laffitte, "a skeletal emaciation which conjured up visions of famine in India, which had earned them the sobriquet of 'Mussulmen' from their guards" (36, p. 7). As they were "all skin and bone," it had become impossible to tell them apart.

Gsell gives this description: "Faces and bodies of the chronically undernourished all look exactly the same, so that the unfamiliar observer finds it difficult to recognize individual persons and not to get them confused" (73, p. 124). The same thing struck Mollison, who visited Bergen Belsen four weeks after its liberation (111, p. 5). The prisoners were so emaciated that he could not use his stethoscope, as it bridged the space between two ribs and could not be made to touch the skin between.

In Amersfoort Borst observed the same phenomenon; he stretched the skin, in order to get his stethoscope to make complete surface contact with it.[7] And Kaas told me that for the same reason physicians in the quarantine camp in Buchenwald had ceased auscultation by stethoscope by the end of 1944.

As malnutrition will be more completely dealt with in subsequent sections, no further remarks on this subject need be made at this point.

The Sick, Their Attendants, and Their Care

Everything pertaining to the medical field was housed in the H.K.B., of which the SS camp physician was the chief. This person will be referred to more than once later on, so that here I can restrict myself to a few brief remarks. He hardly, if at all, attended to treatment of sick prisoners, his duty consisting mainly in making selections (this book, pp. 36 ff.), and deciding whether or not a prisoner was ill. Before a prisoner was officially regarded as ill, he first had to pass a number of "authorities."[8] The first of these was an attendant, who at the

[7] Personal communication.
[8] The following description applies to the Stammlager-Auschwitz, but may, with a few variations, be taken to apply to all concentration camps.

entrance door of the polyclinic decided, often in a manner far from gentle, whether anyone was sufficiently ill to be granted admittance. (It goes without saying that in this, as for that matter in every stage of this procedure, corruption was rife.) If the patient was admitted he reported to the "Arztvormelder," a prisoner physician; [9] the latter had to make his diagnosis amid the often considerable noise of other prisoners and decide whether he thought the patient sufficiently ill to have him shown to the block physician the next day. With the latter lay the decision whether or not he would allow the prisoner to be inspected by the German camp physician. If the patient finally reached this stage, then he would have to wait hours and hours, naked, for the camp physician, who gave his decision without examination. This decision might be:

(a) "Blockschonung" for a number of days; this meant that during this period the patient would be exempt from labour.

(b) Hospitalization in a block of the prisoners' hospital.

(c) Being sent back to work, when the prisoner was not considered sufficiently ill. When this happened too often, the block physician would receive a rebuke, which ultimately came on the head of the "Arztvormelder."

This description might create the impression that in the concentration camps prisoner doctors were people of considerable authority in the H.K.B. This was by no means always the case, as in many concentration camps laymen had more authority than physicians. Borst [10] stated that in the concentration camp Amersfoort, in the early part of 1942, a swimming instructor was the medical boss. Writing about Auschwitz-Birkenau, Lettich recorded: "Birkenau . . . the chief of the hospital . . . was a locksmith by trade" (101, p. 21). Rosencher, on Dachau: "When the *Revier* [11] was first instituted medicine and surgery were practised by persons of doubtful antecedents among the inmates. In June, 1944, internee doctors were attached to blocks" (125, p. 953). Kaas has recorded that "Prisoner doctors were not appointed to functions consistent with

[9] This function I fulfilled in the Stammlager-Auschwitz from September, 1944, to January 18, 1945.
[10] Personal communication.
[11] Another German name for prisoners' hospital.

their profession until a fairly late date, partly owing to opposition on the part of the SS, and on dates which varied considerably in the various camps" (79, p. 627).

When physicians were allowed to do medical work, though often merely as "employed patient," their lack of authority was conspicuous. Rousset observed this in Buchenwald: "Authentic physicians, who are generally nearly all foreigners, a large proportion of whom are French, have no authority at all" (127, p. 122). Kaas, who worked as a doctor in the H.K.B. in Buchenwald, states that "Whether a patient is to be hospitalized in the *Revier*, . . . is not decided by physicians, but by representatives of the upper ten" (prisoners who held leading functions) (78, p. 418). Rosencher expresses himself more strongly when he states that the prisoners' physician "had to dance attendance on the German carpenter, who conducted the sick parade in the block and who amused himself by freely changing diagnoses and treatments" (125, p. 953).

In Auschwitz-Stammlager, during my stay, conditions in this respect were more favourable. After being officially examined by the camp physician (not for medical knowledge, but for physical fitness), doctors were appointed as "Pfleger," which might mean physician, attendant, or odd-job man. From this it should not be concluded, however, that laymen had no authority in the H.K.B. They had, alas, too often.

Treatment of sick persons in the Stammlager-Auschwitz formed a definitely favourable contrast with that in other concentration camps. The H.K.B. was housed in five good stone-built blocks. There was one block for surgery, one for infectious diseases, one for internal diseases, one for "Schonung" [12] and Block 28 (this book, p. 22). The sick lay in three bunks, one above another, on straw mattresses, and were dressed in a shirt (with, later, a pair of drawers added), under two cotton blankets and a sheet. Every week the patients were bathed, and every two weeks they were given "clean" underwear and a "clean" sheet; there were few fleas and no lice. Each berth

[12] In this block the less serious patients and the convalescents were housed. In many camps the "Schonungsblock" housed those who had received temporary "Schonung" (i.e., exemption from labour) from the camp physician.

was seldom occupied by more than two persons. But . . . even patients in a state of high fever had to leave their beds to go to the toilet or to wash in the cold lavatory in the mornings. Because of "organizations" from the SS, there were always medicines, though not in sufficient quantities, including even sulfa drugs; these had been brought in by Jews from every European country. But in many other concentration camps circumstances were decidedly bad. When Kogon was in Buchenwald, "equipment was at first hardly more than primitive, and for many years defective. There was a notable shortage of adequate *medicines*" (87, p. 152).

The same complaint was voiced by Borst with reference to the camp Amersfoort: ". . . because there were no medicines. The principal and generally used drugs were lacking" (75, p. 157).

For 2,000 patients, in the winter of 1944–45, Kaas [13] was given the following:

> 1 litre of cough mixture
> 20 aspirins
> 20 pyramidon tablets
> about 20 grammes activated carbon
> about 400 grammes oak bark
> 20 tablets tannalbin

Twice a week a "flying squad" of the surgical ambulance bandaged wounds with paper.

Shortage of medicines made it necessary in Dachau "to treat only the moderately sick, since the more seriously ill would die anyway and the slightly sick would recover" (125, p. 953).

Conditions in Auschwitz-Birkenau were miserable. Lettich used to work there in the "hospital" of the men's camp. He has given the following record of his observations: "That mass of inconceivable human misery, those multitudes of people suffering from diarrhoea and cachexia were frightening to behold. . . . Every illness, every form of traumatism was represented in that pathological jail: typhus, pneumonia, cachexia, edema, broken limbs, fractured skulls, all thrown promiscuously together. . . . Without medicines and with a few strips

[13] Personal information.

of paper by way of bandages" (101, p. 24 f.). In the women's camp at Auschwitz-Birkenau things were in a horrible state: the H.K.B. was housed in a hut where "the rain leaked through the roof and the walls had enormous, gaping holes" (99, p. 57). And there also ". . . we lacked everything, even bandages. . . ." (99, p. 59.)

To be ill in a concentration camp was a very serious matter. Shortage of medicines, of expert care, of suitable nourishment, of covering, of hygienic measures, etc., hindered recovery. "To fall ill meant, in the inhumanly hard conditions of the camp, for a long time, an almost certain death sentence" (86, p. 69).

Often there were no chances at all of recovery, because many prisoners, who the SS assumed would never be able to work again, were "abgesprizt" (literally, syringed away) by means of intravenous or intracardial injections of phenol, air, or gasoline. In Buchenwald it happened that every Jew brought into the Main Prisoners' Hospital was sure to be killed by means of an injection of poison (86, p. 69).

However, not only Jewish, but also non-Jewish, prisoners were thus driven to their deaths. And in the extermination camps in eastern Europe the Jewish patients, owing to the continuous threat of impending selection for the gas chambers, were in a state of psychological unrest, which in itself was a serious impediment to recovery.

A great part of the medical work done in the concentration camps was manifestly absurd. A chart showing the course of every patient's disease, together with his temperature, pulse, and the medicines dispensed, had to be kept up to date. The absurdity of the procedure becomes apparent from information by Lettich: "As we had no medicines at our disposal, we had to write on the chart those medicines which the patient ought to have received for his case. . . ." (101, p. 23.)

Apart from these circumstances, however, medical work in the extermination camps became completely devoid of sense through the repeated selections for the gas chambers. In these camps the internee physician was constantly wondering if it was any use doing his best for patients who might be snatched at any moment from under his hands to be sent to their deaths.

It is understandable that the influence of this reflection was fatal to the medical attention of the attending physician, as in the last analysis it was a matter of complete indifference whether a patient was sent to the gas chamber after a wrong diagnosis of influenza, or after a correct diagnosis of pneumonia.

To an outsider it would appear that everything in the various concentration camps was being carried on according to normal medical practice; to him the description given by Rosencher of the prisoners' hospital in Dachau must seem fantastic: "The *Revier* (sick-bay) would seem amazingly clean and tidy. It included rooms for eye and E.N.T. clinics, a physiotherapy room with the most modern apparatus (even an electrocardiograph), . . . two magnificent operating theatres with sterilization room, an X-ray department, a dental clinic, a well-fitted laboratory, a well-stocked dispensary. . . ." (125, p. 953.)

The same applied to the prisoners' hospital of the Stammlager-Auschwitz. There were a laboratory, an X-ray room, an operating room, case histories, a large medical staff (specialists, general practitioners, nurses), etc. But for the prisoners there lay, behind this façade, the terrible reality which took such a heavy toll of human life.

The Diseases

I would like to preface a discussion of these by some general remarks. The first must be that man can go through a great deal more without falling ill than is assumed in normal times. To give one instance: One can, after a hot shower, sometimes stand naked in the open air for hours together while the temperature is well below zero, and not even catch cold.

Referring to what he himself had had to go through without experiencing any harmful effect, Frankl exclaims: "The physician among them learns, in the first place, this: Textbooks are liars! Somebody has said somewhere that to go without sleep for more than so many hours would be beyond human endurance. Entirely wrong!" (46, p. 26.)

Also the course and the symptoms of various diseases were often, in concentration camps, different from what is stated in textbooks. A possible explanation might be found in the change in the resistance and the reactive powers of the body consequent upon chronic malnutrition. It was remarkable that diseases which are repeatedly met with in routine practice were far less frequent in concentration camps. Among these should be particularly mentioned urticaria, asthma, influenza, gastric and duodenal ulcers, eczema, hypertension. Because, as is known, hunger favourably affects the carbohydrate metabolism of diabetics, sufferers from this disease showed few of the usual symptoms. Other medical men have recorded similar experiences (cf. 2, p. 127 f.). Rosencher has stated that "After liberation a number of internees developed gastric ulcers—an almost unknown disease at Dachau" (125, p. 955).

The fact that those diseases which in normal times are frequently observed were less frequent in concentration camps can only be partly accounted for by circumstances of nutrition. It is my conviction that at least as much attention should be paid to the indissoluble connection between psyche and body, and their mutual influence. This principle forms the basis of what is called psychosomatic medicine, and its practitioners regard even diseases such as ulcerative colitis, bronchial asthma, gastric and duodenal ulcer, the causes of which were entirely, or almost entirely, unknown, as being "chiefly, if not exclusively, the result of psychogenic factors" (65, p. 2823 f.).

Moreover, of diseases with a known etiology Groen *et al.* found "in a high percentage of cases, an unmistakable and sometimes remarkably strong influence of psychic factors on the first appearance and the course of the disease. This, for example, was the case with patients suffering from pulmonary tuberculosis and recurrent attacks of erysipelas" (65, p. 2824). One disease, the gastric and duodenal ulcer, should be briefly dwelt on. Many writers, such as De Langen and Schweitzer (21, p. 259 ff.) (who also mention Platteel, Veen, Stolte, and Jordans), Groen (64, p. 108), and Bok (22, p. 96), have found that the frequency of ulcers during World War II had increased in the Netherlands, the first two pointing out that "the increase of gastric ulcers was relatively much greater than that of duodenal ulcers" (21, p. 262). This appears to be in complete contrast with what was observed in concentration camps. The explanation put forward by Groen is that "those specific emotional conflicts which we have known as typical of ulcers were absent there" (64, p. 108 f.).[14] I would endorse this, because it is also my opinion that these specific emotional conflicts had ceased to exist, that, at any rate, their acuteness had dwindled, because the individual was entirely absorbed by the psychic stress to which he was subjected in the concentration camps.[15] Therefore I find it impossible to agree with Bok's statement that "gastric and duodenal ulcers were unfavourably affected by the famine" [16] (22, p. 96) for which he holds the impossibility of maintaining an ulcer diet responsible (22, p. 96), for concentration camp food can hardly be regarded as an ulcer diet either. Besides, some doubt as to the accuracy of Bok's observation seems justified, as, among other physicians, Groen has recorded, in connection with the famine winter: *"Then, as food became scarcer and worse, ulcers did not grow larger, but were reduced"* (64, p. 110). The explanation he offers is the same as that for the rare occurrence of ulcer complaints in concentration camps—"the disappearance of *specific* emotional constellation" (64, p. 110). Similarly might be explained the reduced frequency of "normal" diseases in concentration camps, namely that, because of the considerable psychic stress in the concentration camps, the psychogenic factors, which were the causes (or the contributory causes), had disappeared.

A few "concentration-camp diseases" will now be discussed in some detail.

INFECTIONS

Among these I include all infections of the skin, such as scabies, infected wounds, impetigo, furuncles, carbuncles, abscesses, and erysipelas. Their frequency was unprecedented.

---

[14] "An ulcer arises only, (a) if one cannot attain self-realization in one's work, (b) if the craving for love is denied satisfaction, (c) if the patient wants to or has to adjust himself to his emotional conflicts and reacts to this situation with the ambivalence which is characteristic of him" (64, p. 22; italics omitted).

[15] See next chapter of this book.

[16] During the winter of 1944–45, when many people in the western provinces of the Netherlands died of starvation.

Richet draws special attention to erysipelas, of which he observed in Buchenwald "about 1500 cases in less than one year" (100, p. 454).

It is remarkable how slight the symptoms were, even in the case of extensive inflammations, and how slow the process of recovery. Rosencher also observed: "Furuncles were often seen, and were very slow in healing; carbuncles were remarkable for their extent and indolence, and the lack of accompanying fever" (125, p. 954).

FROSTBITE

Anyone who, when winter began, suffered from frozen limbs, would usually not be rid of frostbite until the next spring. Protection against the severe cold was insufficient and the prisoners were in the open all day, the peripheral circulation was poor, and the camp physician seldom exempted prisoners thus afflicted from work. I only saw first- and second-grade frostbite. Kaas [17] observed third-grade frostbite as well in prisoners who arrived in Buchenwald from Auschwitz in the winter of winter 1944–45.

DISEASES OF THE RESPIRATORY ORGANS

From the frequent occurrence of *pulmonary tuberculosis* among the survivors of the concentration camps it appears that tuberculosis was rife there. Richet even calls tuberculosis "the most fearful of camp diseases" (100, p. 454). In Bergen Belsen Mollison found that, if emaciated persons did not quickly recover, they were suffering from tuberculosis. It was notable that they showed hardly any temperature and coughed little if at all. Of 64 persons examined 27 had pulmonary tuberculosis (111, pp. 5 f.). The Medico-Legal Commission of the U.S.S.R. found 2,819 prisoners alive after the liberation of Auschwitz by the Russian army. Of these 223, i.e. nearly 8 per cent, suffered from tuberculosis of the lungs. Among the liberated prisoners were 180 children, who had spent 3 to 6 months in the camp. Seventy-two children, i.e. 40 per cent, suffered from pulmonary tuberculosis or tuberculosis of the lymph

[17] Personal communication.

nodes (155, pp. 189, 191; 135, pp. 259 f.). Gsell has stated that during an examination in Switzerland after the liberation, it appeared that "of 230 concentration camp inmates 112, i.e. 46 per cent, had developed active, 25, i.e. 10 per cent, inactive tuberculosis, and only 44 per cent had sound lungs" (73, p. 146). Gsell holds that, as compared with people living in normal circumstances, active tuberculosis was 200 times as frequent, inactive tuberculosis 13 times as frequent among former concentration-camp prisoners. In 53 autopsies of victims of concentration camps and other camps, Uehlinger established tuberculosis 22 times as the cause of death (73, p. 182).

Of a total of 296 patients at Herisau (Switzerland), made up of ex-prisoners and non-German labourers from Germany, Labhart found 124 cases of active tuberculosis; i.e. 42 per cent. Had only former concentration-camp prisoners been examined, the percentage would have been far higher. Labhart has also pointed out that the most seriously ill patients from the concentration camps were not taken to Herisau, so that these figures are merely minimum percentages; in view of these facts the percentage of active tuberculosis in concentration camps must have been even higher (73, p. 250).

In a prisoner-of-war camp Markowski found 2,000 cases of open pulmonary tuberculosis in a total population of 6,000, i.e. 33⅓ per cent (73, p. 250). Kars has recorded that of the 6,000 repatriated Netherlanders who were X-rayed at Eindhoven (Netherlands) 1 per cent had open (contagious) and between 2 and 3 per cent active closed (noncontagious) pulmonary tuberculosis. From the number of repatriated inhabitants of The Hague who had been registered at the consultation bureau for the prevention of tuberculosis in that city up to January 1, 1946, he drew this conclusion: "Tuberculosis has greatly increased among persons repatriated from Germany. Many of these patients suffering from active tuberculosis had not yet registered at the consultation bureaus early in January, 1946" (80, p. 1658).

In the repatriating centre at Groningen (Netherlands) it appeared, as stated by Koppius, that of 10,000 D.P.'s, 2.68 per cent suffered from active tuberculosis; 0.31 per cent were open cases and 2.37 per cent closed (21, p. 253).

Concentration camps provided all the factors that are conducive to the generation of tuberculosis: overcrowding, severe conditions of life, bad food, and great psychic stress. As a result of the bad, grossly overcrowded "living" quarters, some of the tuberculosis cases, according to Zuppinger and Labhart (73, p. 146), may be accounted for as being caused by exogenous re-infection. Gsell holds that also endogenous re-activation played a part, through the other factors which will cause a diminished resistance (73, p. 146 f.). As causes of the extraordinary frequency of tuberculosis in concentration camps, therefore, neither endogenous re-activation, nor exogenous reinfection, should be overlooked.

Especially during the last stage of the war tuberculosis spread considerably. However, says Rosencher: "So slowly did it develop among the really cachectic that they did not appear to die any sooner than those with simple cachexia" (125, p. 995).

This is in accordance with what Gsell has observed: ". . . that clinically, *during the most serious state of starvation* tuberculosis *becomes entirely subordinate.* The famished body does not appear able to spare nutritive material, even for the tubercle bacilli, and for the time being behaves anergically. *Not until* adequate nourishment has brought about the convalescent state does *pulmonary tuberculosis secondarily* come into prominence" (73, p. 145).

Pleurisy with effusion was treated in Auschwitz-Stammlager with repeated punctures and calcium injections. For this disease, as well as for tuberculosis, the treatment then generally in use—repose, fresh air, adequate nourishment, cod liver oil— could not be applied in Auschwitz; for around the corner "the gas chamber was waiting."

Bronchitis, broncho-pneumonia, pneumonia were likewise very frequent, especially among newly arrived prisoners from highly developed areas.

DIARRHOEA

Under this heading are considered all forms of diarrhoea, even though etiologies might vary. It was not possible always to find the exact cause because the data provided by the laboratories were not always reliable. Possible causes might be typhoid fever, paratyphoid fever, dysentery, intestinal tuberculosis, dyspepsia, and "general physical weakness" (allgemeine Körperschwäche). Treatment in Auschwitz-Stammlager was very simple. The patients were put on a diet consisting of 1 litre of gruel per day and one piece of bread; in addition small doses of tannalbin were administered. I never learned the name of the inventor of the "cure," and was somewhat surprised to find that one day raw-sauerkraut therapy had been introduced. Patients were very badly nursed. When they were no longer able to go to the lavatories they would sometimes lie in their own faeces all day.

It is not surprising that diarrhoea was rife in the camps. Compelled by hunger, the prisoners were far from particular about what they ate. They would eat any food they found lying about on the ground, garbage, scraps from the meals of the sick. As not more than twice a day "coffee" or "tea" from the kitchen could be had, many prisoners drank water from the faucets, against which, in the Auschwitz-Stammlager, they had been officially warned, since this water was decidedly below standard. An examination by Lhotzky in 1941 proved that ". . . the water . . . is so unsuited for human consumption that at this moment, in the concentration camp Auschwitz, it cannot be used even for a mouth rinse."[18] Diarrhoea, as it often became virulent, claimed a large number of victims. Many of the prisoners would not have succumbed if at the first appearance of diarrhoea they could have restricted themselves to "camp tea" and abstained from food. Most of them, however, could not muster sufficient energy to resort to this drastic measure. This opinion is shared by Rosencher: "Simple dieting for 48 hours would arrest the complaint at its onset, but a relapse was easily provoked by fatigue, cold, or too speedy return to a normal diet" (125, p. 954).

18 Document N.I.-5851 *Schnellentwurf* (express scheme) for the control of the water supply in the area of the K.L. Auschwitz, by Dipl. Ing. Lhotzky, assistant headmaster (November, 1941). Available in the "Centre of Contemporary Jewish Documentation" in Paris. See also 32, p. 29.

ACUTE INFECTIOUS DISEASES [19]

Scarlet fever, diphtheria, meningitis, and typhus occurred. A diagnosis of any of these diseases was for patients in the Stammlager-Auschwitz tantamount to a death sentence. Without even entering the room, the camp physician would, as a rule, send these isolated patients to the gas chamber.

GENERAL PHYSICAL WEAKNESS: CHRONIC MALNUTRITION [20]

This condition will arise when a man receives fewer calories than he dissipates. Thus a negative energy balance arises, and to supply the deficiency, the body begins to "consume" itself, which in the concentration camps resulted in the "mussulman" type (this book, p. 58). A graphic description of the appearance of these prisoners is given by Mrs. Lingens-Reiner: "The overwhelming majority were walking skeletons, aged and hideous, keeping on their feet as though by a miracle" (102, p. 44).

Many prisoners suffered from severe malnutrition. The Medico-legal Commission of the U.S.S.R. recorded that of the 2,819 prisoners liberated at Auschwitz "2189 persons or 91 per cent were ill from extreme exhaustion" (135, p. 295; cf. 155, p. 189). Autopsies showed that of the 536 corpses found in the camp "in 474 cases (88.3 per cent) exhaustion was the cause of death" (135, p. 295; also: 155, p. 189).

Hottinger has recorded that at Herisau 171 of the 296 patients "suffered from severe starvation with or without tuberculosis" (73, p. 16; italics omitted); this is nearly 58 per cent. Here again, as in the case of tuberculosis (this book, p. 67), the percentage would have been higher but for the inclusion of non-German labourers. That the latter group has probably influenced the percentage considerably appears from an observation by Rosencher,[21] although this does not apply to non-German labourers, but to prisoners of war: "Of the returned internees, 65% were found to be ill, in contrast with 7.7

[19] Acute infectious diseases mentioned before are not dealt with again here.
[20] The famine winter 1944–45 also made these symptoms familiar in the west of the Netherlands (See 21 and 22 in bibliography). For a detailed description of this disease see 65a.
[21] It should be remarked that this observation is not restricted to starvation, but is a general one.

per cent of prisoners of war" (125, p. 955).[22] If we assume that non-German labourers had not been better off for food than prisoners of war, the percentage of hunger patients certainly becomes higher than the nearly 58 per cent recorded by Hottinger.

A notion of the strong influence of hunger on mortality can be obtained from the following table (9, pp. 112 f.):

MORTALITY RETURNS OF THE JEWISH POPULATION OF THE
WARSAW GHETTO

Period	Total Number of Deaths	Cause of Death			Percentage [1] of Deaths from Starvation of the Total Number of Deaths
		Typhus Fever	Starva- tion	Unknown	
Sept. 1939 to					
Jan. 1, 1940	6,560	5	4	2,056	0.06
1940	8,981	216	91	1,032	1.01
1941	43,239	1,991	10,991	10,653	25.41
Jan. 1, 1942, to					
July 1, 1942	26,116	512	7,254	10,694	27.77

[1] Calculation made by me. For each year the figures would be, respectively: 0.18, 1.01, 25.41, and 55.54. Actually these figures were even higher, as in the column "Unknown" there were a number of people who should have been tabulated under the heading "Starvation."

Mortality statistics of the west of the Netherlands reveal the same picture. Banning has supplied figures, from which I only quote the data relative to Amsterdam (21, p. 34):

	General Mortality, First Half-Year	Proportional Figures (1939 = 100)	Mortality per 1,000 Inhabitants
1939	3,655	100	4.60
1944	4,393	120.2	5.69
1945	9,735	266.3	12.61

Death registration at Amsterdam during the first six months of 1945 shows that in 2,316 cases starvation was the direct cause

[22] Cf. an observation by Koppius in the repatriating centre at Groningen: "The nutritive state was . . . generally satisfactory, except of those who came from concentration camps" (21, p. 248).

of death. This, however, does not completely reveal the effect of malnutrition, for, to quote Banning once more: "Besides those who were officially registered as having died of starvation, there were perhaps an even larger number for whom the bad food conditions, cold, and privation were responsible for the disease from which they suffered ending in death. This applies . . . as a matter of fact to every illness, because of the general weakening of resistive power through insufficient nourishment. Therefore many are inclined to ascribe the increase in mortality in 1945, as compared with the year before, entirely to malnutrition" (21, p. 36).

Death from exhaustion often occurred with surprising suddenness. At Ebensee I found a few times (we slept at the time four prisoners in each berth), one or two men lying dead by my side in the morning. The evening before I had observed nothing in these people to show that their end was near. Rosencher has observed the same phenomenon:"The 'mussulman' died quite suddenly, in his sleep or perhaps at roll call" (125, p. 954).

On the other hand life was sometimes seen to ebb away slowly; this dying was like the gradual going out of a candle-flame.

These two ways of dying were also observed by Fliederbaum: "The sick go out like a lamp when oil has run out . . . Some sick die in bed during the night . . . , in the morning they are often found with a bit of bread in their mouths" (9, p. 111).

Besides the sudden and slow deaths from starvation Bok distinguishes a third, viz. that caused by complications: diarrhoea, pneumonia, and bedsores with sepsis (22, p. 108 f.).

Although I do not propose to discuss exhaustively the complex of symptoms of "general physical weakness," they should not, I think, be left entirely unmentioned. Emaciation sets in, which, according to Gsell (73, p. 124), causes the original body weight to decrease by, on an average, 30 per cent, in extreme cases by from 40 to 50 per cent. The impression made on an outsider by prisoners in this state has been described by Hottinger: "The first impression the patients made on us at their hospitalization was simply crushing" (73, p. 31). Frequently body weights of between 30 and 40 Kg. (66–88 lb.) occurred in people of normal height (73, p. 248). Mollison has (111, p. 5) laid down the serious degree of emaciation in a simple statistical return. He found the average body weight of 18 men to be 44 Kg. (38.7–59.7 Kg. or 85–131 lb.) and of 18 women 35.3 Kg. (25–45.5 Kg. or 55–100 lb.). For the eleven persons who remembered their normal body weight this meant an average loss of 38.8 per cent. That this loss of weight is considerable appears from a comparison with the Minnesota experiment; here the average body weight of the testees had declined, after six months, by about 24 per cent (84, p. 27). De Jongh has recorded a weight decrease of 30 per cent in 600 of the 1200 men and women who visited the out-patients' department. He even observed declines of over 50 per cent in the normal body weight (21, p. 236). In the Warsaw ghetto, with its official daily ration of about 800 calories (9, p. 80), people were regularly weighed. Here too body weights of between 30 and 40 Kg. were observed, which, as compared with pre-war body weights, meant a decline of from 20 to 50 per cent (9, p. 83). According to Gsell, the process of emaciation is as follows: "First the stored fat disappears, next the muscles are reduced, and finally the loss of substance affects the internal organs" (73, p. 124). Stein found at post-mortem examinations that the fat around the internal organs and in the bone marrow also disappears (9, p. 25). Bok states: "even the mesenterial, perirenal, and epicardial fat is virtually absent" (22, p. 128). This emaciation of the body, Gsell asserts, is not only a passive, but also an active adaptability of the body, as "all the *dispensable organ functions cease* or are reduced to a minimum . . . the tendency of the body toward economization reveals itself in a *preponderance of the vagotropic functions: bradycardia, hypotonia, hypothermia*" (73, p. 124 f.).

The body restricts itself as much as possible to its most important functions. Forster has stated in this connection that as the internal organs are being consumed, those essential for human survival will be the last to be thus affected. "Organs of primary importance for keeping alive such as the heart, the brain, the kidneys, and the hypophysis do not suffer a decline in substance until later, and then to a lesser degree" (73, p. 125). Everything that can be regarded as "luxury" disappears; the functions not directly essential for survival—libido and potency—decline or disappear. Thus the testees of the Minnesota experiment mention in private conversations the evanescence of sexual interest as the experiment proceeds (85, p. 66). Of the 28 men who were prepared to submit to this particular test, "Only 57 per cent . . . obtained semen samples at the end of semi-starvation" (85, p. 68).

A statement to the same effect has been made by Rosencher: "Amenorrhoea was common in females, as was a total loss of sexual desire in the males. Azoospermia has been found in several patients since their repatriation" (125, p. 954; see also 9, p. 83).

Finally I may add that the disappearance of libido and potency in chronic malnutrition is also an experience of my own.[23]

A more economic working of the body through a decline in the intensity of its functions was also observed by the experimentators during the Minnesota experiment: "Paralleling the decline in body weight were striking decreases in blood pressure, pulse rate and basal metabolic rate. . . . An equally striking decrease in the size of the heart, progressing as semi-starvation proceeded, was observed" (26, p. 1569 f.).

As to the size of the heart, one meets with various conflicting statements. We have seen that in the Minnesota experiment the heart was found to have decreased in size (85, p. 47). On the other hand, Gsell has stated: *"No change* can be observed *of the heart, in usual* physical and röntgenological *examination"* (73, p. 140).

On the other hand, Piatt and Richet in X-raying ex-prisoners even found enlarged hearts (73, p. 186), as did Rosencher: "On screening, . . . the cardiac shadow [seemed]

---

[23] Sherif records a study made by A. R. Holmberg among the Sirioni (semi-nomadic Bolivian Indian society), who live in a tropical climate in the most primitive conditions. As to the sexual activity of the Sirioni it is stated that: "Food is used as a lure for obtaining a partner in sexual activities; when it is scarce, there is little sexual activity. Sexual orgies follow a successful hunt" (132, p. 83).

enormous . . ." (125, p. 954). In view of these conflicting statements, it seems best not to draw any definite conclusions as to the clinically definable size of the heart in chronic malnutrition.

In the Minnesota experiment the pulse rate decreased to "the astonishingly low value of 37" (26, p. 1570). Also Fliederbaum found in the Warsaw ghetto a decline in pulse rate to 40 to 50 per minute, "exceptionally an acceleration of activity up to from 70 to 80 per minute" (9, p. 94). In the same ghetto Mrs. Braude-Heller counted 55 to 60 beats per minute in children from 5 to 6, who, as we know, have a faster pulse rate than adults. She stated: "The slowing down of the pulse is very characteristic" (9, p. 181).

In the Amersfoort concentration camp Borst also found slowing down of the pulse during starvation. With Brutel de la Rivière he observed a boy of about 20, who, as it seemed to them, was dying of sheer starvation; this boy had a pulse rate of about 30.[24]

Different observations, however, are also recorded. Gsell: "Slow pulse rate, which is characteristic during the first months of malnutrition and regarded as vagus irritation, could no longer be observed in severely ill persons, but mostly a slight acceleration was noticeable, of between 80 and 100. Mollison likewise records an average pulse rate of about 100 in the Bergen Belsen cases" (73, p. 140). And Rosencher: "This bradycardia was interrupted by extreme and prolonged tachycardia on the slightest exertion" (125, p. 954).

As I have also frequently observed a rapid pulse rate, I think it probable that in the starvation state a decreased pulse is characteristic, but that the slightest emotion or physical exertion will cause an increased pulse rate.

The question of basal metabolism is simpler. It is already known from clinical observations that metabolism declines during brief and drastic undernourishment. Meyler mentions the research made by Master, Jaffe, and Dack, who, in heart patients on a diet of 800 calories per day (Karell cure) found metabolism to decline by 20–30 per cent in a few weeks (107,

24 Personal communication.

p. 2773). Meyler put a 67-year-old heart patient weighing 125 Kg. (275 lb.) on this diet; the patient's metabolism declined in one week from +1 to −21 per cent, in two weeks to −33 per cent, and in three weeks to −43 per cent (107, pp. 2773 f.).

De Langen records a research made by Schweitzer in his clinic. In 8 men who were undergoing a Sippy cure an average decline in metabolism of about 12 per cent was observed in 7 days (93, p. 394). It is, therefore, not surprising that also in chronic malnutrition, metabolism should decline. The Minnesota experiment supplied the following data: "At the end of semi-starvation the average basal metabolism, measured as absolute oxygen consumption, had declined 39% from the end of the control period" (85, p. 34). In 70 persons examined, Fliederbaum did not find one single instance of increased metabolism. In most cases he found a decline of 30 to 40 per cent, and in two cases, who were in the final stage of hunger sickness, even a decline of 60 per cent (9, p. 131). This decline in metabolism is regarded by De Langen and Schweitzer "as an adaption of the organism to decreased calorie allowance, by which the calorie requirement of the body is also decreased" (21, p. 272). As further adaptations of the organism they mention the more economical working of the whole organism, a decline in or a cessation of the specific dynamic action of the proteins, particularly of animal origin, because the food is entirely, or almost entirely, lacking in them. In this connection I would like to refer to a commonly held view concerning the protein requirement of human beings, which I think to be a mistaken one. White has stated: "The standard which has become quite generally accepted, assuming the average adult body weight to be 70 Kg. (154 lb.), is 1 Gm. of protein . . . per kilogramme of body weight per day. This protein allowance includes at least a 50 per cent excess to allow for proteins of low biological value. The biological value of a protein is dependent on its amino-acid composition" (40, p. 90). Evans states further:"One gramme of protein per kilogramme of ideal body weight is the minimum for safety" (40, p. 576).

Involuntarily I have proved by experiment that the view that 1 Gm. of protein per Kg. of body weight per day is necessary in order to prevent a breaking up of the body protein, is open to controversy. In view of the quantity of protein I was given in Auschwitz, while my body weight (without edema!) remained constant and my physical strength also did not decline, I am inclined to estimate the daily protein requirement of the human body at much less than is officially accepted. This view is shared by others. Borst states: "With food of high calorie value 25 Gm. of protein are sufficient to keep the nitrogen balance constant; even if no protein at all is provided only little body protein will be lost. A patient suffering from serious protein shortage who is given nourishment of high calorie value and of relatively high protein value consumes the greatest proportion of the protein for reconstruction" (24, p. 2726). And according to Kolff, it is Kempner's opinion "that a daily intake of 15 Gm. of protein is sufficient not to disturb the nitrogen balance, if a diet of high carbohydrate value is provided" (88, p. 428).

In connection with my experiences I am of the opinion that the views of Borst and Kempner are nearer to the truth than those held by White and Evans.

A few more symptoms of chronic malnutrition were:

Decrease in blood pressure: This phenomenon is not surprising, for, to quote De Langen, it is known that "malnutrition and decline in metabolism result in a decrease in blood pressure" (94, p. 3126). Thus Mollison found an average of 91/60 in Bergen Belsen (111, p. 5). Gsell also observed in Switzerland in ex-prisoners: "Blood pressures had generally decreased as low as 80–110 mm. Hg." (73, p. 139).

Blood pressure of the test persons in the Minnesota experiment also decreased (26, p. 1569). In this connection I want to call attention to a statement by De Langen. He observed a few cases of hypertension that had disappeared in people who had been in camps. He has recorded: "That changed, and especially bad, food conditions may cause a certain type of hypertension to decrease, as far as the camps have shown, is beyond doubt" (94, p. 3127). Thus the fact that a number of sufferers from essential hypertension were freed of their complaints in concentration camps may be accounted for.

Decrease in body temperature: People covered themselves up in bed with anything they could lay hands on; also the testees in the Minnesota experiment complained of cold and used to wear, in spite of the hot weather in July, warm clothing. Bok has recorded that he regularly observed rectal temperatures of 34–35° C. (93.2–95 F.).

Weakness of movement: I found that in order to mount a short flight of steps, I had to lift my legs with my hands, and that even speaking tired me. Similar experiences have been related by, *inter alios,* Kouwenaar (89, p. 21) and Bok (22, p. 32). These symptoms may be explained by atrophy of the skeleton musculature, which Uehlinger (73, p. 210) and Stein (9, p. 72) could macroscopically observe in post-mortem examinations of persons who had died of starvation.

Impotence of males and amenorrhoea of females: Both are reversible (22, p. 37; 157, p. 136).

Psychic symptoms: Apathy, retarded reactions, decline of concentration power and of memory.

In the Japanese internment camps Van Wulfften Palthe observed that "In the last phase, that of real starvation, the severity and frequency of mental disturbances most positively increased. The psychopaths became ever more unmanageable, many schizophrenics died, others went into deep stupor. New patients came to the 'mental department,' exhibiting acute confusion, which resembled an intoxication psychosis as is seen, for instance, in bromide intoxication, with great excitement and theatre-hallucinations" (157, p. 138).

I am not in a position to affirm these observations of Van Wulfften Palthe concerning schizophrenics, as I observed only a small number of these patients. Unlike Van Wulfften Palthe, I found no acute confusion in people who were in the last stage of starvation. In this connection the following observation by Glastra Van Loon is noteworthy: "It is indeed an interesting and as yet not fully explained phenomenon that starvation causes quite different symptoms in different countries. . . . For instance, what struck us in the western provinces of the Netherlands was the absence of deficiency diseases and the quiet, nearly symptomless course of starvation, which progressed, via the extreme degree of emaciation, to the silent death from starvation" (discussion in 157, p. 139).

I also noticed no deficiency diseases, and as noted before, not seldom observed silent death from starvation (this book, p. 72).

Finally one more symptom will be discussed: *Hunger edema.* Gsell remarks: "Edemas are generally the first ominous symptom that the body has suffered so much through malnutrition, that henceforth physiological adaptation begins to fail" (73, p. 128).[25] The frequent occurrence of edema in hunger sickness has also been reported by Bok: "Most patients suffering from severe cachexia suffer also, if slightly, from pretibial or sacral edema. Really completely 'dry cases' of extreme cachexia are extremely rare" (22, p. 38).

Gsell regards as characteristic of the mild form of hunger edema: "its *dependence,* in the first place, *on the body position* (with shifts according to position and disappearance through bed repose) and secondly *on the intake of fluid and salt*" (73, p. 128).[26]

In a further stage of chronic malnutrition edemas disappear only through bed repose, and abstention from fluids ceases to have any effect.

Uehlinger has recorded, as characteristic of hunger edema, "preference for the lowest parts of the body (pronounced static localization), lability, quick and easy shifting, quick and easy disappearance in repose, rapid development after heavy labour (intermittent edemas)" (73, p. 223, italics omitted). The last characteristic has also been mentioned by Stein, as an observation by others: "The appearance of the edema is facilitated by the influence of cold and physical exertion" (9, p. 30).

Gsell was struck by the fact that hunger edema patients—in contrast with patients with cardiac or Bright's disease

---

[25] Gsell makes this distinction of the results of chronic malnutrition: "A first phase of *physiological adaptation* of the body to the subnormal intake of nourishment, and a second phase of the *pathological processes* after the exhaustion of the regulating powers at the disposal of the organism, therefore a sickly process which we designate as *hunger sickness*" (73, p. 124).

[26] Bok also points to the easy shifting of edemas (22, p. 39).

edemas—suffer little inconvenience (73, p. 128), while Bok thinks it remarkable that there should be so little dyspnea (22, p. 35). Also Borst has stated, in a description of a patient suffering from hunger edema, that the latter was not dyspneic (25, p. 1039).

I want to point out emphatically that I do not intend to discuss hunger sickness exhaustively. For this reason I will not enter into affections of the skin, pains in the back,[27] neurological aberrations,[28] diarrhoea, the possible connection between edema formation and hypoproteinemia, or Borst's opinion that hunger edema should be partly attributed to a decrease in elastic resistance of the tissue (25, p. 1043). Nor do I propose to discuss the protein content of the blood, the sedimentation rate, hematological changes, blood chemistry, etc. On the other hand, I should like to devote a little space to the period which is necessary for recovery from the effects of starvation. Gsell observed that in medium cases recovery took from 4 to 8 weeks, and in severe cases from 3 to 6 months, "while more subtle changes in the cells are even longer apparent. Light ankle edemas will occur for months afterwards after exertion" (73, p. 168).

Rosencher mentions prolonged "sympathetic hyperactivity" during at least 6 months. He instances sweating on the slightest exertion (125, p. 955). Bok holds that "only after a very long time can complete recovery be spoken of . . . they are easily tired, also mental exertion has become harder than before, it appears that many have become slower in learning, they are apt to get a return of edema about the ankles, when standing or walking, or to have diarrhoea; in females menstruation often does not return until months later" (22, p. 153).

That it takes a long time to regain one's pre-concentration-camp physical and psychic condition I have experienced in my own person.

---

[27] Van Wulfften Palthe mentions the often intolerable pains in the back, in the vicinity of the ileosacral joints, accounting for them as follows: "The disappearance of all adipose tissue and the extreme weakness of muscles, which cause a stretching of the ligaments and overburdening of the joints, with consequent arthrosis" (157, p. 136).

[28] See the lecture by Van Wulfften Palthe and subsequent discussion (157, pp. 135 ff.).

INJURIES

Besides all kinds of injury and fracture, which are effected by violence and which are also met with in normal life, there was one of a different type. One of the many forms of punishment which were imposed was the notorious "twenty-five on the buttocks." For this the SS used a so-called buck, a "particularly constructed wooden table, on which the offender, lying on his belly, with his head in a lower position, with his behind stretched and high, and his legs pulled forward under him, was strapped fast" (87, p. 111).

On the buttocks the prisoner received from 5 to 25 strokes with a stick or a whip. This might be repeated four times at fourteen-day intervals. On April 4, 1942, the following order was issued: "The Reich Führer SS and Chief of the German Police has decreed that when he has decided upon corporal punishment (both for male and female prisoners in protective or preventive custody), if the word 'intensified' has been added, the punishment is to be administered to the *naked buttocks*" (142, Vol. XXIX, p. 329).

The effect was terrible. Least serious were the extensive hematomas, which were very painful. Sometimes the buttocks looked like "raw minced beef." Once I saw a patient die of sepsis consequent on this maltreatment.

Medical Experiments on Prisoners [29]

In various concentration camps medical experiments on prisoners were made. The fact that we are well informed on this subject we owe to the trial which is officially known as "Case No. I, United States of America *vs.* Karl Brandt, *et al.*" (143, Vols. I and II, through p. 352). It took place at Nuremberg before the Military Tribunal I from November 21, 1946, through August 20, 1947, and is also called the "Medical Case" or "Doctors' Trial," because of the 23 accused, 20, among whom there was one woman, were physicians. They were charged with having committed "murders, tortures, and other

[29] See page 114 of this book.

atrocities . . . in the name of medical science" (143, Vol. I, p. 27). Of the 20 physicians, 13 were found guilty. Four were sentenced to death by hanging, the other nine to imprisonment varying from ten years to life.

The aim of the experiments was the collection of data which would enable the German military medical service to give the German soldier better medical aid. Some of these experiments, however, were made to find out what methods could best be applied to prevent the propagation of life and even to destroy life; this is called "*ktenology, the science of killing*" by Alexander (7, p. 325).

The prisoners who had to undergo these experiments had *not* volunteered for them. To everyone who has lived in a German concentration camp this is, despite denials by some of the defendants, perfectly evident. For the many people who are not acquainted with this inferno from their own experience, I think I cannot do better than cite what Taylor, Chief of Counsel for War Crimes, said on this subject in his opening statement at Nuremberg on December 9, 1946: "None of the victims of the atrocities perpetrated by these defendants were volunteers, and this is true regardless of what these unfortunate people may have said or signed before their tortures began. Most of the victims had not been condemned to death, and those who had been were not criminals, unless it be a crime to be a Jew, or a Pole, or a gypsy, or a Russian prisoner of war . . . it is a fundamental and inescapable obligation of every physician under any known system of law not to perform a dangerous experiment without the subject's consent. . . . I fervently hope that none of us here in the courtroom will have to suffer in silence while it is said on the part of these defendants that the wretched and helpless people whom they froze and drowned and burned and poisoned were volunteers. If such a shameless lie is spoken here, we need only remember the four girls who were taken from the Ravensbrück concentration camp and made to lie naked with the frozen and all but dead Jews who survived Dr. Rascher's tank of ice water. One of these women, whose hair and eyes and figure were pleasing to Dr. Rascher, when asked by him why she had volunteered for such a task, replied, "Rather half a year in a brothel than half a year in a concentration camp." [30]

These experiments, made on non-volunteers, will be only summarized here, although the subject is of sufficient importance for an extensive discussion of them to be justified. [31]

HIGH-ALTITUDE EXPERIMENTS: [32]

As Allied planes flew at very high altitudes, the German pilots were forced to follow suit. In order to find out what effect this would have on the human body, experiments were made on prisoners in the concentration camp Dachau in 1942, by means of a mobile low-pressure chamber supplied by the German Institute for Aviation (D.V.L.) in Berlin; Chief of the Institute of Aviation Medicine of the D.V.L. was Ruff. [33] In this chamber atmospheric conditions of the altitude required (from 12 to 20 Km.) could be reproduced. But also pressure in the chamber would very quickly be increased or decreased; in this way investigations could be made as to what happens to a pilot who has to bail out at a considerable height, through a defect in his pressure cabin.

The initiative in performing these tests on human beings was taken by SS Second Lieutenant Dr. Sigmund Rascher, Air Force physician, who is presumed to be dead. On May 15, 1941, he addressed a letter to Himmler to this effect (143, Vol. I, pp. 141 ff.; 110, p. 11 f.; 109, p. 5 f.): "I therefore put the serious question: Is there any possibility that two or three professional criminals can be made available for these experiments? . . . The experiments, in which the experimental subject of course may die, would take place with my collabora-

[30] 143, Vol. I, p. 70 f. In a memorandum (143, Vol. I, p. 245; 110, p. 54; 109, p. 27) written by Dr. Rascher on November 5, 1942, on the rewarming of the victims of freezing experiments by naked women this statement is to be found. This woman appears to have made a deep impression on Rascher, for he writes: "It hurts my racial feelings to expose to racially inferior concentration camp elements a girl as prostitute who has the appearance of a pure Nordic . . ." (143, Vol. I, p. 245).
[31] Extensively treated by F. Bayle (15).
[32] 143, Vol. I, pp. 92–198; 110, pp. 11–41; 109, p. xi and pp. 4–19.
[33] Ruff was a medical aviation expert.

tion" (143, Vol. I, p. 142). The request was granted. Rudolf Brandt[34] wrote to Rascher that Himmler would gladly make the prisoners available. How lavishly this was done appears from the testimony of the ex-prisoner Walter Neff (143, Vol. I, pp. 177 ff.; 110, pp. 22 f.; 109, pp. 18 f.), who had been assigned as an assistant in these experiments; between 180 and 200 prisoners were subjected to the tests, of whom from 70 to 80 persons were killed. Besides a number of prisoners sentenced to death (estimated by Neff at about 30) there were among the testees Jews, Poles, and Russian prisoners of war. Dr. Blaha, who was confined in the concentration camp Dachau from 1941 and held the function of pathologo-anatomist there, testified at Nuremberg on June 11, 1946 (142, Vol. V, pp. 167 ff.) before the International Military Tribunal with respect to high-altitude experiments: "Through a window in the van I have seen the people lying on the floor of the van. Most of the prisoners used died from these experiments, from internal hemorrhages of the lungs or brain. The survivors coughed blood when taken out. It was my job to take the bodies out and as soon as they were found to be dead to send the internal organs to Munich for study. About 400 to 500 prisoners were experimented on" (142, Vol. V, pp. 169 f.).

Although the exact number of testees is apparently not known, it is certainly higher than the two or three professional criminals requested by Rascher. Many died of the consequences of these experiments.

The scientific results were communicated by Rascher to Himmler. He recorded that during sustained tests in atmospheric conditions above 10.5 Km. respiration ceased after about 30 minutes, while in two cases electrocardiographically charted action of the heart continued for another 20 minutes.

On one victim autopsy was begun about half an hour after breathing had ceased. The pericardium contained 80 cc. of clear yellowish fluid; after this had been removed the right auricle of the heart began to beat again; a severe brain edema

[34] Rudolf Brandt was the personal administrative officer of the SS Reich Leader.

was also found, as well as gas embolisms in the vessels of the brain, heart, and liver (143, Vol. I, pp. 145 ff.; 110, pp. 13 ff.; 109, pp. 8 ff.; 15, p. 329 [photostat]).

Though I do not propose to treat these high-altitude experiments in further detail, I think that the following test should not be ignored. Several instances of inhumanity on the part of the SS have already been mentioned; yet this experiment, performed by a physician, fills me with particular disgust. Rascher had noticed that those testees who had been taken up very quickly to an altitude of 14 Km. and then been "dropped" again to sea level, showed serious psychic symptoms, also on ground level, such as retrograde, amnesia, disorientation as to time and locality until about one hour after the experiment; he also observed paralysis, catatony, stereotypy. In the practice of aviation this corresponds to the pressurized cabin becoming damaged (so that the pilot experiences a sudden transition from high pressure to low pressure, and consequent gas embolism may occur), and the following parachute jump. Rascher now wanted to find out to what extent gas embolism, which may have occurred as a result of rapid depressurizing, apart from lack of oxygen, is responsible for these indications. In a report to Himmler (143, Vol. I, p. 152 ff.; 110, p. 17 ff.; 109, p. 12 ff.), he stated that for this purpose "after relative recuperation from such a parachute-descent test had taken place, however, before regaining consciousness, some VP's [35] were kept under water until they died. When the skull and the cavities of the breast and the abdomen had been opened under water, an enormous amount of air embolism was found in the vessels of the brain, the coronary vessels, and the vessels of the liver and the intestines, etc. This proves that air embolism, until now considered as absolutely fatal, is not fatal at all, but that it is reversible, as shown by the return to normal conditions of all the other VP's" (143, p. 154 f.).

Rascher was not the only one to conduct experiments on

---

[35] VP's—Versuchspersonen (testees, test persons or T.P.'s); in this case they were "rassenschänderische Berufsverbrecher—Juden" ("Jewish professional criminals who had committed race pollution") (143, Vol. I, p. 154).

behalf of aviation. The physician Ruff and his assistant Romberg also made experiments on prisoners in the concentration camp Dachau. As it was not proved that the experiments by Ruff and Romberg caused injury or death to the prisoners, they were acquitted by the Military Tribunal I.

FREEZING EXPERIMENTS [36]

On February 24, 1942, the inspector of the Medical Service of the Air Force, Professor Dr. Hippke, instructed Dr. Holzlöhner, who held the chair in physiology at the University of Kiel, to study the effects of freezing on warm-blooded creatures. A research group was formed, consisting of Professor Holzlöhner, Dr. Rascher and Dr. Finke, who started investigations on August 15, 1942, in Block 5 of the concentration camp Dachau. In this block there had been constructed a basin 2 meters long, wide, and deep, which was filled with icy water. As testees 50 to 60 prisoners were used, of whom 15 to 18 died. The experiments of the research group ended in the early part of October, 1942. The results were communicated to Himmler in a detailed report (143, Vol. I, pp. 225 ff.; 110, pp. 41 ff.) and by Professor Holzlöhner personally to physicians who attended the congress which took place in Nuremberg on October 26 and 27, 1942. This congress was devoted to "Medical Questions in Marine and Winter Emergencies."

The research group was disbanded in October, 1942, but this did not prevent Rascher from continuing these experiments and even exposing prisoners to below-zero temperatures during the night in the open air. This Rascher period, which came to an end in the beginning of 1943, cost the lives of 80 to 90 of approximately 300 testees. Although Rascher wrote on September 10, 1942, that no useful purpose would be served by investigating the rewarming of severely chilled people through body warmth (143, Vol. I, p. 220; 110, p. 45), yet he carried out these experiments because Himmler wanted him to (143, Vol. I, p. 221; 110, p. 45). The latter "modestly" remarked in a letter of October 24, 1942, addressed to Rascher: "I am very curious as to the experiments with body warmth.

[36] 143, Vol. I, pp. 198–278; 110, pp. 41–63; 109, pp. 20–33.

I personally take it that these experiments will probably bring the best and lasting results. Naturally, I could be mistaken" (143, Vol. I, p. 244). For these experiments four women were transported from the concentration camp Ravensbrück to Dachau. In a report to Himmler (143, Vol. I, pp. 250 f.; 110, pp. 54 ff.; 109, pp. 27 f.) Dr. Rascher stated his results. The test persons were taken out of the water (temperature 4 to 9 degrees Centigrade or 39.2 to 48.2 degrees Fahrenheit) when their rectal temperature had decreased to 30 degrees Centigrade (86 degrees Fahrenheit), when all were in a state of unconsciousness. The testees were put in one bed either with one or with two naked women. Rascher's "scientific" conclusion stated, among other things: "Only those experimental subjects whose physical condition permitted sexual intercourse rewarmed themselves remarkably quickly and showed an equally strikingly rapid return to complete physical well-being" (143, Vol. I, p. 251).

According to information by Blaha (142, Vol. V, p. 170), Himmler once attended such an experiment.

As to the scientific value of these experiments, I quote the opinion of Bayle: "The experiments carried out by Rascher on his own retained the extreme and unscientific character of the high-altitude experiments; they constitute unheard-of and inexpiable crimes. Rascher's experiments conducted together with Holzlöhner and Finke likewise assumed an extreme character, but they were conducted with a certain scientific rigor, for which Holzlöhner was, beyond any doubt, responsible. Neither deaths nor sufferings were eschewed" (15, p. 532).

MALARIA EXPERIMENTS [37]

From February, 1942, until the end of the war malaria experiments were conducted by physicians on prisoners in the concentration camp Dachau. These experiments were supervised by Professor Dr. Schilling, a famous malaria research scientist and member of the Malaria Commission of the League of Nations. In a trial held before the Military

[37] 143, Vol. I, pp. 278-315.

Court at Dachau in 1945,[38] by which he was sentenced to death, Professor Schilling confessed to having conducted these experiments on non-volunteer test persons, and also said that from 900 to 1,000 prisoners were infected with malaria. The object of these experiments was, according to Professor Schilling, to find a vaccination against malaria. The patients were treated with quinine, neoarsphenamine, pyramidon, and a new dye, No. 2516, after they had been infected either by being bitten by infected mosquitoes or by injections of malaria-infected blood.

The Czech physician Blaha, mentioned before, has stated (142, Vol. V, p. 169) that between 30 and 40 persons died as a result of these malaria experiments, and many more of diseases which ended fatally owing to weakened physical condition consequent on malaria attacks. Deaths also occurred as a result of too large doses of neoarsphenamine and pyramidon.

MUSTARD AND PHOSGENE GAS EXPERIMENTS [39]

Under the supervision of Professor Hirt of Strasbourg experiments with mustard gas on prisoners took place in the concentration camp Natzweiler from November, 1942, until the middle of 1944. The object was to find the most effective treatment for injuries caused by mustard gas. About 220 prisoners were experimented on, of whom some 50 died. The results of these experiments were recorded by Professor Hirt and Dr. Wimmer in a report entitled "Proposed Treatment of Poisoning Caused by Lost [40] Gas" (143, Vol. I, pp. 341 ff.).

In the same concentration camp experiments were conducted by Professor Dr. Bickenbach, of Strasbourg University, and his assistants Helmut Ruehl and Fritz Letz. After the capture of Strasbourg by the Allies the French found in the apartment of Professor Bickenbach the seventh report addressed to Professor Dr. Karl Brandt, the personal physician to

---

[38] Extracts from the trial in 143, Vol. I, pp. 289–299.

[39] 143, Vol. I, pp. 314–355; 110, pp. 157–165; 109, pp. 75–81.

[40] Lost = mustard gas. It was called Lost, because Lommel and Steinkopf recommended its use for war purposes (59, p. 323).

Adolf Hitler and Reich Commissioner for Health and Sanitation; he was responsible only to Hitler.[41]

This report deals only with the protective effect of hexamethylenetetramine in phosgene poisoning. Forty prisoners, probably all Russian prisoners of war, were subjected to phosgene poisoning, resulting in the death of no less than 4 subjects while some of the others suffered severe lung edema.

SULFANILAMIDE EXPERIMENTS [42]

These experiments were conducted in the concentration camp Ravensbrueck from July 20, 1942, until August, 1943. The experimental subjects consisted of 15 male and 60 female prisoners. The latter were all Polish women. Supervisor was Dr. K. Gebhardt,[43] professor of surgery at the University of Berlin (7, p. 301), personal physician to Himmler, chief of the orthopedic clinic at Hohenlychen, Chief Surgeon of the Staff of the Reich Physician SS and Police [44] and (after Dr. Grawitz had committed suicide) president of the German Red Cross. The required surgical treatment was carried out by Dr. F. E. Fischer, assistant at Hohenlychen. One of the co-workers nominated by Dr. Lolling [45] was the female camp physician of Ravensbrueck and assistant at Hohenlychen, Dr. Herta Oberheuser. Cultures of staphylococci, streptococci, and gas gangrene bacteria were made available by the Hygiene Institute of the Armed SS, of which Professor Dr. J. Mrugowsky [46] was chief; this man also held the office of Chief Hygienist of the Reich Physician SS and Police.

The aim of these experiments was to test the efficacy of sulfanilamide on inflammations and particularly on gas gangrenes, for the German troops on the front were sustaining heavy casualties from the many infected wounds. On the question whether these soldiers should be treated with medicines alone,

---

[41] Karl Brandt was sentenced to death by Military Tribunal I.
[42] 143, Vol. I, pp. 354–392, 660–664; 110, pp. 123–145.
[43] Gebhardt was sentenced to death by Military Tribunal I.
[44] Reich Physician SS and Police was Dr. Grawitz.
[45] The medical chief of all concentration camps.
[46] Mrugowsky was sentenced to death by Military Tribunal I.

or only surgically, or with both methods combined, opinion of the German medical world was divided. The death of Heydrich, Chief of the Reich Security Main Office and Deputy Reich Protector of Bohemia and Moravia, resulting from a bullet wound inflicted in an attempt on his life at Prague on May 27, 1942, was a powerful incentive for these experiments to be undertaken. As Mitscherlich and Mielke have recorded: "The effect of Heydrich's death on the later insistence of tests on human beings at Ravensbrueck can hardly be exaggerated" (110, p. 124). For it had been charged against Gebhardt that, if he had given Heydrich better sulfanilamide treatment, the latter's life might have been saved. These experiments gave him an opportunity to rehabilitate himself, and as has been recorded in the sentence of Military Tribunal I: "Gebhardt personally requested Heinrich Himmler's permission to carry out these experiments" (143, Vol. II, p. 223).

The human guinea pigs were surgically infected. Attempts were made to bring about gas gangrene in the testees by imbedding a strip of gauze saturated with bacteria under the fascia of the musculus peroneus longus. Because the effects shown in the testees were not satisfactory, the number of bacilli was increased, bacilli coli and earth were added, so that a process was obtained that resembled that of gas gangrene disease. Still the experimenters were unsatisfied, because the picture was different from that shown by soldiers at the front, and so the prisoners were inoculated with bacteria plus glass splinters or fragments of wood shavings, or both (from animal tests it was known that this would considerably increase the virulence of the bacteria).

During a visit by Dr. Grawitz on September 3, 1942, the latter, however, stated that the conditions under which the tests were being conducted did not conform to those prevailing on the front, as none of the testees had died. In deference to this criticism, in 24 female Polish prisoners the arteries of the muscles which had been inoculated with bacteria were tied off. According to witnesses at Nuremberg, this series of experiments resulted in the death of 5 of the 24 women; according to the defendants Gebhardt, Fischer, and Oberheuser,

3 died. A number of these women were permanently crippled. The results of these experiments were announced by Fischer, after being introduced by Gebhardt, at the Third Conference East of Consulting Specialists from May 24 to 26, 1943, at the Military Medical Academy in Berlin. The address bore the title "Special Experiments on Sulfanilamide Treatment" (143, Vol. I, p. 378). In an affidavit Fischer stated: "It was made perfectly clear during the speeches made by Dr. Gebhardt and myself that the experiments were conducted on inmates of a concentration camp" (143, Vol. I, p. 376). The lecture was attended by a large number of physicians (according to Mitscherlich and Mielke, about 200 [110, p. 143]); among them were Professor Dr. Sauerbruch and Professor Heubner (143, Vol. I, p. 376). As to the response aroused by his lecture, Fischer stated: "This lecture was followed by a discussion. No criticism was raised" (143, Vol. I, p. 375).

BONE, MUSCLE, AND NERVE REGENERATION AND BONE TRANSPLANTATION EXPERIMENTS [47]

These tests were carried out simultaneously with the sulfanilamide experiments in the concentration camp Ravensbrueck. About 75 female Polish prisoners served as testees. Again Professor Gebhardt was supervisor and his co-workers were the physicians: Oberheuser, Fischer, Schiedlausky, and Stumpfegger. Stumpfegger was a disciple of Gebhardt and had been personal physician to Himmler and later, after Professor Brandt had fallen into disgrace, to Hitler.

The results of the bone experiments were published by Stumpfegger in 1944 in the *Zeitschrift für Chirurgie (Journal for Surgery)*, edited by Professor Sauerbruch. An extract appeared in 1946 in a German journal for the practicing physician.[48] An excellently documented description of these experiments was submitted to Military Tribunal I at Nuremberg by two ex-prisoners of the concentration camp Ravensbrueck.

[47] 143, Vol. I, pp. 318–418; 110, pp. 145–151.
[48] *Clinic and Practice*, weekly journal for the practicing physician. Editors: Dr. Herbert Volkmann and Dr. V. E. Mertens, Munich 2, Alfonsstrasse 1. The extract is to be found on p. 14 of Volume I, No. 1, February, 1946, which was the first issue (143, Vol. I, p. 405).

the Polish female physicians Nedvedova-Nejedla (143, Vol. I, pp. 400 ff.) and Maczka (143, Vol. 1, pp. 402 ff.). Only one experiment will be mentioned here, viz., a free heteroplastic transplantation of a bone, mentioned by Fischer (143, Vol. I, p. 394; 110, p. 147; 109, p. 64). Because of sarcoma the shoulder joint of one patient at Hohenlychen had been removed. In this man the German physicians Gebhardt, Stumpfegger, and Schulze wished to transplant a scapula from another living person. For this purpose Fischer removed a scapula from a prisoner and took it to the clinic at Hohenlychen, where it was transplanted in the patient by the above trio. The two Polish female physicians have made no separate record of this operation, but only mention amputations of a whole arm or leg. They have stated that these amputations of whole limbs were mainly carried out on abnormal (mentally ill) patients (Maczka gives their number as about 10), who, if they survived the operation, were killed by injections of evipan.

SEA-WATER EXPERIMENTS [49]

These experiments were carried out in the concentration camp Dachau in August and September, 1944. Forty-four prisoners, for the greater part Gypsies made available by Himmler, served as human guinea pigs. The aim of these tests was to find out how to advise German military men, crews of aircraft after forced landings at sea, and crews of torpedoed ships (who might not be picked up for days); a point of great importance was whether these men should be advised to abstain completely from drinking, or to drink small quantities of sea water. At the same time researches were to be made as to the advisability of making sea water potable by Dr. Berka's method of adding Berkatit, which altered the taste but not the composition of sea water. Dr. Schäfer's improved method, by which through the addition of Wofatit the salt in the sea water is precipitated, was not practicable, because the production of a sufficient quantity of Wofatit required too much silver. A request to Himmler for permission to have these tests carried out was sent in by Professor Dr. Schröder,

[49] 143, Vol. I, pp. 418–495; 110, pp. 63–83; 109, pp. 33–42.

Chief of the Medical Service of the Air Force (143, Vol. I, p. 452).

Directions for the experiments were laid down by a commission, one of whose members was Professor Dr. Eppinger of the University of Vienna.[50] The actual experiments were conducted in Dachau by Professor Dr. W. Beiglböck. Various experiments were made, in which the effects of starving, deprivation of water, intake of ordinary sea water, sea water made potable by means of Berkatit or Wofatit, emergency food rations, etc., were observed in various combinations.

Although the testees who had to submit to these experiments were not spared severe sufferings, no deaths occurred. Professor Dr. Andrew C. Ivy, medical scientific consultant in the trial, pronounced the results of the experiments to be "not scientifically reliable" (143, Vol. I, p. 429).

TYPHUS EXPERIMENTS [51]

Because typhus had become rife in the German armies after the invasion of Russia, a conference was held on December 29, 1941, which was attended by a number of physicians, among whom were Professor Dr. Handlöser, Medical Inspector of the Army, Professor Dr. Reiter, President of the Public Health Department, and Professor Dr. Gildemeister, President of the Robert Koch Institute in Berlin. At this conference it was decided that "as animal tests cannot provide adequate evaluation (of typhus vaccines) experiments on human beings must be conducted" (87, p. 185).

The concentration camp Buchenwald [52] was appointed as the place where these experiments were to be carried out, while Dr. Ding, who later assumed the name of Schuler, was instructed to direct them. When Ding was absent, his duties were temporarily taken over by the camp physician, W.

[50] Professor Eppinger committed suicide in Vienna on September 26, 1946 (15, p. 544).
[51] 143, Vol. I, pp. 508–631; 87, pp. 184–191; 110, pp. 81–119; 109, pp. 42–51.
[52] Typhus experiments were also conducted in the concentration camp Natzweiler and the outside camp Schirmeck of the same camp. They were supervised by Professor Haagen, professor of Hygiene at Strasbourg. These experiments will not be discussed.

Hoven.[53] Thanks to Kogon finding the diary of the late Dr. Ding [54] in the Buchenwald concentration camp, we have ample information on the subject of these experiments. They were conducted in Block 46, to which Block 50 was added in the course of 1943. Block 50 was used exclusively for the production of vaccines, with which experiments were made elsewhere, e.g., in Block 46. The experimental department in Buchenwald was officially called, as of 1943, "Division for Typhus and Virus Research of the Hygiene Institute of the Waffen SS" (Chief, Professor Dr. Mrugowsky). These experiments were not restricted to typhus; experiments were also made with yellow fever, smallpox, paratyphoid A and B, cholera, and diphtheria, while at the same time the possibility of injecting persons with old blood plasma without danger of shock was investigated. As the typhus experiments were the main feature, experiments with yellow fever, etc., will not be considered here.

It appears from Ding's diary that 729 prisoners were experimented on with typhus, of whom 154 died. To these must be added the so-called "passage persons," of whom between 90 and 120 died (143, Vol. I, p. 511). The experiments were carried on as follows: The test persons were inoculated with a typhus vaccine. Some weeks later they were artificially infected by means of scarification of the skin, or by intramuscular or intravenous injections. Infection took place by means of Rickettsia-Prowazeki, the cause of typhus, furnished by the Robert Koch Institute in Berlin. About a year later this strain appeared, according to an entry in Ding's diary, to have lost its virulence: "*11 April, '43*. . . . The strain 'Matelska' of the Robert Koch Institute, which was highly virulent until a year ago, apparently is no longer pathogenic to humans" (143, Vol. I, p. 565). In order to avoid this risk for the future, a number of prisoners in good physical condition, the "passage persons," were each month infected with fresh blood from typhus patients. Thus typhus organisms of high virulence were always

[53] Hoven was sentenced to death by Military Tribunal I.
[54] "Diary of the Division of Typhus and Virus Research at the Institute of Hygiene of the Waffen SS, 1941 to 1945" (143, Vol. I, pp. 557–573; 15, pp. 1134–1146; 84, pp. 143–151).

available. According to information by Kogon (87, p. 186), virtually all these "passage persons" died. Ding's experiments to this effect have been recorded in his diary. To quote an example:

Apr. 13, 43. Preliminary Experiment D.
The following were infected:
   6 persons with 2 cc. each of fresh blood intravenously.
   6 persons with 2 cc. each of fresh blood intramuscularly.
   6 persons with 2 cc. of fresh blood subcutaneously.
   6 persons by scarification.
   6 persons by means of vaccinating scalpel cutaneously.
The 6 *intravenously* infected persons again contracted very serious typhus; 5 died.
Of the 6 infected intramuscularly, one person contracted medium typhus. The others had no serious complications, and were not hospital cases. The surest means of infection to produce typhus in humans is, therefore, the intravenous injection of 2 cc. fresh typhus-infected blood.

Dr. Ding
SS-Sturmbannfuehrer [55]

Several series of experiments were made to find out the protective value of the vaccine used. Among the vaccines investigated were the following: Cox, Gildemeister, and Haagen vaccine; Behring vaccine; Weigl vaccine (of the Institute for Typhus and Virus Research of the Army High Command at Cracow); Durand and Giroud vaccine (from the Institute Pasteur in Paris); vaccine made by the process of Combiescu, Zotta, and collaborators (produced by Cantacuzino at Bucharest); vaccine "Zürich" (from the University of Zürich) and the vaccine "Copenhagen" (from the National Serum Institute at Copenhagen).

The following example reveals Ding's method of experimentation:

Typhus Vaccine, Experimental Series VII
May 28, '43–June 18, '43. Carrying out of typhus vaccination for immunization with the following vaccine:
   1. 20 persons with vaccine "Asid."

[55] 143, Vol. I, p. 566.

2. 20 persons with vaccine "Asid Adsorbat" of the Anhaltini-schen Serumwerke G.m.b.H., Berlin 7.
3. 20 persons with vaccine "Weigl" of the Institute for Typhus and Virus Research of the Army High Command, Army (O.K.H.), Krakow (Eyer).

Aug. 27, '43. Infection of—
20 persons in the series "Asid."
20 persons in the series "Asid Adsorbat."
20 persons in the series "Weigl."
10 persons for control
   by intravenous injection of ¼ cc. each of fresh typhus-infected blood, strain Bu. II, Passage I. All experimental persons contracted very serious typhus.

Sept. 7, '43. Chart and case history completed.
The experimental series was concluded:
53 deaths (18 with "Asid," 18 with "Asid Adsorbat," 9 with "Weigl," 8 control).

Sept. 9, '43. Charts and case histories delivered to Berlin.
                                    Dr. Ding
                                    SS-Sturmbannfuehrer [56]

On request of the I.G. Farben the therapeutic value of acridine and methylene blue was examined; as the test persons did not become ill after inoculation with a typhus strain, this experiment was designated as negative. Experiments in the therapeutic effects of acridine granulate and Rutenol were conducted later, after a preliminary discussion had been held:

Apr. 13 and 14, '43.
Unit of SS-Sturmbannfuehrer Dr. Ding ordered to I.G. Farben-industrie A.G., Hoechst. Conference with Professor Lauten-schlaeger, Dr. Weber, and Dr. Fussgaenger concerning the experimental series "acridine granulate and Rutenol" in the concentration camp Buchenwald (143, Vol. I, p. 566).

The results of these therapeutic tests have been recorded by Ding:

[56] 143, Vol. I, pp. 567 f.

Apr. 24, '43. Therapeutic Experiments Acridine Granulate (A-GR, 2) and Rutenol (R-2)

To carry out the therapeutic experiments "acridine granulate and Rutenol," 30 persons (15 each) and 9 persons for control were infected by intravenous injection of 2 cc. each of fresh typhus-infected blood. All experimental persons contracted very bad typhus.

June 1, '43. Charts and case histories completed.

The experimental series was concluded:

21 deaths (8 with acridine granulate, 9 with Rutenol, 5 control).

Dr. Ding
SS-Sturmbannfuehrer [57]

These typhus experiments deserve a more detailed discussion; as this would, however, fall outside the scope of the object of this book, the matter must now be allowed to rest.

STERILIZATION EXPERIMENTS [58]

The aim of these experiments appears from a statement by Rudolf Brandt: "Himmler was extremely interested in the development of a cheap and rapid sterilization method which could be used against enemies of Germany, such as the Russians, Poles, and Jews. . . . The capacity for work of the sterilized persons could be exploited by Germany, while the danger of propagation would be eliminated" (143, Vol. I, p. 695).

In reply to a request by Himmler, Brack, Chief Administrative Officer in the Chancellery of the Fuehrer of the N.S.D.A.P., informed Himmler of the possibility of sterilizing large numbers of people by means of Roentgen rays. He proposed that these people be asked a few questions over a counter, or be told to fill out a blank form. During the time this would take (from 2 to 3 minutes), he would have them sterilized by means of Roentgen rays. He estimated that from 3,000 to 4,000 persons per day could thus be sterilized. This suggestion by Brack does not appear to have been accorded the attention he had expected, for on June 23, 1942, he wrote

[57] 143, Vol. 1, 566.
[58] 143, Vol. 1, pp. 694–739; 110, pp. 229–242; 109, pp. 131–146.

to Himmler again: "Among the 10 million Jews in Europe there are, I estimate, at least 2–3 million men and women who are fit enough to work. Considering the extraordinary difficulties the labour problem presents us with, I hold the view that those 2–3 million should be specially selected and preserved. This can, however, only be done if at the same time they are rendered incapable of propagating. . . . Castration by X-ray, however, is not only relatively cheap, but can also be performed on many thousands in the shortest time. I think that at this time it is already irrelevant whether the people in question become aware of having been castrated after some weeks or months once they feel the effects. Should you, Reich Fuehrer, decide to choose this way in the interest of the preservation of labour, then Reichsleiter Bouhler would be prepared to place all physicians and other personnel needed for this work at your disposal" (143, Vol. I, pp. 721 f.).

In October the dermatologist Dr. Pokorny brought to Himmler's attention a publication by Madaus on sterilization experiments on animals with an extract of Caladium seguinum.[59] Pokorny wrote: "Dr. Madaus published the result of his research on a medicinal sterilization (both articles are enclosed). Reading these articles, the immense importance of this drug in the present fight of our people occurred to me. If, on the basis of this research, it were possible to produce a drug which, after a relatively short time, effects an imperceptible sterilization on human beings, then we would have a new powerful weapon at our disposal. The thought alone that the 3 million Bolsheviks, at present German prisoners, could be sterilized so that they could be used as labourers but be prevented from reproduction, opens the most far-reaching perspectives. Madaus found that the sap of the Schweigrohr (Caladium seguinum) when taken by mouth or given as injection to male and also to female animals, after a certain time, produces permanent sterility" (143, Vol. I, pp. 713 f.; italics omitted).

This caused Himmler to promote the researches of the biological department of the Madaus Works. Serious difficulties

[59] Caladium seguinum: a plant found in Brazil.

appear to have been encountered, so that experiments on human beings were never started.

The gynecologist Professor Dr. C. Clauberg was more successful. On May 30, 1942, in a circumstantial report (143, Vol. I, pp. 724–728), he suggested to Himmler that sterilization experiments be carried out on female prisoners in the concentration camp Auschwitz; at the same time he submitted a plan for the establishment of a "Research Institute of the Reich Leader SS for Biological Propagation." On July 7 following, a conference was held at which the sterilization of Jewesses was discussed. This conference was attended by Professor Clauberg, Professor Gebhardt, and Himmler.[60] It was decided that the concentration camp Auschwitz be put at the disposal of Professor Clauberg for his proposed experiments on human beings and animals, and further that "by means of some fundamental experiments, a method should be found which would lead to sterilization of persons without their knowledge." [61]

Finally it was decided that examinations be begun, preferably in cooperation with Professor Dr. Hohlfelder, as to the way sterilization of men could be achieved by X-ray treatment.

[60] Memorandum of Rudolf Brandt on this discussion. See 143, Vol. I, p. 728; 110, p. 240 f.
[61] 143, Vol. I, p. 728. Himmler seems to have been somewhat ignorant of the fact that involuntary and unexpected sterilization of women was still in its experimental stage. Witness the following letter, sent by Rudolf Brandt to Professor Clauberg on July 10, 1942:

"Dear Professor!

"Today the Reich Leader SS charged me with transmitting to you his wish that you go to Ravensbrueck after you have had another talk with SS Obergruppenfuehrer Pohl and the camp physician of the women's concentration camp Ravensbrueck, in order to perform the sterilization of Jewesses according to your method.

"Before you start your job, the Reich Leader SS would be interested to learn from you how long it would take to sterilize a thousand Jewesses. The Jewesses themselves should not know anything about it. As the Reich Leader SS understands it, you could give the appropriate injections during a general examination.

"Thorough experiments should be conducted to investigate the effect of the sterilization, primarily from the point of view of determining after a certain time, which you would have to establish, what changes have taken place—perhaps by means of X-rays. In some cases a practical experiment might be arranged by locking up a Jewess and a Jew together for a certain period and then seeing what results are achieved. . . ." (143, Vol. I, p. 729).

These experiments were conducted in Block 10 of Stamm-lager-Auschwitz. On June 7, 1943, although he had been experimenting for not more than four months, Professor Clauberg could inform Himmler that: "The method I contrived to achieve the sterilization of the female organism without operation is as good as perfected. It can be performed by a single injection made through the entrance of the uterus in the course of the customary gynecological examination known to every physician. . . . One adequately trained physician in one adequately equipped place, with perhaps 10 assistants (the number of assistants in conformity with the speed desired) will most likely be able to deal with several hundred, if not even 1,000 per day" (143, Vol. I, p. 731; emphasis omitted).

Adelaide Hautval was an inmate of Block 10 from March until July, 1943. Because she refused to assist in these experiments, she was sent to Birkenau. She has recorded [62] that some caustic fluid was introduced into the uterus in order to cause obstruction of the Fallopian tubes. The testees had to submit to this treatment several times; the result was checked by means of X-rays. Apart from this method researches were also carried on in the concentration camp Auschwitz as to how women might be rendered sterile by X-rays. Kleinova has stated that "The method of Professor Schumann consisted in, first, an application of X-rays on the lower part of the abdomen, i.e. on the internal genitals. After a few of these applications a removal of an ovary was carried out, sometimes bilateral, sometimes unilateral. In the latter case the second ovary was removed later by another laparotomy." [63]

Professor Schumann's experiments were not, however, restricted to females. The effect of X-ray treatment on one or two testicles of males was examined by X-raying the genital area. According to Steinberg (36, p. 2), who was a physician in Block 21 of the Stammlager Auschwitz, the men who had been X-rayed were sent back to the camp; they were exempted from selections for the gas chambers "until further notice." After some time they were questioned as to pollutions, sexual

[62] In 101, p. 44 and 15, pp. 700 ff. Similar reports in 32, p. 74.
[63] In 101, p. 52. Similar reports in 32, p. 73 f.

desire, character changes, etc. They were told to masturbate, and if this had no effect massage of the prostate was applied, first digitally, and later "by means of a kind of crank which was inserted into the anus of the unfortunate person; a few turns of this instrument sufficed to cause erection and an ejaculation of the spermatic fluid" (36, p. 2).

In *German Crimes in Poland* (32, p. 74) it has been stated that the men were also castrated and that, after removal, the testicles were taken to Berlin by Professor Schumann, to be examined. These castrations are also recorded in a report (135, pp. 287 f.) of the surgical department of the prisoners' hospital at Auschwitz covering the months of October, November, and December, 1943. Among the operations performed during this period are found "89 amputations of testicles (castrations)" (135, p. 288).

According to Alexander (4, p. 8) the method of sterilization by means of X-rays was proved to be unsuitable; every one of the 100 males who had to submit to this experiment sustained serious burns. On examining 4 of these victims, who had all been castrated, he found that "Three had extensive necrosis of the skin near the genitalia, and the other an extensive necrosis of the urethra" (4, p. 9).

As I think that the nature of the experiments mentioned so far has been clearly revealed, a bare mention of the rest will suffice. These consisted in experiments with epidemic jaundice (143, Vol. I, pp. 494–508; 110, pp. 119–123), poisons (143, Vol. I, pp. 631–639), phlegmon (143, Vol I, pp. 653–669; 110, pp. 151–157), polygal (a hemostat) (143, Vol. I, pp. 669–684, and phenol (*ibid*, pp. 684–694).

In conclusion I refer to the testimony of Blaha (142, Vol. V, p. 169), to the effect that in the concentration camp Dachau about 500 operations, among which were stomach, gall bladder, spleen, and throat operations, were performed on healthy prisoners from the middle of 1941 until the end of 1942. Many people died on the operating table. These operations were meant to serve instructional purposes and "were performed by students and doctors of only 2 years' training, although they were very dangerous and difficult" (*ibid.*, p. 169).

Jewish Prisoners as Objects of Study on Behalf of Medico-Anthropological Science [64]

In "The Medical Case" only one instance is mentioned, which, however, was described in the "Opening Statement" as "perhaps the most utterly repulsive charges in the entire indictment" (143, Vol. I, p. 54). The "scientific" object that Professor Dr. Hirt, who held the chair of anatomy at Strasbourg University, aimed at, was to form a collection of Jewish skeletons on behalf of this university. In order to realize this Sievers [65] enclosed in a letter to Rudolf Brandt dated February 9, 1942, a report by Professor Hirt (143, Vol. I, pp. 748 f.; 110, pp. 165 f.). The subject was: "Securing skulls of Jewish-Bolshevik Commissars for the purpose of scientific research at the Reich University of Strasbourg" (143, Vol. I, p. 749). In this report the professor states: "Of the Jewish race . . . only very few specimens of skulls are at the disposal of science. . . . The war in the East now presents us with the opportunity to remedy this shortage. By procuring the skulls of the *Jewish-Bolshevik Commissars, who personify a repulsive yet characteristic sub-humanity*, we have the opportunity of obtaining tangible scientific evidence" (143, Vol. I, p. 749; italics mine). He therefore suggests that, when these persons are taken prisoner by the Wehrmacht, they be turned over to the field police. A special deputy is to take photographs and anthropological measurements, ascertain the origin, date of birth, and other personal data of the prisoner. Hirt continues: "*Following the subsequently induced death of the Jew*, whose head must not be damaged, he will separate the head from the torso and will forward it to its point of destination in a preserving fluid in a well-sealed tin container especially made for this purpose. On

[64] 143, Vol. I, pp. 738–759; 110, pp. 165–173; see p. 114 of this book.
[65] Sievers was Reich Business Manager of the "Ahnenerbe" Society. The "Ahnenerbe" was controlled by Himmler, and was, from Jan. 1, 1942, incorporated in Himmler's personal staff, thus becoming a section of the SS (143, Vol. II, p. 188). It was devoted to researches concerning the propagation, the spirit, the accomplishments, and the heredity of the Indo-Germanic people of the Nordic race (143, Vol. I, p. 88). When the collection of Jewish skeletons was begun the "Ahnenerbe" was given an additional duty: "the establishment of the 'Institute for Military Scientific Research' " (143, Vol. I, p. 89; 110, p. 166).

the basis of the photos, the measurements, and other data on the head and, finally, the skull itself, comparative anatomical research, research on racial classification, pathological features of the skull formation, form and size of the brain, and many other things can begin. In accordance with its scope and tasks, the new Reich University of Strasbourg would be the most appropriate place for the collection of and the research on the skulls thus acquired" (143, Vol. I, p. 749; italics mine).

The original plan to use "Jewish-Bolshevik Commissars" for this Jewish skeleton collection appears to have been incapable of execution. In order to attain the object in view in spite of this, Rudolf Brandt gave the following instruction to Eichmann on November 6, 1942:

"The Reich Leader SS has given instructions that everything that is necessary for the researches of SS captain Professor Dr. Hirt, who is also director of a department of the Institute for Military Scientific Research in the 'Ahnenerbe' Society, be put at his disposal. By order of the Reich Leader SS, I therefore request you to enable the projected collection of skeletons to be established. As to details, SS lieutenant colonel Sievers will get in touch with you." [66]

The result of this request appears in a letter (143, Vol. I, pp. 751 f.; 110, p. 166) addressed by Sievers to Eichmann dated June 21, 1943, in which the former states that SS Captain Dr. Bruno Beger had, up to June 15, 1943, selected 115 prisoners in the concentration camp Auschwitz. Of these 115 prisoners 79 were Jews, 2 Poles, 4 Asiatics, and 30 Jewesses. As, in Auschwitz, there was danger of infectious diseases (it was for this reason also that Beger had ended his work in Auschwitz), a request was made for a speedy transfer of these persons to the Natzweiler concentration camp. "At the same time one must provide for the accommodation of the *30 women* in the Natzweiler concentration camp for a short period" (143, Vol. I, p. 752). From a statement made by Joseph Kramer (143, Vol. I, p. 740; 110, pp. 167 f.; 109, pp. 84 f.), at the time camp commander of the concentration camp Natzweiler-Struthof, it ap-

[66] Document NO-089; on file in the "Contemporary Center of Jewish Documentation" in Paris.

pears that about 80 prisoners were gassed there at the beginning of August, 1943, at the request of Professor Hirt. For this purpose a special gas chamber had been constructed at Natzweiler. Kramer gave a detailed description of what took place inside the gas chamber. "I illuminated the inside of the room . . . and observed through the peephole what happened inside the room" (109, p. 85). The complete corpses, not the skulls only, were sent in three shipments to the Anatomical Institute of Hirt in Strasbourg University (143, Vol. I, p. 740). This evidence is corroborated by the testimony of the witness Henripierre [67] (143, Vol. I, p. 740; 110, pp. 168 f.). He testified that at the beginning of August, 1943, three shipments of corpses, 30 female, 30 male, and 26 male, were delivered at the Anatomical Institute of Prof. Hirt and were stored in tanks filled with 55 per cent alcohol.

When the Allied armies approached the city "it was first decided to destroy the evidence of these brutal crimes" (143, Vol. I, p. 741), but this decision was rescinded with a temporary improvement in the military situation. When, however, it appeared that the Allied advance could not be held back, Professor Hirt ordered two assistants to cremate the as yet undissected corpses in the Strasbourg crematory. The assistants being unable to perform this task, the Allies found cast-iron proof of this "scientific" crime in the cellars of the Anatomical Institute after Strasbourg had been liberated.

Photographs taken by the French authorities (143, Vol. I, pp. 905–908) tell, to quote the words of the prosecutor, "the grim story of this mass murder more vividly than witnesses and documents ever could" (ibid., p. 741).

In the "Medical Case" mention is made only of the Jewish skeleton collection. Another medico-anthropological "scientific" research was made, for which Jews were again abused as subjects of study.

This research concerns twins and dwarfs, and was conducted by SS First Lieutenant Dr. Mengele. Twins and dwarfs in the Jewish transports that arrived at Auschwitz-Birkenau were

[67] Henripierre worked in the Anatomical Institute until the capture of Strasbourg by the Allies.

not sent to the gas chambers, but were consigned to a special block. They were allowed to keep their clothes and were well fed and well treated. Dr. Mengele subjected them to a very thorough medical examination and an artist from Prague made drawings of their skulls, auricles, noses, mouths, hands, and feet. The data thus acquired by Mengele and the artist were embodied in reports which, however, were incomplete, as no pathologico-anatomical investigation had been made. The procedure by which Dr. Mengele made this possible was recorded by Nyiszli (117), from whose report these and the following data have been taken. As has already been stated, this Hungarian-Jewish physician had been charged with post-mortem examinations by Dr. Mengele, as he was a pathologo-anatomist and had been educated at a German university. His record of the way in which this camp physician filled up the gap in the reports is therefore based on personal observation.

The twins to be selected were delivered to Nyiszli in pairs. He has described his observations at the autopsies as follows: "In the outer walls of the left ventricle there is a tiny pink spot, caused by a needle and scarcely differing from the surrounding colour. cannot be mistaken. The prick has been made by a very fine needle, evidently an injection needle. He has been given an injection, but for what purpose? . . . I open the heart, starting with the ventricle. Usually the blood is removed from the left ventricle with a spoon and weighed. This course of procedure cannot be applied in the present case, for the blood has coagulated into a solid mass. I break up the clot with a pair of tweezers and carry it to my nose to smell it. I am overcome by the unmistakable smell of chloroform. He has been given a chloroform injection in the heart, that the blood of the ventricle on coagulating shall be deposited on the valves and cause instant death through cardiac arrest" (117, pp. 1669 f.).

In the autopsy reports, which were enclosed with the reports of Dr. Mengele and the artist, and then sent together to the Institute for Race-biological and Anthropological Research at Berlin-Dahlem, Nyiszli did not mention the cause of death.

By killing the twins simultaneously Dr. Mengele obtained "a unique thing in the history of medical science in the whole world. Two twin brothers die together and at the same time, and a possibility has been created to perform autopsy on them" (117, p. 1667).

Euthanasia in the Concentration Camps [68]

In a discussion of this subject, euthanasia as practiced in Nazi-Germany cannot be disregarded, as there was a close connection between the two.

An order concerning euthanasia was given by Hitler to Professor Karl Brandt and Philipp Bouhler [69] on September 1, 1939: [70] "Reichsleiter Bouhler and Dr. Brandt, M.D., are charged with the responsibility of enlarging the authority of certain physicians to be designated by name in such a manner that persons who, according to human judgment, are incurable can, upon a most careful diagnosis of their condition of sickness, be accorded a mercy death" (143, Vol. I, p. 848).

Professor Karl Brandt was the chief of the medical, Bouhler of the administrative division of the euthanasia program. Professor Brandt, according to testimony by Brack,[71] nominated from 12 to 15 physicians to assist him in its execution. Brack remembered the following names: Professor Dr. Heyde,[72] Professor Dr. Nietsche, Dr. Pfannmueller, Dr. Schumann (who made the X-ray experiments in Auschwitz,[73]) Dr. Falthauser, and Dr. Rennaux. The procedure was this: The Reich Ministry of the Interior sent questionnaires, by instruction of Dr. Linden, Councilor in this ministry, to all mental institutions. These questionnaires had to be sent by this ministry and

[68] 143, Vol. I, pp. 794–897; 110, pp. 175–229; see p. 114 of this book.
[69] Bouhler was Chief of the Chancellery of the Fuehrer of the NSDAP.
[70] According to a statement by Karl Brandt ᵃ this decree was signed after the conclusion of the Polish campaign, late in October, 1939, but dated back. This, he said, was done to make it clear "that this decree is the form in which during the war this euthanasia programme and the measures it implies can be carried out. After the war, as I understood it, . . . it will be continued in a different form." ᵇ [ᵃ 110, p. 176 f.   ᵇ ibid., p. 177.]
[71] Brack, as Chief Administrative Officer, was Bouhler's deputy (143, Vol. I, pp. 842 ff.; 110, pp. 177 f.).
[72] Professor at the University of Würzburg.
[73] See p. 100 of this book.

signed by or for Dr. Conti, State Secretary for Public Health of this ministry and Reich Health Leader, as it controlled the mental institutions. The questions to be answered by the chief physician of each institute concerned: [74] the patient's name, civil status, religion, race, war injuries, if any; visits received (if regularly and by whom), duration of illness and of stay in the institution, diagnosis; restlessness, bedridden condition, incurable physical illness, capacity for work, value of work, etc.

After being filled out, the questionnaires were sent to Linden and forwarded by him to the Reich Association, Hospital and Nursing Establishment, a camouflaged name for a division of the euthanasia programme, where photostats of them were made. Of each document a photostat was sent to four physicians, "Gutachter" (experts) who, without seeing the patient and even if the latter had been in the institution only for a short time, gave their decision on life or death, independently of each other. Next the photostats were sent by these physicians to a top expert, e.g., Professor Heyde or Professor Nietsche, who made the final decision, naturally again without examining the patient. The theoretical rule, that a unanimous decision was required was, in practice, not rigidly observed.

That these experts were quick workers will appear from the circumstance that Dr. Pfannmueller disposed of 2,058 cases in 18 days (143, Vol. I, p. 800).

If the decision that the mental patient would be granted mercy death had been taken, word was sent to the institution concerned that the patient was to be transferred to an observation hospital. Then the patient would be transferred by the General Patient Transport Company (again a camouflaged name), via the observation hospital (actually nothing but a temporary dumping place) to the euthanasia institute.

The financial part of the programme which, according to Alexander (4, p. 40) consisted, *inter alia,* in collecting money for expenses from the patient's relatives, was looked after by the Charitable Foundation for Institutional Care, again a name

[74] For a complete questionnaire see 143, Vol. I, p. 850; 110, pp. 182 f.; 109, pp. 96 f.

that served as camouflage for the institution's actual work.

As Brack has stated, there were at least six euthanasia institutes, of which he has mentioned the following by name: Grafeneck in Württemberg, Hartheim near Linz, Sonnestein near Dresden, Bernburg near Dessau, Hadamar in Hessen, and Brandenburg near Berlin. In these institutes one room was set up as a gas chamber.

Brack, who witnessed several gassings, related that the patients were taken to the gas chamber naked and were photographed at the door, for scientific reasons. Gassing, for which no consent of the relatives was asked, was done by means of carbon monoxide, and after a physician had established death the corpses were cremated. The cause of death, as stated in the announcements to the victim's relatives, was false. Brack and Karl Brandt estimate that in this way from 50,000 to 60,000 persons were murdered; in a report of the Czechoslovak War Crimes Commission the number of mental patients and aged people thus murdered is estimated at 275,000.[75]

This German euthanasia was not restricted to adults; even children were not spared. Corresponding to the Reich Association, Hospital and Nursing Establishments, there was instituted for children the Reich Committee for Research on Hereditary Diseases and Constitutional Susceptibility to Severe Diseases. To this committee again Dr. Linden forwarded the questionnaires (filled out by obstetricians, heads of children's clinics, physicians, midwives, etc.). Pfannmueller (143, Vol. I, p. 801) has declared that these children were murdered without the consent of their parents. There were murder centres for children at Eichberg, Idstein, Kantenhof, and Goerden.

Although this form of euthanasia was treated as top secret, many Germans found out what was happening. This caused Himmler to bring the matter to Brack's attention and to ask what measures he proposed to take to prevent rumours from

---

[75] 143, Vol. I, p. 67. "The Jury Court at Duesseldorf states the total number of mental patients killed, although the exact number is not known with absolute certainty, to have certainly amounted to more than 100,000" (110, p. 198).

spreading.[76] Whether or not measures were taken, I cannot tell, but if they were, they were not able to prevent the bishop of Limburg, Dr. Hilfrich, from protesting against these murders to the Reich Minister of Justice on August 13, 1941 (143, Vol. I, p. 845).

Probably through the weight of public opinion, euthanasia of adults was stopped in the autumn of 1941; children continued to be "mercy-killed" until Germany's defeat.

After what has been noted about German physicians, it will hardly be surprising that there were German research workers who wanted to make scientific capital out of these mass murders.

The General Patient Transport Company brought the brains of the victims, in batches of 150 to 250, up to a total of 600 (110, p. 189), to Dr. Hallervorden, who had also given directions as to the method of preserving the brains. Hallervorden gave Alexander what the latter calls "a vivid first-hand account. . . . Hallervorden stated: There was wonderful material among those brains, beautiful mental defectives, malformations and early infantile diseases. I accepted those brains of course. Where they came from and how they came to me was really none of my business" (4, p. 6). Hallervorden also described the procedure which was followed in picking out those patients who were to be killed. Because of the shortage of physicians the remaining doctors had "delegated the selection to the nurses and attendants. . . . The worst thing about this business was that it produced a certain brutalization of the nursing personnel. They got to simply picking out those whom they did not like, and the doctors had so many patients that they did not even know them, and put their names on the list" (4, p. 6).

By those who feel so inclined (as I do not), euthanasia as described so far may still be regarded as a matter of medical science. The euthanasia, however, that was carried on in the concentration camps from an unspecified date in 1941, and

[76] Letter from Himmler to Brack, dated 19 December, 1940 (143, Vol. I, p. 856; 110, p. 194).

designated by the code name "14 f 13," had not the remotest connection with medical science. This is shown by an affidavit of the former camp physician of Buchenwald, W. Hoven. This man has stated that the camp commander had received a secret order from Himmler to the effect that "all mentally and physically deficient inmates of the camp should be killed. The camp commandant stated that . . . all the Jewish inmates of the Buchenwald concentration camp be included in this extermination programme. In accordance with these orders 300 to 400 Jewish prisoners of different nationalities were sent to the euthanasia station at Bernburg for extermination" (143, Vol. I, p. 847).

The former first camp physician of the concentration camp Dachau, Muthig, stated that a commission of four psychiatrists, of whom Professor Heyde was the leader, selected there the prisoners "unable to work" for extermination by gas (143, Vol. I, p. 797).

By the end of 1941 it was decided to start a widespread application of 14 f 13. The inspector of Concentration Camps of Office Group D of the SS Economic and Administrative Main Office sent the following letter to the camp commanders of several concentration camps: "As the camp commandants of the concentration camps Dachau, Sachsenhausen, Buchenwald, Mauthausen, and Auschwitz have already been advised by letter, a medical commission is about to visit the above-named concentration camps shortly in order to select prisoners. A visit to the concentration camps Flossenbürg, Gross-Rosen, Neuengamme, and Niederhagen is scheduled for the first half of January, 1942, for the same purpose. . . . At the conclusion of the check a report to the Inspector of Concentration Camps is to be made, giving the number of prisoners assigned to special treatment '14 f 13' " (109, pp. 118 f.).

The "accuracy" with which the examination of the prisoners was made is clearly revealed in a statement of Muthig, referring to the above-mentioned visit of the four psychiatrists to the concentration camp Dachau: "I know that this commission stayed only a few days in Dachau and that it was impossible for them to examine medically the large number of concentration-camp prisoners in such a short time" (110, p. 210). And the physician Mennecke, who directed action 14 f 13 in several concentration camps, wrote to his wife in a letter dated November 25, 1941, on the subject of the examination of prisoners in Buchenwald: ". . . Afterwards we continued our examination until about 4 o'clock. I myself examined 105 patients, Mueller 78 patients. . . . As a second group a total of 1,200 Jews followed, all of whom do not need to be 'examined,' but where it is sufficient to take the reasons for their arrest from the files (often very voluminous) and to transfer them to the reports. Therefore, it is merely theoretical work. . . . Of this second group (Jews), we completed today: I myself 17, Moeller 15. At 5 o'clock sharp, 'we threw away the trowel' and went for supper. . . . After the Jews, another 300 Aryans follow as a third group who will again have to be 'examined' . . ." (143, Vol. I, pp. 861 f.).

Appearing as a witness in the "Medical Case" on January 17, 1947, Mennecke answered the question, "When you examined a large number of Jews, do you mean that they were all mentally ill at the same time?" with, "I have already given my position on that, to the effect that in my view they were not sick at all, either mentally or otherwise" (109, p. 121).

In connection with the total Employment of Labour, Gluecks, chief of Office Group D of the SS Economic and Administrative Main Office, informed the commanders of the concentration camps on April 27, 1943, that "in future only insane prisoners can be selected for Action 14 f 13 by the medical commissions appointed for this purpose" (143, Vol. I, p. 862); this meant that Action 14 f 13 in the concentration camps had come to an end.

The experience gained in the practice of euthanasia was applied to the "Final Solution of the Jewish Question."

At a conference of Brack, Eichmann, and Wetzel, "Amtsgerichtsrat" in the Reich Ministry for the Occupied Territories, held early in October, 1941, Brack declared himself willing to give full co-operation in murdering Jews unable to work. For this purpose he was also prepared to make persons available who had been trained in the euthanasia programme.

There is extant a draft of a letter to this effect from Wetzel to the Reich Commissioner for the East dated October 25, 1941: "Referring to my letter of October 18, 1941, you are informed that Oberdienstleiter Brack of the Chancellery of the Fuehrer has declared himself ready to collaborate in the manufacture of the necessary shelters as well as the gassing apparatus. . . . Since in Brack's opinion the manufacture of the apparatus in the Reich will cause more difficulty than if manufactured on the spot, Brack deems it most expedient to send his people direct to Riga, especially his chemist Dr. Kallmeyer, who will have everything further done there. Oberdienstleiter Brack points out that the process in question is not without danger, so special protective measures are necessary. . . . I draw attention to the fact that Sturmbannfuehrer Eichmann, the Referent for Jewish questions in the RSHA, is in agreement with this process. . . . As affairs now stand, there are no objections against doing away with those Jews who are not able to work— with the Brack remedy . . ." (143, Vol. I, pp. 870 f.).

This measure, however, was not to be restricted to Jews only. "Reichsgau Governor" Greiser, in a letter to Himmler, dated May 1, 1942 (143, Vol. I, pp. 776 f.), proposed after the "special treatment" of about 100,000 Jews had been completed "to have cases of open tuberculosis exterminated among the Polish race here in the Warthegau." Greiser estimated the number of cases of open pulmonary tuberculosis at 35,000.[77]

As to what was in store for the Russians, E. von dem Bach-Zelewski has related that Himmler early in 1941 had announced in a speech that one of the aims of the coming war against Russia was to decrease the Slav population by 30,000,000 (7, p. 311).

Alexander (7, p. 325) characterizes the genocide of non-German peoples and the elimination of "useless" and no longer loyal Germans as the "master crime" committed by the SS. He further states that, in order to be able to carry out these two items of the programme, Himmler asked for and was given "the co-operation of physicians and of German medical science" (7, p. 325). In this particular branch of medi-

[77] This plan was not carried out.

cal research, ktenology,[78] sterilization experiments were meant to secure those methods which were suitable to prevent the propagation of human life. To find the most satisfactory way of murdering large numbers of people by gassing as quickly as possible was the task of the commission of physicians and experts, under the direction of Professor Karl Brandt (7, p. 326). The third object of research was the best method of unsuspected elimination of single individuals. In many camps intravenous or intracardial injections of petrol [79] or phenol were used for this purpose. Of the latter method Ding has given a description (143, Vol. I, p. 687). Because of the sudden deaths of soldiers who had been given large doses of gas gangrene serum, Professor Mrugowsky suspected that these might be caused by the cumulative effect of the phenol content of the injections. In the presence of (*inter alios*) Professor Schreiber and Professor Killian, according to Ding's statement: "Mrugowsky ordered me to take part in euthanasia with phenol in a concentration camp and to describe the result in detail" (143, Vol. I, p. 687). He also relates that he witnessed the camp physician Hoven administering 20 cc. of undiluted raw phenol intravenously to 4 or 5 prisoners in Buchenwald: "They died in an immediate total convulsion during the actual injection without any sign of other pain. The time between the beginning of the injection and death I estimate at about ½ second." [80]

Without arousing suspicion this method could not be applied to eliminate distinguished Nazi authorities, as the smell of phenol or petrol would give away the actual cause of death. Recourse was had, therefore, to a method designed at Hohenlychen by Dr. Heissmeyer, collaborator of Professor Gebhart's, which had been tested on children in the concentration camp Natzweiler, and which consisted in intravenous injections of a suspension of live tubercle bacilli. This caused acute military tuberculosis in a few weeks, which was above suspicion as a cause of death.

[78] See p. 82 of this book.
[79] The female camp physician Herta Oberheuser murdered prisoners of Ravensbrueck by means of intravenous petrol injections (110, p. 149).
[80] 143, Vol. I, p. 687. Hoven said "within a minute" (143, Vol. I, p. 686).

In this chapter, dealing with the medical aspects of concentration camps, I have cast my net wide; I have also drawn attention to the medical experiments, medico-anthropological researches, and euthanasia. These were not a feature of every concentration camp and cost the lives of a comparatively small number of people, so that I may have laid myself open to the criticism that I should have left them out.

That I have discussed them is due, in the first place, to the interest the physician will take in them, but especially because the conception that anything could be done to a prisoner was part and parcel of the concentration-camp system.

That several German physicians took part in practices which were a corollary of the Nazi conception of a concentration camp was an additional reason for not omitting a treatment of the various forms of medical experimentation.

CHAPTER THREE

The Psychology of the Concentration-Camp Prisoner

DURING his stay in a concentration camp the prisoner passed through various stages, which may be classified as:

    I. the stage of initial reaction;

    II. the stage of adaptation;

    III. the stage of resignation.

The Stage of Initial Reaction

In this category I place all those reactions which manifested themselves on one's entry into the concentration camp, the reception, the metamorphosis into a "prisoner," [1] and the first information on the camps—in other words, the first day of concentration-camp life.

The nature of the initial reaction was determined by the psychological condition of the victim, which means *that the conception he had formed as to what would happen to him was the determining factor.* If this conception conformed to reality, the initial reaction was not very violent, as I have personally experienced. On being notified in prison that I was to be transported to the concentration camp Amersfoort (Neth-

[1] The metamorphosis into a concentration-camp prisoner: the processes by which one was turned from an ordinary citizen into a prisoner—being robbed of personal property, having one's hair cropped and the prison-number tattooed on the lower part of the left arm (only at Auschwitz), being bathed and compelled to put on prison dress.

erlands), I had a fairly accurate idea of what was in store for me. I had read much on the subject of concentration camps in Germany and had met a few people who had been confined there for some time. The concentration camp Amersfoort had been the subject of talks with people who had been inmates for shorter or longer periods, so that I was in a position to form a more or less true image of what Amersfoort would be like.

In a letter, surreptitiously written in prison, I expressed my awareness that the odds that I would not leave the concentration camp Amersfoort alive were very great. I entered the camp with the knowledge that inhuman conditions prevailed and that I was very likely to die there.

The batch to which I belonged was lined up close to the entrance gate. The first thing I perceived was a prisoner who was so violently kicked and beaten by an SS man that he was left lying on the ground for dead. Presently I saw the dreary spectacle of the entry of the labour groups.

My reaction to this, I observed, was an apparent splitting of my personality. I felt as if I did not belong, as if the business did not concern me; as if "I were looking at things through a peephole"; I felt untouched by any compassion either for the prisoner, who had probably been beaten to death, or for the incoming labour group.

This state, which is an estrangement from the surrounding world, may be regarded as an *acute depersonalization*. According to Le Coultre an acute depersonalization manifests itself as "an estrangement from one's ego, an estrangement from one's own body, and an estrangement from the surrounding world" (34, p. 370). This triad did not develop in my particular case. Thus I never thought for a moment that I had lost my personality, nor did I ever speak of my actions in the third person or see myself in the camp.

Still I think that my reaction may be regarded as an acute depersonalization, as it was a subject-object split. In my view the term "acute depersonalization" can therefore also be used if not all three estrangements mentioned by Le Coultre are present.

This acute depersonalization developed, I believe, in those who had formed an image of what a concentration camp was like, and were thus prepared for what was going to happen. As, in spite of the conception formed, the reality was too terrible for the ego to realize its immediate import, this acute depersonalization occurred, which I regard as a defence mechanism of the ego.

This reaction, to my mind, was limited to a very small group of the new arrivals. The overwhelming majority had no notion, or only the vaguest notion, of what a concentration camp really was. Kogon is of the same opinion: "There was only a very small proportion of prisoners who had any conception, before their first arrival in a concentration camp, of what awaited them" (87, p. 69).

Bettelheim, who was in the camps Buchenwald and Dachau in 1938 and 1939, discusses experiences similar to those mentioned by myself: "The writer gained emotional strength from the following facts: that things happened according to expectation; that, therefore, his future in the camp was at least partly predictable by what he was already experiencing and by what he had read" (17, p. 431).

It strikes him that during the transport to the camp and the first days in it, his behaviour is different from the normal. At first he thinks that this is an effect of the unusual situation in which he finds himself, but presently he notices "the split in his person into one who observes and one to whom things happen" (17, p. 421), and considers it as a "typical psychopathological phenomenon" (17, p. 421).

Later he states even more clearly that "these horrible and degrading experiences somehow did not happen to 'him' as a subject, but only to 'him' as an object" (17, p. 431). It is remarkable that Bettelheim refuses to call this phenomenon depersonalization, because there "seem to be so many differences between the phenomena discussed . . . and the phenomenon of depersonalization, that it seemed advisable not to use this term" (17, p. 432).

This conclusion does not appear acceptable to me without further evidence. What Bettelheim describes is, to my thinking, a subject-object split, and would, therefore, be considered a depersonalization.

My reaction on arrival in the concentration camp Auschwitz was an entirely different one. What I had expected to find there must be considered before my reaction to what I did find it to be.

During my confinement in the "Judendurchgangslager Westerbork" (Jews' Transit Camp Westerbork, Netherlands) I compared (like many others) Auschwitz to the camp at Vught (Netherlands), on which I had reliable information, thanks to the prisoners transferred from there to eastern Europe by way of Westerbork. The result was that I pictured Auschwitz as a concentration camp and a Jews' camp which were strictly separated, and where the prisoners of the two camps were treated differently. What concentration-camp treatment was I had experienced in the Amersfoort camp; I had, however, formed an entirely different mental picture of the treatment in a Jews' camp.

My conception that Auschwitz would consist of a concentration camp plus a Jews' camp was strengthened by:

(a) The farce of the so-called criminal cases at Westerbork. These were Jews, who, from the German legal point of view, had some offence on their record: going into hiding, not wearing the Star of David in the streets, making purchases in non-Jewish shops or out of shopping hours fixed for Jews, etc. They were confined in separate huts, had no freedom of movement, had their skulls shaved, were forced to harder labour, and their names could virtually not be removed from the transport lists. Sometimes, by way of special favour, the German commander would allow them to go to Auschwitz with an ordinary transport instead of with a penal transport.

(b) The stories told by several prominent persons in Westerbork, who claimed to know that criminal cases had ended up at the concentration camp Auschwitz.

(c) An announcement by the Jewish chief physician of Westerbork that he had received a cable from Auschwitz to the effect that physicians were urgently needed there.

I cannot deny that I cherished this delusion, and that everything that did not fit in was repressed.[2] Thus I refused to consider the deterioration of conditions in the Jews' camp at Vught. Nor did I leave any room for the thought of the gassing of Jews, of which I could surely not have pretended ignorance. As early as 1942 I had heard rumours about the gassing of Polish Jews, and it was assumed by everyone in Westerbork that the transport of the patients of the Jewish mental institution "Het Apeldoornse Bos" (Netherlands) on January 26, 1943, had suffered the same fate. No one expected either that the Germans would have any scruples in respect of the aged and sick people removed from Westerbork. That in spite of all this the thought of gassing was repressed seems to me beyond any doubt. Nobody had ever heard, however, *when* these gassings took place, and it was definitely not known that people were gassed immediately upon arrival. Other writers too noticed that the victims arrived in the camps in complete ignorance of their fate. De Wind has stated: "Nobody realizes that this arrival will probably be his end . . ." (156, p. 2); and Frankl: "When night came we learned the significance of the game of the pointing forefinger" (46, p. 20). Would Mrs. Lengyel have sent her mother and her eldest son to the "wrong" side, if she had known that she was sending them to death by gassing? (99, p. 15 f.).

The conclusion appears justified that none of the new arrivals had ever heard anything about the first selection and that repression did not come in at all. Real ignorance was accountable for the fact that they did not suspect that the SS man past whom they were filing decided on life or death.

Because the contact we had with several prisoners who performed certain duties during our metamorphosis into prisoners was very brief, it was not until later that we learned

---

[2] Repression is an unconscious mental process. A clear definition has been given by Groen *et al.* (repression of impulses from the id are not considered here): "Repression is generally taken to mean a process by which all unpleasant affective experiences are removed from the conscious." The three grades of repression which they distinguish are noted here for the sake of completeness:
(1) Repression: What has been repressed cannot through volition nor by simple talks or events be brought back to consciousness. (2) Suppression: What has been repressed can be restored to the conscious by talks or events. (3) Control: the person is conscious of his unpleasant emotions, but their discharge is deliberately checked (65, p. 2830).

from other prisoners the significance of the performance on the "station platform."

As my arrival in a concentration camp, the gassing of my family immediately upon arrival, and the possibility that I might shortly be dead, found me unprepared, I experienced an *acute fright reaction* when I found myself faced with the inevitability of realization. This reaction, I believe, only developed in those whose conception did not conform to reality —in the majority of the new arrivals, therefore.

Arrival in the camp and the transformation into camp prisoner did not always follow the same pattern. Kogon has given a detailed account of what he terms "the welcoming ceremonies" in the concentration camp Buchenwald. This often consisted in many forms of torment, physical torture, and humiliation, to which the new prisoners were subjected by the SS. Many new arrivals did not survive the reception: "Those who wore ties likewise had no occasion to laugh when they were garroted" (87, p. 71).

Bettelheim has related his experience: "This transportation into the camp . . . is often the first torture which the prisoner has ever experienced and is, as a rule, physically and psychologically the worst torture to which he will ever be exposed. This initial torture . . . is called by the Gestapo the prisoner's 'welcome' to the camp" (17, p. 424).

Mrs. Lengyel has told us of her arrival in Birkenau. There were threats of beating and a few were beaten. She felt it a terrible humiliation that she was forced to undress in the presence of "about twenty soldiers, most of whom were drunk" (99, p. 17), and that she had to submit to "a thorough examination in the Nazi manner, oral, rectal, and vaginal . . . All that in the presence of drunken soldiers who sat around the table, chuckling obscenely" (99, p. 19).

On the first day of our arrival in Auschwitz there were very few acts of violence. De Wind, who came with the same transport as I, distinguishes six phases on the first day: "being deprived of one's luggage, the separation of families, the impressions of the prisoners at work in the open air, the view of the camp with its electrically charged barbed wire, having one's

skull shaved and the prisoners' number tattooed, and particularly the information imparted to the newly arrived prisoner
from the elder prisoners" (156, p. 4).

We had, indeed, to go through all this; it is, however, remarkable that De Wind lays far less emphasis on what I consider was the most important psycho-trauma for the new arrivals: the realization that 80 per cent of our transport, among
whom were all the mothers with their children, had been
driven into the gas chambers. It is evident that in the various
publications the personal element plays an important part;
this may be accounted for by the individual way of assimilation (because one person will be more, or less, distressed by the
impact of a given disaster than another), by the "reception,"
which might vary considerably in individual cases, and by the
enormous difference it made whether one's family was gassed
or not. Quite apart from this personal element, memory distortions strike across many a page of concentration-camp literature. These distorted reflections of actual events in the concentration camps are not surprising, for *everyone* is subject to
emotional memory distortions, which are all the more compre-
hensible with respect to concentration camps.

Unlike De Wind, I will not make a distinction into six
phases, but include all in *one phase,* during which on the first
day events bore down upon us with tremendous rapidity. One
instance of the overwhelming effect this produced is that, after
we had been ordered to undress in the open air, and been
driven inside, I never suspected (nor, I am convinced, did any
one of us) that the sprays of the shower baths would deliver
anything but water.

De Wind is of opinion that the reaction of this first day may
be regarded as equivalent to "the reaction of a violent acute
fright: the result being a state of stupor" (156, p. 4). I share
this view, though not on the strength of the motives stated by
De Wind, who considers his six phases comparable to "the
most violent traumas with which we are acquainted in the
domain of fright neuroses" (156, p. 4). In this I disagree, as
during the first five phases there were none of the somatic
symptoms which are often observed in fright reactions, such

as vomiting, diarrhoea, polyuria, paling, fainting, tremor, inability to walk (when I was arrested I found that I was unable to walk). Neither was there oblivion, which Vroom mentions as a result of fright (149, p. 37), for De Wind's description is proof that he has remembered very much. Also, the experiences one went through during the metamorphosis into a prisoner were so many and succeeded each other so quickly that nobody had time to realize them completely. For it may happen, Vroom says, "that an incident, . . . unfolds so quickly, that there is no time to be frightened," as the incident is already over "before we know it" (149, p. 137). In my view five phases of De Wind's classification cannot be compared to the most violent traumas in the domain of fright neurosis. I remember that until after the metamorphosis, there was no trace of panic among the new arrivals; that they conversed quietly, and could (still) laugh at the "clothes" they were given. There occurred, however, a most violent psycho-trauma when they learned that there were gas chambers. The thought of gassings, which had been repressed, now suddenly came into the unprepared consciousness, causing a fright reaction. This reaction, in my experience, was very violent in those who then heard that their wives and children had already been murdered at that moment.

As to the occurrence of fright, Vroom states: "It was not the suddenness and unexpectedness of events that caused fright, but the realization that they implied the presence of a death threat" (149, p. 125).

Freud defines the meaning of fright: "the condition induced when danger is unexpectedly encountered without previous anxious readiness" (51, p. 330).

Freud defines "previous anxious readiness" as "danger, which expresses itself in heightened sensorial perception and in motor tension. This expectant readiness is obviously advantageous; indeed, absence of it may be responsible for grave results. It is then followed on the one hand by motor action, taking the form primarily of flight and, on a higher level, of defensive action, and on the other hand by the condition we call a sensation of anxiety or dread" (51, p. 330). Vroom explicitly mentions the presence of a death threat. Freud uses the term "danger," but I believe that in this word "danger" the death-threat is implied. Freud points especially to previous anxious readiness. The views of both appear of importance to me for the occurrence of a fright reaction. My definition of fright reaction, therefore, would be: the reaction which occurs on the sudden awareness or reawareness of a death threat in an unprepared consciousness.

In this connection a remark by Carp on the view of fright held by Reik should be noted: "If it is true that in a situation that inspires fright, there generally occurs a sudden and unprepared recognition of a danger at one time realized as imminent, then it is quite conceivable that uncontrolled aggressiveness may be the fateful response . . ." (29, p. 42).

The restriction expressed here, to which the occurrence of fright is subjected, the recognition "of a danger at one time realized as imminent" may be applied to the fright reaction of the prisoners in Auschwitz, as every one of them knew that he was entering "a darkness." Whether "uncontrolled aggressiveness may be the fateful response" is hard to decide, because any manifestation of aggressiveness, which I did not once perceive, meant certain death. Consequently I see no occasion to revise my definition of fright reaction.

Because the forcible termination of repression caused us to become suddenly aware that in this camp death was imminent, a narrowing of consciousness resulted, "which focuses attention exclusively on one aim: self-preservation. Although a person may be outwardly calm and collected, yet the instinct of self-preservation is very strong. This is not always sufficiently appreciated by those who have not experienced it in their own person" (149, p. 93). I also had only one thought left: How can I survive? My experience gained at Amersfoort helped me to realize that my only chance of survival lay in the medical field. When on that first day in Auschwitz we were sent on to the outside camp Buna, my sole object was to contact the physicians and nursing staff of the prisoners' hospital there and learn what course to pursue so as to be allowed to join the medical attendants of the camp. The interests of my fellow prisoners I did not consider at all. Mrs. Lingens-Reiner has stated that her reactions were entirely similar: "Will you survive, or shall I? As soon as one sensed that this was at stake everyone turned egotist" (102, p. 23).

The thought of suicide did not occur to me for a single moment. Nor did it to Bettelheim: "He wondered all the time that man can endure so much without committing suicide or going insane" (17, p. 430).

All the same, other people appear to have considered suicide. Mrs. Lengyel has recorded an attempt by a Hungarian woman physician. She herself thought it very important that she had succeeded in keeping the poison she had brought with her (99, p. 18). Bondy states that in Buchenwald, at the time of the November action in 1938 against the German Jews: "Life in Buchenwald was so wild and unbearable that many of the inmates committed suicide by severing an artery or running into the electrically charged barbed wire. . . . It was especially bad during the first few days and nights . . ." (23, p. 456).

From this it appears that people reacted in different ways. There were those who considered suicide, and even committed it. Although it is not easy to form an accurate assessment, I am inclined, because of the small number of suicides which I observed, to put the number of people who contemplated or carried out self-destruction at a fairly low figure.

Summing up, then, the *initial reaction* can be considered as follows: If the new arrival was subjected to a "ceremony of reception" that corresponded to what he had more or less expected, *acute depersonalization* would frequently result. This acute depersonalization may be regarded as a protective measure, a defence mechanism of the ego.

Quite differently situated were those who bore repression with them into the camp. The facts observed forced them to renounce this repression, and to admit suddenly into the conscious ego everything that they had heard before about concentration camps and the gassings, and that had been repressed. At that moment it was also realized that the situation into which they had been thrust contained a serious death threat for which the consciousness had not been prepared. The response to this was a *fright reaction*.[3]

Because our "reception ceremony" at Auschwitz had passed without violence, I think that the fright reaction here arose only through psychical processes. Had the "reception ceremony" been different, the fright reaction would probably have been caused both by the psychical process, and by the acts of violence of the SS (cf. 149, p. 127).

Of course there must have been persons who experienced no initial reaction. To these persons the following quotation from Vroom may be applicable: "He *may* be 'undaunted' if the conscious refuses to trace the meaning of the threat, or, in doing this, finds itself equal to the situation, and refuses to be 'daunted' " (149, p. 135). I am of opinion that to the "un-dauntedness" in a concentration camp only the first part of this quotation can be held to apply, that is, that in spite of everything the repression was retained. For anyone whose conscious recognized the meaning of the threat of the concentration camp, to remain "undaunted" appears to me highly improbable.

The Stage of Adaptation

During this stage the individual would prove whether or not he could adapt himself to the concentration-camp system.

This stage, which Kogon has called the "process of selection" (87, p. 377), was for some time decisive as to survival or death. For some time—the concentration camp being a dynamic community, in which conditions were in a constant state of flux—nobody was certain of anything: one could be transferred, or lose the function to which one owed a measure of security, or fall into disgrace, or be caught in an offence.

Even in normal life the adaptation to new conditions is difficult. As Cavan puts it: "Arrests, illness, the breaking up

[3] A more exhaustive discussion of the fright phenomenon has been omitted; readers are referred to Vroom (149).

of a home, change of residence—anything, in fact, which changes the external relationships to which one is accustomed may lead to severe emotional disturbance" (30, p. 165).

To adapt oneself to, and find one's place in, concentration-camp life was immeasurably more difficult. There was a world of difference between the conditions in which one was now forced to live and those of one's former existence. How wide the gulf was will appear from a discussion of some aspects of concentration-camp routine:

Working hours. The prisoners were on their feet from early in the morning till late at night, with only one short break at noon; when working hours began and ended would vary in accordance with the camp discipline prevailing in various concentration camps, and with the seasons.

Labour. Almost without exception the new arrivals were set to work with the outside labour groups, who were strictly guarded by the SS; also the new arrivals had to be trained in how to deal with the SS, nor did they know the Kapos and the foremen. They still had to learn the tempo of work, and had no experience in picking out the appropriate tools. Labour was often unfamiliar and physically exhausting. In each group, however, there were differences of degree, and finding the easier divisions took some time. In the outside labour groups there was never any protection from the weather. Sufficient hardiness to be abroad in all weather conditions was only acquired after a considerable time.

Food. The newly arrived prisoner had to train himself not to be nauseated by the "camp soup," and to conquer his disgust of mouldy potatoes and the leaves of trees (used by way of soup greens). To provide himself with a "Schuessel" [4] and a spoon was a problem not easy to solve.

Sleep. Several prisoners had to share one bunk, which might or might not contain a straw mattress, while the covering was always insufficient; they suffered the more from the cold, as they were forbidden to keep on their outer garments. In an

---

[4] A bowl in which the prisoner got his food. Generally there were too few, so that several prisoners had to share one "Schuessel," which, naturally, was not cleaned first.

overcrowded and often stuffy hut, sleep was all but impossible owing to the sounds of other sleeping, or sometimes dying, prisoners, and the polyuria of one's roommates and oneself; the "conveniences," moreover, were generally outhouses. All this, taken together, made the night's sleep sheer torment, until one got accustomed to it.

General hygienic care. After the prisoner had awakened in the morning, and once more realized his condition (no pleasant occupation), he was often faced by the impossibility of taking any hygienic care of himself at all. Not only was there no toothbrush, toothpaste, soap, towel, etc., but also very important was the very limited period of time before morning roll call, so that one had to wash in a hurry. Because, however, the number of faucets was insufficient for so many people, and also because occasionally there was no water available at all (99, p. 44 f.), going to the "lavatory" often became a mere formality. General hygienic conditions were unfavourably influenced by the fact that each prisoner had only one suit, one set of underclothing, one pair of socks, and one pair of shoes. Nor could the medical care to which one had been accustomed in normal life any longer be taken for granted.

As the newly arrived prisoners had not yet acquired "camp" experience, and were therefore as yet unable to "organize," they had for some time to make shift with what they had been given. For them to secure a handkerchief, a cake of soap, a towel, a scrap of paper to be used as toilet paper, was to be faced by so many unsolvable problems. Of the conditions under which the prisoners had to live Mrs. Lingens-Reiner has given this striking description: "The women prisoners would work the whole day, stand in the pouring rain for two hours or more during roll-call, and go to bed in sweaty, wet clothes, to wake the next morning at five, chilled to the bone and forced to get on to their tired feet" (102, p. 43).

One or several of the conditions mentioned obtained not only in concentration camps, but to an equal or lesser degree also in prisoner-of-war camps, "preference," and "staging" camps. There were also, however, factors that were operative to the same extent in each type of camp. Only the three "fundamental facts" mentioned by Vischer with reference to prisoners of war will be dealt with here, viz.: "Loss of liberty for an unpredictable period in community with others" (146, p. 6 f.; italics omitted).

Normal personal liberty is very important. Arntzen (10, p. 446 f.) observed 10,000 to 20,000 German prisoners of war, interned in Canada. This study is particularly revealing in that the prisoners of war did not lack for anything except personal liberty; they were well fed, not made to do hard work, housed in comfortable and well-heated huts, given good hygienic care. They also enjoyed normal opportunities for recreation and cultural developments in concerts, a library, church services, games. There was indeed restriction of spiritual liberty: letters and newspapers were censored, and the Germans were allowed to speak with Canadians only through an interpreter. The original enthusiasm for long walks, once they were allowed to take them under supervision, faded very quickly. Arntzen's explanation is "that people can gradually so accustom themselves to restriction of spatial liberty that the possibility of greater freedom of movement no longer holds great attraction, so long as full liberty is denied" (10, p. 447).

I had the same experience in the Jew's Transit Camp Westerbork. I was a physician there and often said (and many people there harboured the same reflection) that I would not n.ind remaining interned like this until the end of the war, since outside the camp there was no normal personal liberty. And the point that inside a concentration camp there was no vestige of personal liberty need not be labored.

More serious than one's lack of liberty was that *one did not know how long one was to be imprisoned* and that nothing one did would ever result in shortening the duration of one's imprisonment. "This uncertainty about the duration of the imprisonment is probably what unnerves the men most" (23, p. 464, cited from 146). In this respect the camp prisoners were far worse off than criminals, who know the term of their detention and can shorten it by good conduct.

Ignorance of the duration of imprisonment led to an existence which, as to concentration camps, has been formulated by Frankl: "The life of a concentration-camp prisoner can be defined as 'provisional detention without time limit' " (46, pp. 98 f.). And he goes on to say: "Now any human being who cannot see the end of a (provisional) form of existence, is unable to live toward an aim. *He can no longer,* like a human being in normal life, *make plans for the future"* (46, p. 99).

This view is open to objection. I am of the opinion that the non-Jewish prisoner, despite the reality of the concentration camp,[5] did make plans for the future, the most important consideration being that his nearest relatives were still alive. So also did Jewish prisoners who had married non-Jews, or whose next of kin were still alive, either in the concentration camp, or else in hiding.

Frankl's view, however, holds good partly for those Jewish prisoners whose entire family had been exterminated. This does not imply that they had now also abandoned the hope of leaving the concentration camp alive; this hope remained in spite of everything, but plans for the future were not made, at least not at the beginning. Later, when they had entirely, or partly, adapted themselves, the future was indeed considered, though generally in the spirit of "We'll wait and see." And, naturally, they were convinced that no situation in ordinary life could ever compare in difficulty with "normal" concentration-camp life. At this stage, however, plans for the future were not entirely ruled out; I remember having made a "date" with a woman prisoner in Auschwitz, for after the liberation.

As far as the other types of camp are concerned, Frankl's view will not hold either. As Utitz has stated, the majority of the Jews in Theresienstadt considered that "this existence represented a path linking the past with a future and still unknown existence" (145, p. 73). Herzberg noted in his diary on December 19, 1944, in Bergen Belsen: "Will anybody who will read this in the future ever understand? This is meant as a note to be worked out in detail later. Perhaps it will be a

---

[5] "Everyone knew that he was not likely to survive the camp, everyone had to reckon with the sacrifice of his life" (120, p. 201).

testament . . . which no one, no one, will ever open" (67, p. 238). Bondy relates of prisoners of war that "they know that their mental and physical energies are decreasing, that perhaps they will be unable to go back to their former professions because they are losing experience and are not able to follow up the newest developments in their special fields" (23, p. 465). Of the German prisoners of war who after World War II were confined in Russian prisoner-of-war camps, it has been stated by Gollwitzer: "The only thought and the only topic of their talks, one only question that incessantly occupies them all: their fatherland and the return home" (62, pp. 92 f.).

Unlike Frankl, Utitz points to the benefit that can be derived from viewing camp life as a "provisional existence": "In the concentration camp one lives as in a summer resort; here, however, one knows when the holidays will be over; in the concentration camp, fortunately one does not, and that is an enormous piece of luck" (145, p. 71). Apart from the fact that Utitz dares to call the Theresienstadt ghetto a concentration camp and dares to compare a concentration camp with a "summer resort," he is right. How many of those who managed to survive the concentration camp would have stuck it out if they had known beforehand the number of years they were to spend there? I do not believe that I could have mustered sufficient strength to keep up the continuous struggle in the concentration camp if in October, 1942, I had been told that I should not be liberated until May, 1945.

The last factor that obtained in each type of camp, which must be discussed here, is that the prisoner was *never alone*, not even when occupied in his normal vegetative functions; there was nowhere for him to settle down for a single moment; he had not a shred of private existence left. To live continuously in the company of others became agony. As Dostoievsky, who spent ten years, from 1849 to 1859, in the penal camp at Ostrogg in Siberia, has put it: "Besides the loss of liberty, besides the forced labour, one more torture in the convict's life . . . , which is almost harder to bear than any other: this is the *forced community of life*" (39, pp. 43 f.). Many other writers have dealt with this subject in much the same spirit:

Vischer (146, p. 13) with reference to prisoners of war in World War I, Utitz (145, p. 12) in regard to the Theresienstadt ghetto, Kogon (87, p. 387), Bakels (14, p. 107), Hunsche (75, p. 69), and Frankl (46, p. 71) of concentration camps, and Mrs. Pfister (120, p. 217) with reference to the refugee camps in Switzerland.

It is therefore not surprising that many prisoners became very irritable as a result of this forced daily community with people who were widely divergent in character. Kautsky holds this to be mainly responsible for the atmosphere of irritability that pervaded the concentration camps: "It is my opinion that the condition of never being alone added most to irritability" (81, p. 191).

Although there were more points in which life in the various types of camp was similar, these will not be dwelt on here. The three factors considered—lack of personal freedom, ignorance as to the duration of imprisonment, and the impossibility of ever being alone—obtained in each type of camp in equal measure. Not common, however, to every camp to the same degree, was:

HUNGER

Whereas in concentration camps hunger became an important feature soon after one's arrival, in other camps it did not make itself felt until much later. Moreover, the effect of hunger in concentration camps was much deadlier, as in these camps the prisoners' working power was totally exploited, which was not done, or was done to a much lesser extent, in the other camps. As the new arrivals came to the concentration camp reasonably well fed, and were often first, for some time, placed in quarantine (during which period they were still exempt from labour), hunger did not torment them in the beginning, and moreover their appetite had suffered through the initial reaction. Presently, especially when they had to turn out with the labour groups, this would change, and food began to play an important part, ultimately becoming the dominant factor in their lives. Anyone who has ever been in the company of hungry people knows how conversation almost invariably turns on the subject of food. In their report on the Minnesota experiment Keys *et al.* have recorded: "Favourite topics of conversation were food, farming, and rural life, a fact which was bitterly resented by some of the men" (84, p. 25). There were, however, exceptions: "Some passed through a stage of excessive food interest and then apparently rebelled against their acquiescence to this domination of an 'animal instinct.' Several of these men at times became almost violently irritated by wishful discussions of food" (84, p. 34).

In the concentration camps too, food was a very favourite topic of conversation. The prisoners would go "dining" out together and exchange recipes for special dishes: Hungarian Jews told me again and again how goulash used to be cooked at home (cf. 62, p. 92; 157, p. 138). These food discussions are called by Rümke "culinary dry screwing" (128, p. 460), while Frankl uses the term "gastric masturbation." The latter thinks these talks unwise, as they unnecessarily tortured the organism, which had already partly adapted itself to the small quantity of food (46, p. 43).

This view of Frankl's may be correct, but the fact cannot be denied that food occupied a predominant position in the thoughts of the majority of prisoners, and was constantly discussed (far less frequently, of course by the "prominents"). Nor is this surprising, for, as Bondy has related: "The main thing was to get something to eat and to drink. When food was brought in, an excitement ensued which one can otherwise observe only among animals" (23, p. 455). In order to appreciate this excitement about food, one must presumably have experienced it oneself. If there were not enough Schuesseln, I could hardly restrain my impatience enough to wait until another man had gulped down his soup. Without cleaning the Schuessel I would receive my ration with trembling hands. What suspense would come over me, when the soup was being ladled out of a "good" kettle: would I be in time for my ration? How happy I felt when I was, and when I had much substance (potatoes, macaroni) in my portion. With what violence the room seniors and room attendants would beat the thronging prisoners, to make them fall in line and wait their turn. Whenever "Nachschlag" [6] was being doled out the prisoners behaved like animals, which in these circumstances cannot be regarded as otherwise than normal: devoid of all that is commonly called civilization, the behaviour of the starving man did not differ in any respect from that of the starving beast. For the hunger drive is equal in both: it demands to be satisfied. And if it was not, it sought satisfaction in the imagination, which may explain the interminable discussions of food; as Miss Bluhm does, treating these conversations: "The auto-erotic nature of this pleasure in which the real object was replaced by fantasy" (20, p. 20). The fact that some of the testees in the Minnesota experiment refused to discuss food may be regarded as a defence against the unsatisfied hunger drive.

Before going into details on the problem of the hunger drive, it must first be stated that of this, as Rümke (128, p. 460) and De Sauvage Nolting (129, p. 429) have recorded, little is as yet definitely known. The latter writer points to the interest taken by physiology in the problem of hunger, but, he goes on to say, it is strange that whereas the sexual life has been thoroughly studied by Freud, "less attention has been paid by him to the very important hunger drive than this interesting drive deserves" (129, p. 429). That the hunger drive is of paramount importance appears from its analogies with sexuality which Rümke has noticed: "Just as in sex-starved individuals sexuality occupies the central position in thought, we find in the hungry individual a preoccupation—we may even say, an obsession—with food and everything connected with it, perhaps to a higher degree than is ever met with in sexuality, except for pathological cases" (128, p. 460).

The significance attached by De Sauvage Nolting to the hunger drive is apparent from the possibility he suggests that "our highest aspirations are, in the last analysis, rooted in the two primitive drives: hunger and love" (129, p. 449).

As the object of the hunger drive is the maintenance of the

---

[6] Nachschlag: If, after everyone had had his ration, and after the "organization" by the "prominents," there was anything left, this remainder was distributed.

individual, it is of necessity "a relentless and an indispensable drive, whereas the sexual drive remains, after all, something of a luxury" (129, p. 432).

By what has so far been stated, as well as by what will be stated below, it will be sufficiently proved that the hunger drive is completely overpowering, sparing nothing and no one. Also in the prisoners' dreams food, not sex, figured prominently (cf. 31, pp. 528 f.) [7]; the sex drive was completely subjected to the drives of hunger and thirst (of thirst only in prisoners who were starved of drink). "Under the grim pangs of hunger, the relative importance of other motives, such as sex, tends to fade" (132, p. 87). In this connection it should not be forgotten that through starvation the physical potency in the field of sex will decline.

The psychological incompatibility between hunger and sexuality has been pointed out by De Sauvage Nolting: ". . . the erotic drive only really manifests itself if hunger is absent, just as the hunger drive declines, if there is a strong desire to love . . . the animal nature drive, hunger, finds it impossible to coexist with its more aesthetic sister" (129, p. 434).

In the concentration camp man was beaten back to his most animal basis. His only concern was with that which would help to keep him alive. This was a regression to the primitive phase of the drive to self-preservation. Primitive was the blissful feeling of the prisoner when he had his stomach filled with a liberal portion of food and a "Nachschlag" into the bargain. Hunger was satisfied.

Primitive was his envy of those people who had got something he had not. General Wainwright, who was a prisoner of war in Japan, writes, "If a man received a bean in his soup, and another did not, it made for hard feeling. This must be hard to imagine, but it is true" (132, p. 88; italics omitted). And how I envied another man for some potatoes in his soup, when I had none! Examples could be given almost ad infinitum.

With all the strength which is characteristic of a drive, the

---

[7] See 31; this paper contains a detailed description of the dreams of concentration-camp prisoners, including those after they had been liberated.

hunger drive broke through every restraint found in human beings under normal circumstances. Least objectionable was that the civilized manners of normal existence were disregarded. In the concentration camp, prisoners were regularly seen to lick their Schuessel clean, or to scrape out the empty food kettles. Also in the Minnesota experiment etiquette was seen to disappear: "In the period of rehabilitation the excessive interest in food and abnormal eating habits, such as plate-licking and 'souping' of foods with hot water [8] continued . . ." (85, p. 71).

A more serious consequence was that Allied officers taken prisoner by the Japanese sometimes found it impossible to abide by their refusal to work for the enemy when promised an extra ration of rice (132, p. 88). Or, as happened in camps with a mixed population, women were prepared to sell their bodies for food. Herzberg has related of Bergen Belsen that "hardly any eroticism, not because of moral sense or of prudery, but because of hunger and weakness" was observed (66, p. 25) until the Kapos assumed control. Apart from the pains the Kapos took to seduce the women, "A piece of bread or sausage, a little sugar or margarine, all delicacies which could be obtained by the Kapos" (66, p. 25), would do the rest. Prostitution for the same reason was observed in Theresienstadt (145, p. 52).

The women's camp at Auschwitz-Birkenau was regularly visited by male prisoners who had various jobs to do. These men could be reckoned among the "prominents," and consequently had desirable foods; this resulted in prostitution (99, pp. 48 ff.).

Indeed, hunger recognized no restraints of any kind. As Minkowski has remarked, hunger "incites every kind of baseness" (108, p. 294).

One example will serve to illustrate this. Bloch (19, pp. 335 ff.) was one of the first American officers who visited various liberated German concentration camps. In the concentration camp Lensing (Austria) he examined 547 Jewish women. About one woman he has recorded copious data. She was a

[8] In order to get their stomachs better filled; see also 62, p. 92.

"cultured and aristocratic British woman," became French through her marriage, "and was noted in her former life for her generosity, benevolence, and humanitarian interests." She told Bloch: "I decided I wanted to live. Nothing else counted but that I wanted to live. I could have stolen from husband, child, parent or friend, in order to accomplish this. . . . I would remain close to those who were too far gone and too weak to eat their meagre rations of ersatz coffee or soup, and instead of pressing them to eat so that they might exist, I would eagerly take it from them and wolf it down if they gave the slightest evidence that the effort for them was too great. I would count a day as lost and would become terribly depressed if I had been able to accomplish nothing in this mad desire for a little more in order to live" (19, p. 338).

If any attempt is to be made to explain the attitude of this woman, I think it of primary importance to take into account that the superego acquired new values in a concentration camp so much at variance with those which the prisoner bore with him into camp that the latter faded.

We owe to Freud the concept of the superego as part of the ego; of the way the superego comes into being Freud has propounded this theory: "The broad general outcome of the sexual phase governed by the Oedipus complex may, therefore, be taken to be the forming of a precipitate in the ego, consisting of these two identifications in some way combined together. This modification of the ego retains its special position; it stands in contrast to the other constituents of the ego in the form of an ego-ideal or super-ego" (49c, p. 153).[9]

The formulation by Anna Freud is somewhat simpler: "It is the continuation of the voice of the parents which is now operative from within instead of, as formerly, from without. The child has absorbed, as it were, a part of his father and mother, or rather the orders and prohibitions which he has constantly received from them, and made these an essential part of his being" (48, p. 85).

[9] Freud epitomizes the concept of the ego: "The ego represents what we call reason and sanity, in contrast to the id which contain the passions" (49, p. 30).

To this are added the precepts and prohibitions of parents, teachers, and society.[10]

As the function of the superego which has a profound effect on the ego Freud mentions "self-observation, the moral conscience, the censorship of dreams, and the chief influence in repression" (49a, p. 69). And to this superego another component was added in the concentration camps, which at the time was stronger than its original content; this is clearly proved by the words of the woman quoted by Bloch: "I would have stolen from husband, child, parents or friend" (19, p. 338).

The conscience (one of the functions of the superego) of this woman had to be silenced for her to behave as she did, and this was made possible by the example set by the "authorities," who showed that the standards of normal society did not obtain in the concentration camp. Theft, egotism, lack of consideration for others, pitilessness, disregarding of laws, all this was prohibited in pre-concentration camp days; inside the concentration camp, however, it was normal.

To evade the laws and instructions issued by the SS as much as possible was even a necessity. Mrs. Lingens-Reiner's reaction

[10] Flugel (44, pp. 34 ff.), mentions four sources from which the superego derives:

(I) During the development of the human being a part of the libido is directed to the real self. "But this 'real self' does not permanently satisfy our narcissism; as we develop, we become all too painfully aware of its defects and limitations, physical, mental, and moral; and we compensate by building up in imagination a sort of ideal self . . . the ego-ideal, and to this another portion of our narcissistic libido . . . becomes directed" (44, p. 35).

(II) The introjection "of the precepts and moral attitudes of others, particularly of one's parents or of other persons *in loco parentis* in one's youth" (44, p. 35).

(III) Because many wishes of the young child cannot be fulfilled, the child will experience a sense of frustration, which tends to arouse anger and aggression. This aggression may be either not expressed at all or insufficiently expressed toward the frustrating parents. "But he always has himself as a possible object for his anger. . . . The superego, which represents the internalized, forbidding parents, is already endowed with the aggression. . . . It is now reinforced by the child's own aggression; and in this way (among others) it becomes more stern, cruel, and aggressive than the actual parents" (44, pp. 36 f.).

(IV) A still uncertain source is the sado-masochistic relation which exists sometimes between the ego and the superego.

The only source to be considered in this book will be introjection, as much of my argument is based on this.

did not differ from mine. In a way she felt free in the camp "because I never felt bound by a single one of the rules laid down by the SS. I observed them only as far as I considered them of benefit to the prisoners and felt free to break them whenever I was unobserved" (102, p. 142).

The only restriction which still held the attempted satisfaction of the hunger drive in check, was the *reality principle* [11]; if this principle could permit the hunger drive to be satisfied without peril to the individual's life, it would be satisfied. If, however, danger to life threatened to a greater or lesser extent, the reality principle prevented attempted satisfaction of the hunger drive, or at least caused it to be delayed for some time, unless the drive was so powerful that it also blew the last fuse. Was there in Bloch's example danger to the woman's life, if she had simply taken away the prisoner's food? There was indeed, as in that case she would have been expelled from the prisoners' community. This was the reality principle which decided her to delay the satisfaction of the hunger drive until the enfeebled fellow-prisoners offered her the food. But it does not seem impossible that in this woman the weakened original values of the superego were still active. The reason why I have chosen this example is that I did the same thing in the sick bay of the concentration camp Amersfoort. I "helped" the sick to eat, and, while grudging them every bite, I would wait until they refused further food and offered me the remainder in gratitude for my "help." Nor did I take any pains to press more food on the sick prisoners.

But not everyone turned complete egotist. Mrs. Adelsberger has recorded that "Themselves already on the verge of starvation, they would sell their own bread ration, in order to buy potatoes for a dying comrade, and thus give him a last happiness" (2, p. 130).

[11] "The task of avoiding pain becomes for them almost equal in importance to that of gaining pleasure; the ego learns that it must inevitably go without immediate satisfaction, postpone gratification, learn to endure a degree of pain, and altogether renounce certain sources of pleasure. Thus trained, the ego becomes 'reasonable,' is no longer controlled by the pleasure-principle, but follows the *reality-principle*, which at bottom also seems pleasure—although a delayed and diminished pleasure, one which is assured by its realization of fact and its relation to reality" (51, p. 299).

There were indeed also prisoners who were not completely dominated by egotism, but who still had room for altruistic sentiments, and who had compassion with their fellow men. Apparently concentration-camp conditions did not produce the same effect in them as in the other prisoners, but the original values of their superego could maintain themselves unimpaired. This might be explained by a constitutional factor (a less violent drive element in their lives), or by their character,[12] in the sense that in character they were superior to many other prisoners. To my mind superiority of character was more significant than the constitutional factor.

In the majority of prisoners, however, egotism reigned supreme, and one aim was constantly kept in view—survival. Mrs. Lingens-Reiner has said, "We camp prisoners had only one yardstick: whatever helped our survival was good, whatever threatened our survival was bad and to be avoided" (102, p. 142).

During his research Bloch arrived at the same conclusion: "Behaviour is reduced to survival activities. The records display a constant morbid preoccupation with the destruction of the family and isolation from the rest of the world. There is strong evidence of traumatic shock, excessive apathy, an intense desire for survival, profound insecurity, and fear" (19, p. 336).

This will to live, according to Frankl, manifests itself "in a total devaluation of anything that does not serve this exclusive interest" (46, p. 47).

Thus the hunger drive, which is somehow always connected with the will to live, became in the concentration camps a ruthless and unscrupulous drive.

A factor only indirectly connected with food, but of very great importance, was the sudden unavailability of the "stimulating poisons," coffee and tobacco. Of these tobacco was the most desired article, and one which the prisoner could only secure after some time had elapsed. The importance of these poisons to which all civilized peoples are more or less addicted

[12] "The character proper is always a conglomeration possessing a certain unity and inner organization not to be found in the original disposition. No one, therefore, is born as a character, but in the course of development one may or may not grow into a character" (72, p. 123).

will appear from an observation made by an American: "The first three items asked for by the liberated peoples of Europe, even in starving western Holland, were tobacco, coffee and white bread" (85, p. 18).

The passionate longing for tobacco might even cause the prisoners to barter a large or small part of their scanty rations for it. It will be understood that this only accelerated their physical ruin. The remarkable aspect is that the vital hunger drive was subjected to the passion for tobacco, which might be accounted for by the restraining influence of nicotine on hunger. The force of the hunger drive, moreover, tends to decrease in the long run, as I personally experienced. During the last weeks before the liberation I was not greatly tormented by hunger when I was working; only when food was being distributed could I with difficulty control myself. A certain measure of habituation must possibly also be taken into account.

Having dealt with the hunger drive I will now examine the part played by the *sexual drive* in the concentration camps. To this end the prisoners should be classified in various groups.

(1) The new arrivals. Although these were, as a rule, still in a good state of nutrition, they did not show the least sexual interest. This may be accounted for by the initial reaction and its consequences, or, as Bluhm has put it: "Sexual energies, like other libidinal energies, were withdrawn in order to rescue the ego from an overpowering excitation. The ego, frustrated by the outer world to an almost unbearable extent, abandoned its genital claims as it abandoned other forms of object libido" (20, p. 12).

(2) The great mass of prisoners, exclusive, therefore, of the new arrivals. For this category, whose state of nutrition was bad or moderate and who had to fight a hard struggle for survival, the sexual factor was of no importance. Kautsky states that 90 per cent of the prisoners had no sexual needs (81, p. 195), and Bakels, "The absence of sexual drive. . . . As if one had been castrated" (14, p. 67). This absence of sexual impulse in adults can be accounted for by (a) starvation (see this book,

p. 134), and (b) regression, which played an important part. Friedman has stated: "This abstention from sex, which was one of the most striking effects of life in the concentration camps, is characteristic of the primitive and narcissistic stage to which the inmates had regressed" (56, p. 604). In addition, (c) the struggle for existence, I think, demanded so much of the prisoner's psychical energy that he had not enough of it left to indulge in sexual matters. Popularly expressed, he had other things to worry about. And finally there was (d) the important circumstance that there were no members of the other sex in the concentration camps.

(3) Prisoners in a good state of nutrition. These were a small group, formed by the "established" prisoners, mainly prominents. They were not hungry, and not engaged in a fierce struggle for life; to them the sexual drive was indeed of importance. This drive demanded gratification and could be gratified, either through masturbation or through homosexual practices. This problem naturally presents itself in all exclusively male camps. As to the prisoner-of-war camps, Vischer records that "Homosexual practice is probably not so frequent as is generally assumed. Cases of mutual masturbation may be the most likely to occur. On the whole prisoners prefer not to speak on this subject. It is therefore rather difficult to form an opinion" (146, p. 18).

Bondy, on the other hand, holds that "The everlasting talk about sex and smut may be considered as compensatory satisfaction. Homosexual acts are likely to occur often in the camps" (23, p. 462).

My experience differs from Bondy's. I am not asserting that sex was never discussed; it was, though not often. Frankl also states "that in contrast to mass existence in other military communities (barracks and suchlike), here (in the concentration camp) there is *no smut talk*" (46, p. 46). I am also convinced that homosexuality was not frequent in the camps. That there were prominents who practised homosexuality appears very likely to me, and also that they bought the objects of their love for food, by placing them in the less hard labor groups, etc. Federn, who spent a considerable time in Buchen-

wald, has made a much more positive statement: "Many German anti-Fascists could not resist a handsome boy, so that
homosexuality claimed its sacrifices by degrading life and
character" (43, p. 77). And in *Synthèses* he writes: "Young
men, the camp prostitutes, stalked through the streets, while
lovers made dates or greeted each other in passing with a
special sign. Love affairs were always developing. . . . The
part played by these young prostitutes with the high function-
aries of the camp. . . . Numerous are the couples who, like
married people, became inseparable in the most tragic circumstances" (42, p. 95).

In view of this information by Federn, the evidence of acts
of homosexuality by the prominents seems irrefutable; I myself, however, did not observe it, although I know masturbation to have been very frequent.

No mention has as yet been made of the normal satisfaction
of the sexual needs of the male prisoners, namely by sexual
intercourse. This was made possible from the middle of 1943
through the establishment of brothels, to which only "Aryans"
were, however, admitted.[13] Of these, the "green" prisoners in
particular visited the brothels, whereas the "red," the political,
prisoners seldom put in an appearance. The conduct of the
latter has been accounted for by Kogon, as follows: "The purpose pursued by the SS was the corruption of political prisoners, who were given precedence. They were to be watched
and distracted from political activity. The prisoners in the
camp had received and passed on secret instructions not to
patronize the brothels, . . . Most of the political prisoners
obeyed these instructions, so that the objective of the SS was
foiled" (87, p. 199).

Outside the brothel the opportunity for sexual intercourse
was non-existent for the male prisoners, as they did not come
into contact with women. An exception is found in the concentration camp Auschwitz, as has already been pointed out
with reference to the women's camp at Auschwitz-Birkenau.
But also the Stammlager-Auschwitz, though it was a men's

[13] "In the summer of 1943 Himmler issued a Reich Directive to the effect that
brothels were to be established in the concentration camps" (87, p. 198).

camp, offered an occasional opportunity. For a considerable time there were many women, confined for medical experimentation, in Block X. Access to Block X was made difficult, the windows having been wire-netted, but despite all, several prominents managed to get inside. On the strength of the stories spread about the camp, sexual intercourse appears to have been practiced in Block X, which personally I think very probable, but this privilege could only be enjoyed by a very small proportion of the male prisoners. I am not in a position to judge whether female prisoners had any intercourse with SS men; Mrs. Lingens-Reiner has recorded one case (101, p. 62).

In summary, it may be concluded that for this group the satisfaction of the sexual drive through sexual intercourse was of secondary importance (in Auschwitz it was given a little more thought, owing to occasional opportunity), but this satisfaction, according to Vischer, was principally obtained by masturbation, and by a small number of prisoners through homosexual acts.

At the beginning of his life in the concentration camp, things were not made easy for the newly arrived prisoner. He would feel some disappointment at the *lack of compassion* with his hard fate on the part of many of the older prisoners. This lack of compassion was a result of repression of normal sensations, for without this repression the individual could not have survived. At the same time it tended to grow through habituation, for what is constantly perceived will cease, in the end, to produce reaction. As described by Frankl: "The suffering, illness, dying, and death of human beings has become such a common sight after a few weeks of life in a concentration camp, that it no longer has the power to move" (46, p. 32 f.; italics omitted). Vrijhoff puts forward another possible explanation: "In the word 'compassion' the phenomenological principle is already implied: the directing of one's mind toward one's fellow man, the being-with one's fellow man" (150, pp. 65 f.). Because in the relation prisoner–SS, as well as in that between prisoner and prisoner, this element of positive mutual interest, the positive sense of mutual relationship, was lacking, compassion, according to Vrijhoff (150, p. 65), was, of necessity, ruled out. The evanescence of compassion in concentration camps has also been observed by Vogel (147, p. 27), Kalmar (20, p. 8), and Wiechert (*ibid.*). It has been noticed as a characteristic, not only of life in concentration camps, but in prisoner-of-war camps (19, p. 338), and such places as Bergen Belsen (66, p. 84), as well (cf. also 62, pp. 60 f. and p. 101).

After the liberation many writers were struck by the callousness of the former prisoners, and particularly by their apathy when relating their experiences, even the most horrible. Information on this subject is to be found in the publications of Padover (118, p. 287), Friedman (56, p. 602; 57, p. 504) and Minkowski (108, p. 291). The latter calls this mental state "anesthésie affective." This, however, is a mere term which explains nothing. In my view, repression in the camps was a sheer necessity, because otherwise the ego could not, through the weight of misery, have kept up the struggle for survival; this repression, however, did not always endure (this book, p. 173). That after their liberation ex-prisoners could not at once abandon this behaviour seems to me not to need further explanation.

The process of adapting oneself to *degradation* was very difficult. Most Jewish prisoners had been thrown into camps innocent of any crime. Their only "offence" consisted in being Jews; this caused the Jews in Buchenwald, for example, to say that their imprisonment was merely due to a "birth defect." [14] Hence for the majority, there was not the slightest occasion to regard themselves as criminals. This feeling of being innocent and yet having to suffer all this misery aroused self-pity and weakened the energy that was essential for survival. Much the same has been observed by Kautsky: "As they (the Jews) had committed no crime whatever, they felt innocently persecuted, and quarreled with their fate" (120, p. 202).

The case of non-Jewish fellow prisoners who had been placed in concentration camps, partly officially convicted,

[14] Personal information.

partly neither examined nor sentenced, was entirely different. These "Aryan" prisoners also (I am only referring to political prisoners), did not consider themselves criminals, but were, on the contrary, proud of their imprisonment, an attitude that helped to lessen their sense of degradation: "The politically educated prisoners found support for their self-esteem in the fact that the Gestapo had singled them out as important enough to take revenge on", (17, p. 425). In addition to this, political prisoners received much support from their elder fellow victims. They were accepted into a "fraternity," they were not lonely, and they profited by their comrades' advice.

The Jews and the political prisoners, therefore, had this in common, that they did not regard themselves as criminals. This struck Bloch (19, p. 336) when he examined 547 Jewish women. Most of these considered themselves victims of forces beyond their control, while a large percentage of them regarded themselves not only as martyrs, but at the same time as superior to their guards and to those responsible for their detention. This feeling of superiority was partly founded on reality, partly compensation for the inferiority feeling caused by degradation. For, innocent as these women might feel, there was no getting away from the fact that they were prisoners.

Degradation was accentuated by the entire absence of civilized manners, as manifested in the language. Thus, in addressing the prisoners, the pronoun "du" (the familiar form of address) was always used, whereas it was compulsory for the prisoners to use "Sie" (the polite form) when they spoke to the SS. The sense of degradation was fostered by the show of respectfulness that prisoners were expected to observe toward the SS.

Apart from the fact that for every newcomer his transformation into a "prisoner" meant a degradation, there was also the *loss of his name.* That this was no trifling circumstance should be apparent from the great importance which, according to Freud, a man attaches to his name. This is, in Freud's view, sufficiently proved by "the fact that savages regard a name as an essential part of a man's personality, and as an important possession: they treat words in every sense as things" (53, p. 56). And children are, by the same token, supposed to conclude that, if two objects are called by the same name, there must be a "deeper correspondence" (*ibid.*) between them. Moreover, Freud holds, "Even a civilized adult may be able to infer from certain peculiarities in his own behaviour that he is not so far removed as he may have thought from attributing importance to proper names, and that his own name has become to a very remarkable extent bound up with his personality" (*ibid.*).

Anyhow, whether one agrees with Freud or not, the loss of one's name is not without significance, for the name is a personal attribute. Because he no longer had a name, but had become a number, the prisoner belonged to the huge army of the nameless who peopled the concentration camp. The prisoner was summoned by his number and then reported with the words: "Number — reports present." Who the man behind the number was, what and how he was, was a matter of complete indifference. It did not even matter whether he was dead or alive. Those prisoners who were beaten to death during working hours had to be brought back to the camp, and had to be produced, even at roll call; for the *number* was all-important. The Kapo had to see to it that the number of prisoners in his gang, as reported before march-out, tallied with the number he brought back at night. Dead or alive, sick or well, nothing counted, so long as the numbers tallied. Thus it could happen that in Melk (April, 1945), owing to three prisoners having escaped, the morning roll call did not produce the required number. Consequently, during the day, the prisoners had to fall in repeatedly, to be counted again. The two dead in our block had over and again to be dragged out to roll call and back. As only the number meant anything for the SS, the block senior and the block clerk were in a position, if a friend had been picked out as a victim for the gas chambers, as in Auschwitz, to cross out his number and substitute another for it.

Everyone being nameless, one knew at best the given names of one's fellow prisoners. (This made it particularly difficult to trace the whereabouts of ex-prisoners after the war.) There were a few exceptions to this general rule. Compatriots often retained an interest in each others' names: likewise, prisoners who had become friends. In the H.K.B. the members of the staff would know each other by name. But the usual procedure was for every feature of human beings in normal life to be obliterated. Name, age, residence, occupation, none of these counted any longer. One had become a cipher, and it was a long time before one became "somebody" again. Living as they did in a crowd who, apart from being counted, having to be fed, and being set to work, were free to go under, prisoners had no opportunity to be "somebody" again until they had proved to be able to adapt themselves.

In this connection it will be expedient to go into the question: *What individuals were best fitted to adapt themselves,* so that there was at least a possibility of their surviving a concentration camp?

It has been generally observed that the longer a prisoner had been in the camp, the greater was his chance of survival. Considering the death rate in concentration camps, this statement may cause a certain surprise. It becomes plausible, however, when viewed in the light of our present knowledge, that the high death rate was mainly due to the large number of newcomers who did not survive the first months of their imprisonment in the concentration camps. Bettelheim explains this phenomenon as follows: "Either because they did not care to survive by means of adapting themselves to the life in camp, or because they were unable to do so" (17, p. 438).

That especially the first months were of crucial importance to the newly arrived prisoner appears from a statement by Kogon: "Within three months at the outside one had either gone under in an almost continuous downward curve, psychically, if not physically, or one had begun to 'adapt oneself' to the concentration camp" (87, p. 380).

It would, however, be doing the numerous dead the greatest injustice if the fact were not taken into account that many newcomers were not given the chance of adaptation: either because, as in the extermination camps they were gassed immediately upon arrival, or because they simply collapsed under the hard work and the abominable circumstances.

To return to the point in question: Many writers, such as Kautsky (120, p. 201), De Wind (156, p. 7), Frankl (46, p. 51), Kaas (78, p. 419), Vrijhoff (150, pp. 7 ff.), and Bluhm (20, pp. 25 ff.), agree that it was of the greatest importance that a prisoner had some *spiritual life*,[15] albeit each defines this conception of spiritual life in different terms. Thus De Wind refers to the bonds of religion, and the great significance he attaches to this appears from the following quotation: "Generally speaking, we see in the camp that anyone in whose life there are certain religious bonds (using the term in its most comprehensive sense, so as to include the devotion to a political system or a humanist view of life), manages to recover the most quickly, after the initial stupor. It is therefore no mere accident that the convinced Christians as well as the Communists, who would seem to be their psychological opposites, should have shown the greatest power of resistance in camps, and even managed to set up certain forms of anti-Fascist organization" (165, p. 7).

For me, the Zionist side of my life has been very important. In order to make this clear, I shall have to go briefly into the subject of the Zionist movement. This movement, since its foundation in 1897 by Theodor Herzl, has aimed at a solution of the Jewish problem through the creation of a publicly guaranteed home for the Jewish people in Palestine. This effort has since been brought to a successful conclusion in the Jewish state of Israel.

One of the causes of the Jewish problem, and therefore of anti-Semitism, was considered by the movement to be the existence of Jewish minorities in the midst of various non-Jewish majorities; this plea was substantiated by the unmentionable sufferings inflicted on the Jewish people in the course

---

[15] The conception "spiritual life" is here used to comprise all spiritual values in their widest sense, such as morality, knowledge, emotion, intellect, character, religion, etc. According to Vrijhof, who applies the term "spiritual self property" to my conception of spiritual life, "culture in its widest sense constitutes, as it were, the raw material from which the building stones for the structure of inner self-possession were derived" (150, p. 67).

of history. And today, in the twentieth century of Christian civilization, I, in my turn, found that I was being kicked and beaten, merely because of my Jewish origin; that the fact that my parents, my wife, my child, my sister, my relations, and my friends were Jews was sufficient motive for their being murdered by means of poison gas.

This, however, does not exhaust the Zionist side of my spiritual life. If before 1940 I had, not only in theory, but also in practice, by settling in Palestine, taken the active consequence of my Zionist views, I would at the time have had to face an uncertain future, and instead of doing intellectual work, I should have been put to hard physical labour. I was not at the time able to muster up sufficient courage for what then appeared a real sacrifice. The result was that when I was forced to the hardest physical labour in a concentration camp, under inconceivable circumstances, I was often haunted by the reflection that it was all my own fault. I reasoned to myself: "If you had not preferred the illusional safety of a physician's existence in the Netherlands, but had suited your actions to your words, you would not have had to go through all this." Thus I could not deny a measure of justice to my fate, and this made my sufferings less difficult to bear.

In much the same situation were those prisoners who, because of their spiritual life, were hostile to national socialism and on this ground had resisted it, actively and passively. These prisoners knew that they and the Nazis were mutually hostile, and so they knew *why* they found themselves in a concentration camp; this made it possible for them to think of their detention as motivated. Needless to add that this reflection did not apply to what they had to go through in the camps.

But any form of spiritual life had another decided advantage. If a prisoner found himself unable any longer to bear the reality of life in a camp, he found in his spiritual life a possibility of escape that cannot easily be overestimated—an escape into regions of the mind which the SS were unable to corrupt. Thus there was no need for him to attempt to get away from reality by living in the past, as those prisoners did

who had little or no spiritual life. Dwelling on a past that was
no doubt very attractive in comparison with the horrors of
the camp [16] weakened their inner resistance, a very serious
consequence of which was that they found it impossible to
adapt themselves to the concentration camp.

In the foregoing I trust I have shown that a prisoner's spiritual life was of very great importance, that it fitted him better
for adaptation, and that through it he might considerably add
to his chances of survival.[17]

The next condition essential for adaptation was *the lowering of one's own spiritual standard*. One example of a person
who found himself unable to lower his spiritual standard may
be mentioned here. At Auschwitz I had a Jewish colleague
who could not get over the fact that he, a physician, was forced
to burn the contents of garbage cans. His psychical attitude, I
am inclined to believe, must have hastened his death. I, on the
other hand, did not feel my function of "lavatory inspector,"
added to that of "room physician," to be a disgrace. To my
way of thinking this attitude, the conscious lowering of my
own spiritual standard, was inevitable, since, if one wanted
to survive, one could not but accept the standards prevailing
in the camp. These were naturally different from those of
normal society. While in the "preference camp" Bergen Belsen
there was still maintained some form of organized administration of justice (66, pp. 43 ff.), in the concentration camps justice was entirely unorganized (apart from that administered
by the SS, which will not be considered here).

One of the few standards recognized by unorganized justice
was that spies were not tolerated. Kaas has recorded the way
this worked in Buchenwald: "Through the cooperation of
prisoners who were employed in the 'political department'
with the administrative room . . . and the labour record office,
a certain form of 'resistance' could be set up, which knew how

[16] Compare also Dostoievsky's experience in the camp at Ostrogg, where
most of the prisoners were habitual criminals whose memories of their former
life were not pleasant: "Usually that past was not spoken of, they disliked telling
of it, and were apparently concerned not to think of it either" (39, p. 20).

[17] The great significance of a spiritual life was also experienced by Gollwitzer
in Russian prisoner-of-war camps. In his book he repeatedly stresses the great
comfort he derived from his Christian belief (see, for example, 62, pp. 90 f.).

to get rid of all sorts of unreliable characters and spies for the SS" (79, p. 620).

"Organizing," even at the expense of fellow prisoners, was considered normal in the concentration camp, though in this case there were limits which could not be overstepped, as Kogon has related: "Anyone who stole bread was lost as soon as he was caught in the act, as he simply could not be tolerated in the camp, even when driven to theft by hunger, since otherwise the other comrades, who likewise had only the barest necessities, would have come into further difficulties" (87, p. 110).

Thus the most elementary needs of the prisoners were safeguarded. What needs would be considered as elementary would differ from camp to camp. Sherif, to give one example, has related that he was told by a physician out of a camp that stealing a bottle of liqueur from a man who had a store of them was not looked upon as theft, "but taking a man's cheap flashlight (which was irreplaceable) was a heinous offence" (132, p. 178).

However, all the factors that determined which individuals could most easily adapt themselves have not yet been indicated. I am certain that I owe my life in great part to my being a physician. In Amersfoort it caused the "hospital Kapo" to take me under his protection. And in Auschwitz physicians, once they had safely passed the first selection and had eventually got themselves inside the prisoners' hospital (often after being first accommodated there as patients), enjoyed special protection.

It was particularly remarkable that the camp physician in Auschwitz, who at the selections decided who was to live and who was to die, seldom, if ever, sent to the gas chambers the physicians (among whom there were many laymen who pretended to be physicians, which could be the more easily done, as at the prisoners' arrival at the camp they had been deprived of all their personal papers), the attendants, and the technical staff of the prisoners' hospital. The only explanation for the conduct of the camp physician that I can put forward is that, despite everything, he continued to regard the prisoners' physicians as colleagues. His conduct toward the rest of the prisoners' hospital staff may be considered as the normal attitude of every physician toward the hospital staff. But also the attitudes of the prisoners and the SS towards the physicians was somehow different. The general primitive respect in which the physician is held by the layman made its influence felt even in the concentration camp.

The medical man is the bearer of mysterious forces and can be compared to those persons whom, among the savages, Freud holds to be invested with taboo.[18] Taboo, according to Freud's definition, is "a number of prohibitions to which these primitive races are subjected. Every sort of thing is forbidden; but they have no idea why, and it does not occur to them to raise the question. On the contrary, they submit to the prohibitions as though they were a matter of course and feel convinced that any violation of them will be automatically met by the direst punishment" (53, p. 21).

According to Freud, all these prohibitions seem to be founded on a certain theoretical basis; as if the prohibitions were necessary because "certain persons and things are charged with a dangerous power, which can be transferred through contact with them, almost like an infection" (*ibid.*). The strangest part of it is that anyone who has broken such a restriction "himself acquires the characteristic of being prohibited— as though the whole of the dangerous charge had been transferred over to him" (53, p. 22).

All people, according to Freud, who are out of the common run possess this power. Although not specifically mentioned by Freud, the "medicine man" among primitive races may probably be regarded as such an uncommon person.

The respect in which the physician (who may naturally be considered as the continuation of the former "medicine man") is generally held must, I think, be based on the taboo concept

---

[18] As Freud's *Totem and Taboo* will be quoted from repeatedly, it must be pointed out that the theories and hypotheses propounded in this book have met with much criticism among ethnologists. The reader is in particular referred to a paper by Houwink, who even holds that "the direct application of the Freudian ideas in *Totem and Taboo* has resulted in complete failure" (74, p. 49).

as developed by Freud. There appears to be no occasion to regard either the prisoner or the SS as exceptions, which would perhaps account for the relative quiet enjoyed by the whole of the prisoners' hospital staff. (It is perhaps unnecessary to point out that it was not in every concentration camp that medical men enjoyed the privilege of their profession. There were obviously both SS men and prisoners who were not affected by taboo.)

An additional explanation is to be found in the occasional need of medical care, which no prisoner, even if he were a prominent, could ignore. This tended to create a tie between the prisoners and their physician, which enabled the latter, though often he had no authority in the camp, sometimes to achieve something on the prisoners' behalf. This tie might even arise between the prisoners' physician and the SS, as not infrequently the SS preferred treatment by the prisoners' physician to that by his officially appointed medical officer. This conduct both on the part of the SS and on that of the prisoners' physician may cause a certain surprise, though it allows of a ready explanation. To the SS medical officer the SS soldier was one of a large number, and he was treated briefly and in a businesslike manner. To the prisoners' physician the SS man was one of those powerful beings who might at any moment make a decision on life and death, and who was accordingly treated with due respect. In order that any misunderstanding may be avoided, it should be stressed that respect is not to be taken here in the sense of esteem, but rather in that of awe, inspired by the awareness that any show of disobligingness towards the SS man might have the most disastrous results. Moreover, it was much more convenient for the SS man to have himself treated by the prisoners' physician, as the latter was expected to be at his disposal at any time of the day or night. And possibly the ability of the SS medical officer was not rated very high. As Kogon puts it: "They usually were more adept at 'organizing' than at healing, and as a rule they were less concerned with the art of saving people's lives than with that of killing" (87, p. 154).

The prisoners' physician could of course have refused—and

signed his death warrant at the same time, which he would also have done, had he given his patient a bad treatment, and been found out. But the patient-physician relation which automatically sprang up during the period of treatment might have very valuable consequences for the prisoners' physician, as well as for his fellow prisoners. The SS man would become communicative, so that the physician might gain an impression of the atmosphere prevailing in the enemy's camp, and become acquainted with army news; this, in the form of rumours, percolated the whole of the camp. Through the same channels the prisoners might be informed of imminent changes in the camp. The object of gaining something to one's own advantage—added protection, cigarettes, and extra food—was naturally a weighty consideration on the part of the physician, but no undue significance should be attached to this. The professional standard of the prisoners' physician was therefore, as a rule, too high.

Besides the medical practitioner, carpenters, mechanics, tailors, etc., might also owe a measure of protection to their occupation.

In general all those who were proficient in any occupation or pastime which was appreciated by the SS or the prominents added to their chances of leaving the concentration camp alive, whether they excelled in boxing, painting, chess, singing, or whistling through their fingers, etc. The benefits thus to be gained by the prisoners were the coveted prizes of the concentration camp: a tolerable labour group and food.

To the factors already discussed another may be added, though admittedly it is a purely hypothetical one—namely, *the drive for self-preservation, which is not equally strong in all people.* Leaving the constitutional factor on one side, this drive is probably strongest in those who have been most thoroughly trained in the struggle for life. This training, in order to be effective, should have started in the individual's childhood, and the determining factor is whether or not every prize life has to offer has been won by the individual by physical and spiritual effort. It does not seem inconceivable that anyone who by dint of arduous labour has "got somewhere" has been better trained in the struggle for existence than another who has not felt the need to exert himself. Consequently the former would have a stronger drive toward self-preservation, which would add to any individual's chances of surviving the concentration camp, than the latter.

It does not seem possible to say that a given group or individual could adapt to the concentration camp and that others could not. A whole complex of factors determined the adaptability of a prisoner: having a spiritual life; a character which to a certain extent could force itself to meet the demands made on it by the concentration camp; a not too easy life in the past, so that the drive for self-preservation had been highly developed; one's profession or trade; outstanding qualities; and in addition to these, others such as age, health, luck, shrewdness.

There was one factor, entirely outside the control of any prisoner, described by Miss Bluhm as "one great unpredictable force that ruled over life and death on the inmates. It was the *anarchic power of accident*" (20, p. 5). The classic example of it is this: An SS man "playfully" threw a prisoner's cap over the wire strung before the electrically charged fence, and ordered him to fetch it back. If the prisoner obeyed the order the SS soldier in the watch tower would shoot him, and if he disobeyed he would be shot by the SS man who had thrown the cap. The "anarchic power of accident" vested in the SS could hardly, if at all, be influenced by the prisoner; and it claimed many victims. Because he was aware of this, the seasoned prisoner would avoid contact with the SS as much as possible.

Finally I shall discuss one factor which, though not strictly one of the requirements of adaptation, could have a considerable influence on it. This factor is mourning, the definition of which I quote from Freud:

"Mourning is regularly the reaction to the loss of a loved person, or to the loss of some abstraction which has taken the place of one, such as fatherland, liberty, an ideal, and so on" (49, p. 153). According to Freud, mourning fulfils a function, which he calls the "work of mourning." The object of this is that "grief, by declaring the object to be dead and offering the ego the benefit of continuing to live, impels the ego to give up the object" (49c, p. 169). Through the compelling forces of reality, all libidinal ties with the lost object must be given up, and it is understandable that this cannot be done without a struggle, and that consequently it takes time for mourning to disappear.

In mourning as felt by the normal individual, unlike that felt by the neurotic, ambivalence toward the dead person plays no part.[19] In primitive peoples, according to Freud, the taboo of the dead is based on this very ambivalence (53, pp. 51–52); his name must no longer be mentioned, his body is regarded as unclean. Even today, in the Jewish religion, the dead body is regarded as unclean; hence it is the rule for Jews on leaving the deceased's house or the cemetery to wash their hands. One is apt to wonder why in normal individuals of today ambivalence should have almost disappeared. To account for this, Freud assumes "that the psychical impulses of primitive peoples were characterized by a higher amount of ambivalence than is found in modern civilized man. It is to be supposed that as this ambivalence diminished, taboo (a symptom of the ambivalence and a compromise between the two conflicting impulses) slowly disappeared" (53, p. 66).

Freud holds that even now in normal man this ambivalence is present in its elementary stage, but so weak that civilized man easily represses the hostile component. Besides the causes of this decline suggested by Freud—constitutional changes and improved family relations—another cause may perhaps be taken into consideration, namely that present-day normal society is less cruel than that of savages.

Mourning in normal man is never morbid and requires no medical treatment, although a temporary mental disturbance may occasionally occur. This has been pointed out by Musaph, who states that "a lack of objective awareness of reality may occur in the distressed person, the individual stricken by mourning (It is not true! You lie! He cannot be dead!), but

---

[19] "In almost every case where there is an intense emotional attachment to a particular person we find that behind the tender love there is a concealed hostility in the unconscious. This is the classical example, the prototype, of the ambivalence of human emotions" (53, p. 60).

before long this will disappear, and give place to the normal respect for reality" (114, p. 93).

If we go on to view the prisoners' mourning in this light, it must first be stated that at the beginning of their stay in a concentration camp, mourning varied in violence with various prisoners. In general it would be less violent in the non-Jewish prisoners than in the Jewish. The former had to live down the loss of more or less normal living conditions, with everything that goes with a normal life—personal liberty, work, recreation, dwelling, food, family life, sexuality, community. The latter, the Jewish prisoners, had moreover to bear the knowledge that their husbands or wives, their children, parents, etc., had been murdered. Although there were individual differences, it is no exaggeration to say that virtually every Jewish prisoner mourned the loss of one or more members of his family.

Another difference between these two categories of prisoners must, however, be pointed out. Many non-Jewish prisoners, before they came to the concentration camp, had an opportunity partly or entirely to overcome their mourning, in prison; hence it seems likely that the non-Jewish prisoners, once they entered the concentration camp, were not unduly bowed down by mourning. On the other hand, the majority of Netherlands Jews, for example, came to the concentration camps after a brief stay in the transit camp at Westerbork. Apart from the fact that, as a rule, they had had no time to overcome that particular mourning which the non-Jewish and Jewish prisoners had in common, they had to digest mentally the news of the murder of their families.

In conclusion it may be said that owing to the difference in intensity of the grief suffered and owing to the fact that the Jewish prisoner had to live down his mourning almost exclusively in the concentration camps, mourning interfered more seriously with the process of adaptation in the Jewish than in the non-Jewish prisoners.

From what has been related so far, it will be evident that the newly arrived prisoner in the concentration camps had to possess very great adaptability. There would, therefore, have been little cause for surprise if suicide had spread like an epidemic among the prisoners; this, however, was not the case. That suicide may assume the character of an epidemic is shown in the paper devoted by Van Loghem (103, p. 4069) to the mortality figures published by the Netherlands Central Statistics Bureau for the first half of 1940. Whereas the average number of suicides for the month of May of the last five years prior to 1940 was 71.2, 371 cases of suicide were registered for May, 1940, 151 of which were committed in Amsterdam.

But in the camps there was no question of any epidemic of suicides. Of the Japanese prisoner-of-war camps Colaço Belmonte has recorded: "A single individual will sometimes make an attempt at suicide, which, to my knowledge, never ended fatally, not even during the darkest periods of imprisonment" (33, p. 420).

In the preference camp Bergen Belsen, only four cases of attempted suicide were witnessed by Tas (139, p. 687), three of which were saved with great effort, while in the Stammlager-Auschwitz only one successful attempt came to my knowledge. This does not mean that there were not more, but their number was certainly small. Kaas,[20] on the other hand, witnessed several attempted suicides in Buchenwald. He has remembered three that were successful (two by hanging, one by rushing into the electric fence). He also knows of prisoners who were known to be depressive cases, and who were shot down when during the night they had deliberately gone out of bounds. As compared with the large number of prisoners, the number of suicides, however, was very small.

That the prisoners were restrained from suicide by fear of death does not appear likely. In the concentration camp death was such a common occurrence that Miss Bluhm, who has become acquainted with concentration-camp life only by studying twelve "autobiographical accounts" has expressed her surprise that there were any survivors at all: "Death in a Nazi concentration camp requires no explanation. Survival does.

[20] Personal information.

Detailed knowledge of the techniques of torture and extermination had made us 'understand' the outcome of nine to ten million dead. What bewilders us are the survivors" (20, p. 3).

In the concentration camp death was our constant companion, so that he came to lose his terrifying quality. From various writers, such as Frankl (46, p. 28), De Wind (156, p. 5), Rost (126, p. 196), Miss Adelsberger (2, p. 129), only the last will be quoted. She says: "We counted on death every minute and on life, for perhaps only another week or only another day, or perhaps even only another hour . . . . . And thus life in the face of death became something quite concentrated and condensed, from which everything unessential and superficial glanced off. . . . This sublimation was the more pure, as it was free from the fear of death. . . . Death was near and concrete and one became familiar with him. One struggled against him, but one was no longer afraid of him. And to anyone who has ceased to fear death, life belongs truly completely, and without any restriction" (2, p. 129).

Kaas, on the other hand, states: "Most of the prisoners repressed the thought of death, thrust it from their consciousness. . . . The ordinary man in the camp was not ready for death, because he never dared realize the proximity of death" (78, p. 421).

I cannot subscribe to this view, because as has already been stated, I am of opinion that through habituation death had lost its terrifying character. One example may illustrate this: One afternoon in the summer of 1944 "Lagersperre" (confinement to barracks) was suddenly decreed in the Stammlager-Auschwitz. Beside our block a few hundred prisoners were lined up, who appeared to belong to the Sonderkommando (see p. 30 of this book) of the Auschwitz-Birkenau gas chambers. Although the SS tried to keep up the pretence that these people would be sent on an "ordinary" transport, they told us quietly, without any trace of fear, that they would be sent to the gas chambers. In this particular case it must not be left out of consideration that because of their work as members of the Sonderkommando they were undoubtedly burdened by senses of guilt. Perhaps the reason why approaching death inspired no fear was that they felt that to die would be a redemption of their guilt.

The fact that the prisoners knew no fear of death does not mean that they deliberately sought it, but only 'that when death came, it was acquiesced in. It was not fear of death, I think, that prevented the prisoner from committing suicide; why, then, did he not kill himself? It might be argued that the prisoner who did not want to go on living need not actively commit suicide, for, as Tas has related, "the only thing one had to do, was, as explained before, to give up the grim struggle for life; i.e., the struggle to do everything possible to obtain food and keep up one's spirits. If one did give this up, then death came by itself" (139, pp. 687 f.). This form of suicide, which might be called passive suicide, is one that eludes observation; hence no estimate of its frequency can be made, and it must be left out of account in an attempt to explain the small number of suicides.

A factor that should not be overlooked is that in the concentration camps (and certainly in Auschwitz), there were generally few elderly people. For there is a connection between suicide and age. In this connection Schwarz has recorded that "The infrequency of suicide among young people presents a contrast to the aggregate of suicides in the more advanced age group" (130, p. 11). He proves his point by the suicide statistics of Switzerland covering the years 1901–1940. From these he has calculated that the maximum of suicides occurred among women of between fifty and sixty and among men of between sixty and seventy years. Schwarz is convinced that, apart from the influence of the climacteric (a most momentous period in the life of woman), the greater frequency of suicide among the elderly should be accounted for by "the sense of no longer fitting in with people, of being henceforth outside their community, (which) conduces to real weariness of life" (130, p. 13).

Hence, according to Schwarz, suicide at a later age shows "unmistakable relations to balance suicide" (ibid.). (The concept of "balance suicide" will be discussed below.) Although the complete or almost complete absence from the concentration camps of people over middle age was undoubtedly co-responsible for the rare occurrence of suicide, the importance of this factor should not be over-emphasized. For in the "preference camp" Bergèn Belsen there were indeed a number of old prisoners, and here too, as has been related by Tas (this book, p. 158), the number of suicides was small.

Another possible explanation is supplied by a theory developed by Speyer, who—following Freud—sets forth that "the individual who commits suicide not only destroys his own body, but, at the same time, through his act gives expression to the tendency to hatred, the murder impulse, directed toward another individual. Through a narcissistic identification with the renounced object, which causes the hatred to be absorbed in the ideal ego, the suicide can treat his own body as an extrinsic object" (136, p. 59).

In Speyer's view the point is, that "an individual only kills himself if in fact he has murder impulses directed toward another, which is most clearly apparent in melancholia, but which also obtains in other cases of suicide" (136, p. 94).

If Speyer's view is considered together with a statement by Vrijhof, "In such concentration-camp literature as I have studied, hatred, as a dominating force, on the part of the prisoners never loomed large" (150, p. 65), then the rare occurrence of suicide might be accounted for by the absence of emotions of hatred toward the SS, and the consequent absence of murder impulses directed toward the SS; so that, in the last analysis, there was no psychic motivation for self-destruction. If it be assumed that in rare instances emotions of hatred were present, the occasional cases of suicide would be understandable. But again this explanation is not good enough, as the prisoners only lost their hatred of the SS during their stay in the concentration camp (see this book, p. 197).

After these somewhat negative statements, I would put forward my personal opinion on the matter. Of primary importance was, I am convinced, that just as the prisoner had to acquiesce in bad food, bad accommodation, bad treatment, etc., he likewise had to resign himself to the great probability of having to die. He came to regard *death* as normal, as in his former existence he had looked upon *life* as normal. In pre-concentration-camp days death, to him, was a contingency that might occur, but with which he ordinarily reckoned only little. In the concentration camp, however, death was normal and his behaviour with regard to the dead was in keeping with his familiarity with death. Death had become an everyday occurrence, which had ceased to inspire him with either awe, fear, or reverence. It is normal that people should live in the "realm of life"; in the concentration camp, however, one lived in the "realm of death." In the "realm of life" one can escape from life by committing suicide; in the "realm of death" one can escape from death by living. In the concentration camp one could escape into the "spiritual" life. While the SS could get at the prisoners in the domain of material life, they could not be pursued into the domain of their spiritual life. Escape from the "realm of death" was possible only for those who had a spiritual life, and this way of escape was open to most of the prisoners.

Finally it remains to be considered whether the life instinct and the death instinct played any part in this question of life and death.

Freud regards these two instincts as the primal instincts: the life instinct or Eros "comprises not merely the uninhibited sexual instinct proper and the impulses of a sublimated or aim-inhibited nature derived from it, but also the self-preservative instinct" (49, p. 55), and it is the task of the death instinct "to lead organic matter back into the inorganic state" (*ibid.*).

I will refrain from discussing the death instinct, partly because the matter is not within my competence, partly because the Freudian death-instinct theory is still far from being generally accepted. Le Coultre refers to "the bewildering complexities of the death-instinct theory. Reading articles by its adherents, one feels bogged, the number of contradictions increases with every page" (34, p. 88).

Whereas Speyer is prepared to accept the existence of a death instinct, although not in the Freudian sense, but as "a striving after a continuation of our existence, in whatever form" (136, p. 79), Musaph concludes that "the conception of the death instinct cannot stand the test of critical consideration" (114, p. 231). Carp expresses his view as follows: "Life instinct and death instinct: this polarity postulated by Freud, or, more accurately these fundamentals of the human instinctual life as such, are on the strength of the foregoing considerations reduced to a vital and a supra-vital life instinct, which aim at development during mundane life, but beyond this at perfection in the super-mundane life" (28, pp. 253 f.).

These few references will suffice to show that even on the question of the existence of a death instinct there is no general consensus of opinion; hence to discuss the death instinct in connection with the occurrence of suicide in the concentration camps would serve no sensible purpose.

However, the assumption seems justified that the life instinct played a very important part, consciously and particularly subconsciously. Of myself I know that I was not continuously occupied by the reflection: I am going to win through. The actions which contributed to my survival were performed instinctively rather than consciously. Thus it was possible for a patient of De Wind to save his life at a selection by giving his occupation as storeroom clerk instead of his actual one of diamond worker. Like animals warned by their instinct that danger is imminent, we would act instinctively at critical moments. These instinctive acts must, I think, be considered as manifestations of the life instinct. If the life instinct is not strong enough, the instinct will desert the individual, and instead of rising to the emergency, the individual will succumb, whereas a stronger life instinct would have seen him through. One instance will be given to illustrate this: at the last selection in Auschwitz, the senior block prisoner had instructed me to take up a position whence I could watch the windows, so that none of the prisoners might try to escape by jumping through them. When the room was all but empty, the roll-call officer, one of the most dreaded SS men in the camp, came in for an inspection. Apparently he wondered what I was doing there, for after ordering me to come up to him, he asked me a few questions. My behaviour and my replies did not appear to annoy him, and with a deep sigh of relief I watched him depart. I felt that I had never before been so near to the gas chambers. My behaviour was certainly not inspired by intellectual motivation, but, as I still think, purely instinctive.

If it is true that our behaviour in the concentration camps was mainly determined by instinct, and also that this instinct is a manifestation of the life instinct and functions better in proportion as the life instinct is stronger, then all this, taken in conjunction with my hypothesis as formulated on page 161, would provide yet another answer to the question why one individual could more easily adapt himself to camp life than another. If the life instinct is strong, then the individual has the strength to escape from the "realm of death" into the spiritual life (see this book, pp. 148 ff.), from which he again derives the courage to persevere. This has been very clearly shown by Bakels. Alongside his life in the concentration camp he built up a life of the imagination: "Writing, imagining, I went on living. . . . They deepened, these imaginations, until they assumed individual features, and thus suddenly arose in my mind, so forcibly and impressively that they thrust everything else from my thought" (14, p. 13).

If an individual is devoid of spiritual riches, or if he has ceased to regard them as valuable, then he will not know whither to escape; his attempt to escape will be vain, and the outcome will be his extinction. This extinction may occur as follows: the individual's failure to escape arouses aggressiveness, so that either (a) he clashes with his surroundings—and if he clashes with the SS or with the prominents, his doom is sealed; or (b) he realizes that he cannot direct his aggressiveness toward the outside world; then the aggressiveness will turn upon the individual himself and may result in active suicide.

Another possibility is that the life instinct is weak, and the prisoner, because he resigns himself to being in the "realm of death," will sooner or later die.

If I attach great importance to the life instinct, so does Miss Adelsberger when she says, "But surely one of the most powerful factors . . . was the will to live (thanks to which the number of suicides was extraordinarily small). It is difficult to balance the conscious against the unconscious elements of this aid to survival" (2, p. 128). To my thinking Miss Adelsberger's explanation is incomplete, as it does not take account of the spiritual life, which afforded the possibility of inward escape.

Also Friedman, who made researches among the internees in Cyprus [21] stresses the great importance of the life instinct among the survivors of the German concentration camps. "In all the survivors of the Nazi camps, one might say, the self-preservation instinct became so dominant that it blotted out all the other instincts. Indeed, it would seem that the whole libido had to be withdrawn from the outer world and focused on the struggle for survival" (56, p. 604). Summarizing, I will put forward this explanation for the rare occurrence of suicide in the concentration camps: Apart from the fact that the prisoners considered dying in the camp normal (the SS had taken them to the camps for this), the life instinct and possession of a spiritual life were of very great importance. A strong life instinct without spiritual life might lead to suicide; and as most of the prisoners had a spiritual life, suicide in the concentration camps was rare.

Of an entirely different order was the behaviour of those Jews who had been arrested during the raid of February, 1941, in Amsterdam and had come to Mauthausen by way of Buchenwald. About the fate of these persons Kogon has given the following information: Of the 341 Jews who arrived there, 50 were immediately driven naked into the electrically charged fence. On the second day the remainder were set to work in the quarry, where, burdened with heavy stones, they were forced to run up 148 stairs at the double. "Many were driven to suicide through despair, jumping into the abyss from above" (87, p. 219). On the third day the SS chased many into the guard line,[22] where they were shot. "On the next day the Jews no longer jumped into the pit alone, but after they had joined hands, the first would pull from nine to twelve comrades with him into terrible death" (87, p. 220).

[21] From 1946 any Jews who tried to enter Palestine 'illegally' were interned in Cyprus by the British mandatory.
[22] Cordon of SS soldiers.

In trying to find an explanation for this suicide epidemic, I start from the assumption that these people may be considered to have been spiritually normal individuals. The question whether suicide occurs among the spiritually sane need not be discussed,[23] because such a situation as described has never been foreseen by any writer. In view of the horrible condition in which these Jews arrived in Mauthausen, I also feel justified in not trying to find an answer to the question introduced by Musaph in his discussion of the suicide epidemic in the Netherlands in May, 1940, namely: ". . . how many neurotics, whether manifest or not, there are among suicides, . . . and how great is the percentage of psychically completely sane" (114, p. 50). As to who are completely normal, I agree with the definition given by Schwarz, who holds any individual normal who "has proved by his general behaviour that in unfortunate life circumstances, with which man has to reckon and which therefore may be designed as more or less 'physiological,' his reactions will be such as may be expected from a sensible person" (130, p. 81). Taking normality in this sense I believe these Jews may be regarded as mentally sane; and these people knew they were to die within a few days. While in the normal concentration camp it was still possible to cherish some hope, these Jews were denied any spark of hope. Leaving the possibility of a panic reaction, which Kogon does not mention at all, out of consideration, it appears very probable that they asked themselves: Shall I today voluntarily renounce life, or suffer myself to be killed tomorrow by the SS? The answer to this question could not be "balance suicide." [24]

Two conditions must be fulfilled in order that the diagnosis "balance suicide" may be made:

(1) There must be "living conditions . . . , far exceeding the 'physiological measure,' which are so difficult that the voluntary departure appears psychologically sufficiently understandable" (130, p. 81).

[23] The reader is referred to 114, pp. 47 ff.

[24] "Balance suicide . . . means that the balance sheet of life has been drawn up, and the result is that the decision of self-destruction is made and carried into effect" (130, p. 81).

(2) ". . . The person committing suicide must be able to comprehend these circumstances and to evaluate their effects correctly; therefore we must be able to assume that he is capable of forming a judgment" (130, p. 81).

These two conditions were fulfilled in the case of the suicides committed by the Jews in Mauthausen, but as they obtained in every concentration camp, one other factor must be added to account for these particular suicides, which is that, as has been stated before, they had not a spark of hope left of leaving Mauthausen alive. In the light of this circumstance I can subscribe to the observation made by Schwarz: "it must always be possible to ascertain an extra-psychical event, for the ensuing act to be an understandable reaction. . . . The outward, . . . i.e., extra-psychical event. . . is so overwhelming, that to an outsider it reveals the suicide act as a simple and sensible solution" (130, p. 82).

Probably not only the drawing up of the balance sheet of life, but also the "infectiousness" of these suicides, was responsible for this suicide epidemic.

The adaptation to concentration-camp life and the residing in the "realm of death" cause death to lose its terror, for death has become normal. This will also account for the quietness with which those prisoners who knew they were going to the gas chambers met their fate. Miss Adelsberger (2, p. 130) may be right in saying that the victims did not revolt out of consideration for their fellow prisoners, because they knew that serious reprisals would be taken upon the latter by the SS. This view is shared by Kogon, as he states that the political prisoners did not resist when they were taken to the place of execution (87, p. 388). I am inclined to think that the most likely explanation of the prisoners' equanimity in the face of death was the normal occurrence of death in the concentration camp, and people as a rule will not resist the normal. On the other hand, the possibility of repression should not be overlooked. When reading in Mrs. Lengyel's record of the concentration camp Auschwitz-Birkenau that sick prisoners thought that after a selection they would be sent to a central hospital, while fully aware of the existence of gas chambers in the camp, one realizes the full magnitude of this particular repression.

In a detailed consideration of the psychology of the stage of adaptation a subdivision into two parts can be made: (1) *the effects of the initial reaction;* (2) *the regression.*

(1) The momentousness of the initial reaction and its effects will appear from a statement by Miss Bluhm: "This initial shock acted, from the beginning, as a principle of selection between those who were, virtually, fit for survival, and those who were not" (20, p. 7).

(a) The initial reaction was a fright reaction. About the after-effect of an acute fright on the inner life there are various opinions. Kleist (149, p. 35) distinguishes three stages: First, the after-effect of the fright stimulus—i.e., that fright wears off slowly, leaving the individual jumpy for days. Second, a decrease of affect, which is characterized by loss of interest in self-preservation or in one's nearest relatives, also by loss of compassion, while the intellect continues to function normally: this is the apathy of fright, also termed Bältz's "paralysis of emotion." This state is of short duration. These two after-effects of fright "may be fixed secondarily through the process of auto-suggestion, in which case they will last much longer" (149, p. 35). Third: an euphoric mood: "a markedly heightened sense of vitality, no feeling of tiredness, a very good appetite" (149, p. 121).

Bonhoeffer also regards Bältz's phenomenon as an effect of fright, and calls it fright stupor (149, p. 142). Vroom, on the other hand, holds that "the after-effect of an acute fright and terror experience . . . is characterized by a strong attachment to the reality of the moment, often accompanied by a euphoric mood, a rejoicing, as it were, at 'having got through.' This is a sensation that could aptly be compared to an ideal holiday mood" (149, p. 142).

It is difficult for me to judge how the prisoners' mentally assimilated fright, because in Auschwitz I suffered from "paralysis of emotion," and consequently took little interest in others. This does not appear a very serious drawback, since I can hardly imagine that I was an exceptional case. Frankl also has stated: "After the first stage of shock the prisoner slipped into the second, the stage of relative apathy" (46, p. 30).

In my opinion the after-effect of the fright reaction in most prisoners was followed by the phase of apathy, which for many was a period fraught with extreme danger. As they took no interest in their surroundings and did not strive after self-preservation, reacting tardily and behaving as if they had been "sandbagged," their behaviour was not such as is best suited to a concentration camp. The duration of this fright apathy is limited; I would estimate it at no more than one or two weeks. But after this the prisoner was not yet in a condition to make an attempt at adaptation, for with the dwindling of his apathy, mourning made itself felt to its fullest extent, and the mournfully depressive phase set in. In accordance with Freud's conception of mourning, this phase was characterized, among other things, by loss of interest in the outer world, with all the disasters consequently ensuing therefrom. As the mourning of one prisoner would be greater than that of another, depression would vary in intensity, so that one individual would recover more quickly than another (see this book, p. 157).

In general, the period of mournfully depressive phase lasted from three to six months, although in the case of prisoners who could at once join an influential (e.g., political) group, it might be shorter. For very many prisoners the period proved too long, so that they never had an opportunity to engage in the struggle for adaptation. Through their behaviour they broke the golden rule, "Be inconspicuous," and brought themselves to the attention of the SS. Not only external factors hastened their end, but also the insufficiency of their urge for self-preservation. My views in this respect are diametrically opposed to Frankl's, who holds that during the phase of relative apathy "every effort, as well as the entire emotional life, is focused on one single issue: sheer survival" (46, p. 41).

That a small part of the new arrivals managed, after all, to survive this period is due to the fact that it was impossible for the SS to murder all the prisoners. If they killed everybody, they would have made their own function in the concentration camp superfluous. Moreover, there was a constant influx of new prisoners, who would then become more conspicuous. And finally a perfectly working life instinct saw a number of prisoners through this period. The factor of luck, however, should not be disregarded; I myself owe much to sheer luck.

Although I have no personal experience of this, I do not think it impossible that in a number of prisoners the fright reaction effected *euphoria*. Thus, ignoring the reality of the concentration camp, they developed aggressiveness and had to pay for it with their lives. In this light can be viewed the following observation by De Wind: "They refuse to be 'pushed around' and their behaviour is rather presumptuous; they try to set aside the law of the concentration camp with iron persistence and make a show of bravado. They, too, succumb quickly" (156, p. 4).

To summarize: I hold the effect of the initial reaction, if it was an acute fright reaction, to consist for most of the newly arrived prisoners in an apathetic phase lasting for some weeks, and a subsequent mournfully depressive phase. The two together lasted from four to seven months. In a small proportion of prisoners the effect of acute fright might be a state of euphoria, but I cannot set myself up as an authority on this question, because I did not personally observe it.

(b) If the initial reaction revealed the phenomenon of *acute depersonalization,* this state would last for some time.

I have already stated my view that acute depersonalization occurred in that small proportion of new arrivals who had formed a mental picture of what they would find in the concentration camp; likewise, that the reality was too terrible for the ego to assimilate it immediately, and that for this reason I regard acute depersonalization as a defence mechanism of the ego.[25] Miss Bluhm's view agrees with mine; she regards the depersonalization in the concentration camps as "protective blocking mechanisms . . . under which the ego was able to

[25] See p. 117 of this book; cf. Carp: "It might be thought that the sense attending estrangement of outer and inner observation is the expression of an escape from a reality which, for the ego, is unbearable" (28, p. 165).

function without breaking down" (20, p. 9). This depersonalization, which was attended by a disturbance of the affective reactions (brought about by the repression of the emotions), resulted in self-observation. This is why I consider this small group of prisoners so important, because ". . . self-observation always includes also the tendency to observe others" (20, p. 10), so that their descriptions should be accorded an especial value. Miss Bluhm, who has made a study of concentration-camp literature, remarks with reference to self-observation, "In the case of our authors, the healthy component of self-observation was strengthened by an additional and most essential factor. Luckier than their less articulate comrades, they were privileged by the relieving gift of *self-expression*. The close association of depersonalization, self-observation and self-expression, comes forth in several of their reports" (20, p. 10).

Self-expression she takes to include, among other components, the mental preparation for writing a book, the study of the behaviour of one's fellow prisoners, painting a picture in one's mind. Her final conclusion is: "The association between self-observation and self-expression became a most successful mechanism of survival" (20, p. 11). However true this may be for the authors of the books read by her, it is inapplicable to the prisoners in general, because only a very small proportion of them could apply themselves to this kind of self-expression. Also the close connection she assumes to exist between self-expression and the state of depersonalization seems to me to be based on error. I would not care to deny that this connection might exist (Bakels' diary (14) being proof sufficient), but Vogel (147) and Rost (126) are among those who have proved that there were diaries written by authors not in a state of depersonalization. It is my view, therefore, that self-expression was not of great significance to the prisoners.

None the less I attach great significance to acute depersonalization and its attendant self-observation and disturbance of the affective reactions. The newly arrived prisoner in this state found himself in a more advantageous position than another who was passing through the apathetic or the euphoric phase.

Because he did not suffer from fright stupor with its familiar symptoms, and because his intellectual faculties were unimpaired,[26] he could assess the events of the camp more precisely and draw accurate conclusions. He did not make himself conspicuous, in contrast to others who did and who were consequently maltreated, given particularly hard work, etc. He observed this without feeling compassion; perhaps he even rejoiced in it. However, it should be understood that seeing another man beaten did not give him pleasure, but merely the fact it was not himself who was being beaten.

In other camps depersonalization also occurred, as is shown by Herzberg: "A kind of stupor, . . . sometimes made us see what happened in Bergen Belsen, no longer as a reality, but as a stage performance, or—even more fantastically—as a shadow show, as a motion picture. Were we truly there, as we were, or was it our shadows that we saw playing their parts in an all too gruesome play? Many a man had left his soul and sense at home, . . . and if he did recognize himself in the camp, this was no more than recognizing oneself in a photograph" (66, p. 61).

Acute depersonalization, which, as we have seen, affected mentally sane people, was a benefit to them, in that it heightened their chances of survival during the dangerous first period. It is not easy to state accurately the duration of acute depersonalization, though probably it did not last longer than one or two months, after which the depersonalization either disappeared or passed from the acute into the chronic stage. It is also hard to estimate whether chronic depersonalization was of frequent occurrence. I am inclined to be sceptical, because of my personal experience and the conversations I took part in or heard in the camp. Besides the visible manifestation of depersonalization, the absence of affective reactions allows of a different explanation, namely as the effect of repression (see this book, p. 143); for affective reactions were indeed noticeable when, for example, a good friend suddenly turned up in

---

[26] "Much like in other cases communicated in analytical literature, the ego of the prisoners refused to accept the estrangement it was subjected to. It, therefore, turned the experience connected with the loss of its feelings into an object of its intellectual interests" (20, p. 9).

the concentration camp. Also, during the many selections I witnessed, I found that hardly any one of the Jews on the prisoners' hospital staff remained unmoved. On these grounds chronic depersonalization will not be further discussed.

(2) *Regression: the process of adaptation in a narrower sense.* Adaptation had already begun during the stage just considered, but through the effects of the initial reaction, this adaptation did not come into prominence. Often these effects were so serious that the prisoner died before having a chance to adapt himself. If, however, he did survive them, he had to adapt himself to the factors discussed. If he was successful in this, the prisoner came to belong to the category of old and seasoned inmates; he had ceased to be a greenhorn.

What exactly was this process of adaptation? In normal life the adult enjoys a certain measure of independence; within the limits set by society he has a considerable measure of liberty. Nobody orders him when and what to eat, where to take up his residence or what to wear, neither to take his rest on Sunday [27] nor when to have his bath, nor when to go to bed. He is not beaten during his work, he need not ask permission to go to the W.C., he is not continually kept on the run, he does not feel that the work he is doing is silly or childish, he is not confined behind barbed wire, he is not counted twice a day or more, he is not left unprotected against the actions of his fellow citizens, he looks after his family and the education of his children.

How altogether different was the life of the concentration-camp prisoner! What to do during each part of the day was arranged for him, and decisions were made about him from which there was no appeal. He was impotent and suffered from bedwetting, and because of his chronic diarrhoea he soiled his underwear. He had not a penny in his pocket, though from time to time he might be given a "premium note" by way of pocket money, and he paid no taxes. His interest did not go beyond the question: How shall I win through? which meant: How shall I obtain more food and get into a tolerable labour group?

[27] In Auschwitz the prisoners were obliged to rest in bed every Sunday from 1 to 3 P.M.

This way of life and this attitude towards life cannot, I think, be viewed as anything but regression. The term "regression" is used here in its general sense, that is, as a "reversion from a higher to a lower stage of development" (51, p. 287). The dependence of the prisoner on the SS, which may be compared to the dependence of children on their parents, caused regression. Friedman observed this even in Cyprus: "Many of the survivors even after liberation showed strong evidence of complete infantile dependency" (56, p. 604).

Another cause of regression, as Flugel puts it, was that "punishment and frustration tend naturally to cause regression; if we cannot satisfy our present impulses, we are liable to fall back upon earlier and more primitive development stages" (44, p. 162).

Through regression the prisoners became "helpless instruments in their masters' hands. This was the so-called 'educational' purpose of the concentration camps" (20, p. 15).

Regression was noticeable in the turn the prisoners' talks took. When Bettelheim deals with their tall stories about the past, the way they had hoodwinked the SS, the sabotage of labour, he remarks: "Like children they felt not at all set back or ashamed when it became known, that they had lied about their prowess" (17, p. 446). Also the prisoners' behaviour revealed a noticeable regression. Kautsky observed this very strikingly in his own person: "I myself can declare that often I saw myself as I used to be in my school days, when by sly dodges and clever pretexts we avoided being found out, or could 'organize' something" (81, pp. 188 f.).

Striking too was the use of words denoting parts of the anal and genital regions. Similar experiences have been put on record by Colaço Belmonte from the Japanese prisoner-of-war camps: "During the increasing austerity of life, later passing into chronic starvation . . . every trace of adult sexuality tended to disappear from conversation and many scatological jokes were made, which sometimes caused everybody to titter like children when one of them expelled wind. (33, p. 420).

It is fairly obvious that apart from regression, degradation and a general coarsening of manners played an important part. Conversation at a low level was not peculiar to concentration camps, for Vischer has stated that also "in many camps verbal usage in conversation sinks to a very low level, both in cultured and uncultured people" (146, p. 16).

Generally speaking, regression was marked by concern with animal functions. During working hours the prisoner had to ask permission from the SS every time he wanted to urinate or defecate, "as if the education to cleanliness would be once more repeated" (17, p. 445).

But also the prisoner himself revealed regression, for instance, by not even trying to keep back his wind. More serious than this was the disregarding of the laws of personal anal cleanliness. With reference to this phenomenon Miss Bluhm has pointed out that it is not at all unusual that people in extraordinary circumstances, for example soldiers in wartime, "are able to give up their habitual standards of cleanliness without deeper disturbance; yet only up to certain limits" (20, p. 17). The rules of anal cleanliness, she adds, are not disregarded. "Their neglect means return to the instinctual behaviour of childhood" (ibid.).

To this statement I can subscribe in broad outline, although one should not lose sight of the fact that regular cleansing requires time, water, soap, towels, and paper; as these were denied to many of the prisoners, they were, also through external circumstances, forced to return to the infantile phase of their life. Fundamentally Miss Bluhm is right, but lack of cleansing material should be taken into account as a highly conducive factor.

Regression became very serious if the prisoner refused to get up at night to urinate, and befouled his bed. The bed-wetting was seriously aggravated by hunger edema and the watery food of high carbohydrate content,[28] which forced the prisoner to get up repeatedly, and encroached seriously upon the few hours of his night's sleep; many, however, were over-fatigued and hence too listless to get up.

Regression in the field of excretory functions is explained

[28] The burning of carbohydrates releases more water than the burning of proteins and fats (see 22, p. 33).

by Miss Bluhm, because "the inhibitions of disgust and shame were not strong enough to prevent an individual from a return to childhood reactions" (20, p. 17).

This appears very plausible to me, since I am convinced that the superego of some of the prisoners was so much weakened that the inhibitions taught by the parents to their children concerning the functions of the bladder and the rectum had totally or partly disappeared, so that there was no longer any check on their drives. Thus many prisoners returned to the primitive infantile stage of humanity.

This regression is more or less inherent in the stay in the concentration camp. According to Colaço Belmonte it also obtained in the Japanese prisoner-of-war camps, and even in the military community in general. He holds that regression is bound to occur

if all people are treated alike, as boys are in a large family,

if all must pay respect to one man . . . ,

if food, accommodation and clothing are no longer an individual concern, but authoritatively regulated, as they are for the child in a family,

if the men no longer receive any money, and are consequently relieved of every financial responsibility toward the outer world (rent, taxes, etc.),

if the soldier or the prisoner of war has to get up, eat, and go to bed punctually, . . .

if he is kept away from women, . . .

In hundreds of ways the soldier, and to an even greater extent the prisoner of war, is given to understand that he is a child. . . . Then dishonesty, mendacity, egotistic actions in order to obtain more food or to get out of scrapes reach full development, and theft becomes a veritable affliction of camp life (33, p. 420).

All these conditions obtained in the concentration camps. One aspect deserves particular attention, as in my view it was of outstanding importance and had far-reaching consequences: "if all must pay respect to one man. . . ." In the Japanese prisoner-of-war camps this one man was a Japanese, in the concentration camp it was the SS man. The SS man was all-powerful in the camp, he was the lord and master of the prisoner's life. As a cruel father he could, without fear of punishment, even kill the prisoner [29] and as a gentle father he could scatter largesse and afford the prisoner his protection. The result was that for nearly all the prisoners the SS became a father image.

If regression is taken into account, through which the prisoners were in a position of infantile dependence on the SS, the conclusion appears logical *that only very few of the prisoners escaped a more or less intensive identification* [30] *with the SS.* Hence my opinion that this identification cannot be restricted only to the Kapos and the other prominents.

Dealing with the concept of identification, Freud has stated: "Identification, in fact, is ambivalent from the very first; it can turn into an expression of tenderness as easily as into a wish for someone's removal" (49a, p. 61).

This ambivalence can be "translated" by the concept of hate and love, but also by that of contempt and admiration. If it is assumed that in the prisoners the identification with the SS manifested itself as admiration or contempt, it will be evident that this identification was not invariably the same as the Kapo mentality, for some of the prisoners felt contempt of the SS and did not make the SS their ideal. In these prisoners the identification was only partial. Freud mentions the occurrence of partial identification (49a, p. 64); in the case under consideration it led to the frequent use of such words as "arse," "shit," "to shit upon," etc.; the bawling at fellow prisoners; irritability, hitting about on the slightest provocation. And identification on the part of the prisoners with the anti-Semitism of the SS was experienced by many Jews.[31]

Kaas also points out that it is possible "that a prisoner comes to identify himself with the SS. No need for him to become a Kapo or a foreman. In daily life too, there are plenty of occa-

[29] Examples are to be found in concentration-camp literature. I refer only to 87, pp. 95, 97, 101, 119.

[30] "Identification endeavours to mould a person's own ego after the fashion of the one that has been taken as a 'model' " (49a, p. 63).

[31] There may be another explanation for bawling, irritability, hitting about, anti-Semitism. Flugel states: "The process of regression . . . may also lead to greater aggressiveness, inasmuch as the pregenital levels are essentially more aggressive than the genital one" (44, p. 162).

sions on which such characters will be able to vent their aggression on defenceless people" (78, pp. 418 f.).

In this connection I point to a study published by Anna Freud, who observed that children may protect themselves from fear by "identification with the aggressor" (47, pp. 117 ff.). The explanation she offers is: "The child introjects some characteristics of an anxiety-object and so assimilates an anxiety-experience. Here the mechanism of identification or introjection is combined with a second important mechanism. By impersonating the aggressor, assuming his attributes or imitating his aggression, the child transforms himself from the person threatened into the person who makes the threat" (47, p. 121).

The great benefit to be derived from "identification with the aggressor" has been stressed by Flugel: "When effective action against an impending danger is impossible, imitation may be the next best thing, and that regression to childish make-believe may have its uses when we are reduced to childish impotence. In spite of its unrealistic and often utterly fantastic character, it can nevertheless help us to overcome fears that might otherwise be paralysing, and thus give us time, courage, and the power of thought to adapt ourselves to a situation to which we might otherwise utterly succumb" (44, p. 73).

"Identification with the aggressor" can also be partial. Anna Freud relates the case of a boy visiting a dentist who has hurt him. After this visit the boy wants to destroy several objects: "The child was identifying himself not with the person of the aggressor but with his aggressions" (47, p. 120).

Similarly, I am certain, the partial identification of the greater number of the prisoners with the SS must be explained: it is not with the moral standards of the SS, which he despises, that the prisoner identifies himself, but he cannot escape identification with the aggressive manifestations of the SS. Thus the fact that these prisoners adopted aggressive behaviour but not the standards of the SS may be accounted for.

Those prisoners who had the Kapo mentality, and therefore admiration for the SS, and who wanted to be like them, identified themselves completely with the SS; the qualities of the SS

were absorbed in their ego. The moral standards of these prisoners were displaced by the standards applied by the SS. In all
probability this group was not numerous; its representative is
the Kapo—about whom more presently.

I am aware that my statement, to the effect that only a small
number of the prisoners, perhaps not even one, was able to
escape a certain measure of identification with the SS will cause
some surprise. My conclusion, as I have shown, is based on
these grounds:

(1) That for all of us the SS was a father image, of such
ambivalence, however, that the intensity of the identification
varied from one instant to the next.

(2) That through regression, which was an essential of adaptation, "identification with the aggressor" occurred. In most of
the prisoners this identification was merely partial.

The stage of adaptation was the most important phase in
the life of the prisoner. When he had succeeded in adapting
himself to concentration-camp life he was an ex-greenhorn,
he had settled down. Roughly this would take him about a
year; but only a small percentage of the prisoners survived
this stage, which is not surprising, as abnormally heavy demands were made on them. Once more I want to stress one
factor that was entirely outside the prisoner's control: luck,
fate, accident—call it what you like—which often caused the
prisoner's life to take an unexpected turn.

The Stage of Resignation

The prisoner who had reached this stage had again turned
from nobody into somebody. He now belonged to the category
of the "old numbers," was given sufficient food, wore better
clothes, was placed in a tolerable labour group, and had made
contacts in the camp. Thus he had won the first round in the
struggle for existence in the camp, though it must once more
be observed that there was no such thing as security in a concentration camp (see this book, pp. 125 f.).

He lived in the camp, camp events were significant to him.
As Bettelheim puts it: "Old prisoners seemed mainly con-

cerned with the problem of how to live as well as possible within the camp. Once they had reached this attitude, everything that happened to them, even the worst atrocity, was 'real' to them" (17, p. 437).

The "old" prisoner had resigned himself to concentration-camp life and because the improvement in his material conditions made it easier for him to accept things as they came, he enjoyed the pleasures that even this life had to offer. Remarkable as it may seem, there were pleasures to be enjoyed. In Auschwitz, for example, there was a band composed of prisoners that was supposed to provide light music in the morning and at night when the labour groups were coming in or going out. This same orchestra, however, gave good concerts on Sunday afternoons (when all work was stopped), thus providing exquisite pleasure for many prisoners. Adequate performers provided excellent cabaret shows, to the accompaniment of a special jazz band. This cabaret was sometimes attended by the SS. A few times in Auschwitz we were allowed to watch a screen play. Games were also taken up, and a Netherlands professional boxer gave a few demonstrations with a sparring partner. Similar pleasures in other camps have been put on record. Kogon (87, pp. 141–146) has related that in Buchenwald there were an orchestra, a string quartet [32] and a cinema. Unless the SS issued a prohibition, it was possible to listen to radio programmes by means of amplifiers. Newspapers (naturally only those published in Germany) could be read, and there was even a library [33] in which anti-Nazi literature could also be found by the initiated. In Auschwitz only non-Jews were allowed to read newspapers, a prohibition that could naturally not be enforced. In this camp there was no library.

At the same time prisoners in this stage had more leisure for conversation, albeit the camp and everything connected with it were usually the main topics. Physicians were apt to abandon the custom, prevalent in their normal existence, of conversing on medical subjects. Most likely this was to a great extent due

[32] I have been informed by Kaas that this string quartet was conducted by the second violinist of the Capet quartet of Paris.
[33] Also in Dachau (see 126, p. 10).

to the lack of medical literature, the senselessness of their medical work in the camp, the authority laymen enjoyed over, the physician, the pains the latter had to take in order to retain his position in the prisoners' hospital, etc.

Some authors have made a point of the great significance of humour in the camps. Frankl has said, "Humour is a weapon of the mind in the struggle for its preservation. For it is well known that humour is better suited than almost anything else in human life to attain aloofness, to rise superior to the occasion, albeit, as has been stated, merely for a few seconds" (46, p. 61).

Great significance has been attributed to humour by Kautsky, who even goes so far as to call it "the most infallible means to keep up morale . . . not so much the bitter witticism, . . . but the laughter at some harmless joke or comic situation, the laughter that is a relief. Incredible as it may seem . . . , laughter was often heard in the camps" (120, p. 204).

The prisoners who had not yet adapted themselves and still found themselves in the midst of the struggle for daily existence, had little sense of humour. Therefore the statements of Kautsky and Frankl should be taken as applying exclusively to the wholly or partly adapted prisoner.

The effect of humour, as Flugel quotes from Freud, is that "the ego adopts the point of view of the super-ego and from this height looks down upon itself like a kindly parent smiling at the petty concerns and quaint behaviour of a little child" (44, p. 181).

Referring to two examples of humour in cases of serious peril of life, Flugel has stated that characteristics of humour are indifference toward life, a deliberate ignoring of the seriousness of the situation, a half-playful assumption that all is normal and that consequently normal standards still obtain. He even regards these characteristics as a "quality of exaltation. From the point of view of the super-ego the ego sees its own unimportance, with a consequent indifference to its extinction, but at the same time presents a bold, united (we might say heroic) front towards a hostile and menacing reality" (44, p. 181). This, I think, applies to the concentration camps as well. On the one hand the prisoner knew no fear of death (see this book, pp. 158 f.); on the other he was driven by his life instinct (pp. 163 f.) to persevere in spite of reality.

Once he had adapted himself, the prisoner was no longer a mere egotist, but could allow his altruistic feelings to manifest themselves. This brings us to the problem of comradeship. A measure of comradeship was experienced and given by everyone. The necessity of this is stressed by Kaas: "It must be continually realized that life in the camp is so full of hardships and dangers that it is almost impossible for the 'lone wolf' not to perish" (78, p. 410). Kautsky makes the same point: "No word in the camp was surely oftener and more objectionably abused than comradeship. . . . Everybody demanded comradeship from the other man and only very few were prepared to extend it. But—most curious inner contradiction: nobody could have survived in the camp, had there been no comradeship" (81, p. 175).

As the camp was a conglomeration of many sorts and conditions of men, every one could join a bigger or smaller group. Groups might be formed because people remembered each other from former days; had heard each other's names mentioned; hailed from the same town, region, or country; spoke the same dialect or language; were members of the same political party or religious sect—and so on. Thus aid and support were received and given. Kautsky even holds that he owed his life to this group support: "I myself in Buchenwald participated in this aid, without which I surely should not have lived to see the liberation" (81, p. 178).

I also received help from others, though to my mind only he could give aid who was not in the starvation stage. To put it even more strongly: Only those who had attained to a considerable degree of adaptation or had already reached the stage of resignation, and hence enjoyed a certain measure of "camp prosperity," were able to aid others. Not until the difficulties inherent in the process of adaptation had been overcome, could people show their comradeship. That there were many who even then did not choose to do this, can only be deplored.

For this reason I believe that there is no need for me to retract what I have already noted on egotism and altruism (see this book, p. 139). Far be it from me to underrate the occasional significance of comradeship, but it must not be overrated either. To my mind Kaas is guilty of exaggeration when he says, "Nearly all the prisoners who returned owed their lives to comrades who made great sacrifices on their behalf" (78, p. 411). My personal experiences were otherwise. I found that, if everybody's life is at stake, very little comradeship is evident. Then people will not make sacrifices or take any risk. There is still a sharp imprint on my mind of the last night in Ebensee, on which I was ordered out. When on that occasion I tried to hide, I was prevented from doing so by my fellow prisoners, who even brought me to the attention of the senior block prisoner. Absence of comradeship is most conspicuous when there is danger of life. With reference to an account, illustrated with photos, of the sinking of the German battleship *Bismarck*, published in *Harper's Magazine* of February, 1942, Bondy, considering the behaviour of the German sailors, remarks: "It seems that men can stand a tremendous amount of danger and suffering, but that the point is eventually reached where only the bestial instincts of self-preservation remain. Ultimately, there is only the will to survive" (23, p. 456).

More conformable to truth than the view held by Kaas appears that of Kautsky, who believes in the existence of "selective" comradeship: "One could not let one's sun shine on the just and the unjust; in the camp there was not so much that we could give away. One had indeed to select the objects one was prepared to aid. . . . In the last analysis nobody can be expected to give away of his food, so long as he himself goes hungry" (81, p. 178).

Though not denying the existence of comradeship in the camps, I am convinced that it did not reveal itself until individual danger of life had ceased to be prevalent.

I would be doing an injustice to Kaas if I were to ignore the experience he had in Buchenwald and of which he privately informed me. More than once he observed excellent comradeship among the group of political prisoners, even when its members were in danger of losing their lives.[34] Hence I leave open the possibility that among those groups in the camp whose members were united by a common ideal, good comradeship existed. A most likely example of such a group may have been that of political prisoners.

In the stage of resignation the prisoner regarded concentration-camp life as real life, but not as his definitive life. This should not be misunderstood. The prisoner knew that one day he would leave the concentration camp, either dead or alive. Until that moment the best thing was to accept reality dispassionately, in the simple awareness that one had got to live in the concentration camp for the time being. This is what I mean by the real life. After his liberation he hoped to enjoy life again to the full, and by this is meant the definitive life.

Of course there were also individuals—for example, the "greens" (the criminals)—for whom concentration-camp life was not only the real, but also the definitive life. Many of them, who attained to high functions, had never had such a good time as they had now in the concentration camp; there was nothing they would rather do than continue this existence.

Because the "old, seasoned, adapted" prisoner saw life in the camp as the real life, life outside the camp assumed a quality of strangeness. Frankl has put this very strongly: "So far as he can look beyond the camp, life there appears to him as it may appear to a deceased person, who looks upon the world from the Great Beyond" (46, p. 101).

The "greenhorn" had no such perception, hence the difference in behaviour between the old and the new prisoners. Bettelheim observed that the greenhorn used his money "to smuggle letters out of the camp or to receive communications without having them censored" (17, p. 439). The old prisoners, on the other hand, employed their money "for securing for themselves 'soft' jobs, such as clerical work in the offices of the

[34] Federn, on the other hand, holds that "True comradeship and fidelity existed only in very small groups" (43, p. 78).

camp or work in the shops where they were at least protected against the weather while at work" (17, p. 439).

Toward those who lived outside the camps in freedom, a definite reaction developed in the old prisoners. They hated and were jealous of "all those living outside the camp, who 'enjoyed' life as if we were not rotting away" (17, p. 442).

A similar view has been set down by Bondy: "The prisoners are envious of all those people who lead a better life, who are free . . . who have more to eat" (23, p. 463); while Kautsky holds that the world outside the concentration camp "had no inkling of the conditions inside the camp" (81, p. 191). It cannot be denied that the old prisoners both through their envy and because they knew that the outside world had no idea of what they had to go through, suffered their attitude toward the new arrivals to be affected. I repeatedly observed this, not only in myself, but also in others. Even in Westerbork, a camp that could not really be likened to a concentration camp, I found myself not very friendly to the new arrivals nor very willing to help them. I reflected, "You have lived so much longer in liberty (I wanted to forget that this was not the same thing as freedom), you have enjoyed a better life so much longer than we did, without worrying about us; now you can also look after yourselves." In Auschwitz this behaviour was even more manifest. Unless a newly arrived prisoner was a good friend of former years, I would ignore him. My jealousy caused me to take revenge on those who had been so lucky as to remain outside a concentration camp longer than myself, and my revenge took the form of neglect, and the reflection, "Let them find out for themselves what the difficulties of a concentration camp are." The same observation has been made by Kautsky: "The prominent forgot that as a new arrival he had experienced the same feelings as the prisoners now under him, and if he remembered this at all, it seemed only right to him that the others should have their turn now" (81, p. 174).

So I was jealous of those who lived outside the camps. And . . . perhaps I still am. This may explain the contempt I feel for those who do not know by personal experience what a concentration camp is. I am jealous of those who have been so fortunate; who could go on living in quiet, who kept their positions or even improved them, whose families have not been destroyed, whom, after the liberation, it did not take a number of years to adapt themselves again to society.

Jealousy is an effect which occurs in very young people. Anna Freud has explained this: "The child who has now left his infancy and his first year behind him suddenly learns that his mother does not belong to him alone. The family . . . has other members—father and brothers and sisters. . . . They all, indeed, assert a right to the possession of the mother. It can easily be understood that the small child regards his brothers and sisters as his enemies. He is jealous of them and wishes them out of the way so as to restore the original state of affairs, which alone is satisfactory to him" (48, pp. 27 f.).

Anna Freud points out that anyone can observe this behaviour in a child, at the birth of a baby brother or sister, and that it sometimes causes children to do each other an injury. She goes on to say that this form of jealousy, which her father called a "family complex of the first sexual period" (50, p. 232), is nothing but "a comparatively harmless prelude to another and much more powerful conflict. His brothers and sisters are not the only rivals who compete with him for the possession of the mother: the father is far more important. . . . The boy hates him as a rival when his father acts the part of the rightful owner of the mother. . . ." (48, p. 31). And this is known as the oedipus complex.

According to Freud, jealousy, like mourning, may be classified as one of the normal effects. If conscious jealousy is absent in a human being, Freud assumes that it is subject to a strong repression and is active in the subconscious. Cases of abnormally strong envy, with which analysis is concerned, prove to be of three degrees. These three degrees or layers of envy may be designated as (1) *competitive* or normal; (2) *projected;* (3) delusional (50, p. 232).

Normal jealousy is made up, according to Freud, of "grief, the pain caused by the thought of losing the loved object, and of the narcissistic wound, in so far as this is distinguishable from the other wound; further, of feelings of enmity against the successful rival, and of a greater or lesser amount of self-criticism which tries to hold the person himself accountable for his loss" (50, p. 232).

Normal jealousy is "under the complete control of the conscious ego; for it is rooted deep in the unconscious, it is a continuation of the earliest stirrings of the child's affective life, and it originates in the Oedipus or family complex of the first sexual period." (ibid.).

The second layer, projected jealousy, "is derived in both men and women either from their own actual faithfulness in real life or from impulses towards it which have succumbed to repression" (50, p. 233). Anyone who denies these impulses "will nevertheless be impelled so strongly in the direction of infidelity that he will be glad enough to make use of an unconscious mechanism as an alleviation. This relief . . . he achieves when he projects his own impulses to infidelity on to the partner to whom he owes faith" (ibid.).

The third layer, delusional jealousy, originates in "repressed impulses towards unfaithfulness—the object, however, in these cases is of the same sex as the subject. Delusional jealousy represents an acidulated homosexuality, and rightly takes its position among the classical forms of paranoia" (50, p. 234).

After this detailed exposition of the Freudian view on jealousy, I will attempt to explain the jealousy of the old prisoners and the ex-prisoners. It may be partly explained by the general regression that occurred in the camps; but this regression does not explain all, for, first, jealousy is not exclusive to youth (adults can also be jealous); secondly, jealousy remained after the liberation and after regression had disappeared.

I suggest that the matter be viewed in this light: Because of conditions in the concentration camps a part of the jealousy was normal. When I restrict this view to the Jewish prisoners, as it is they whom I can most fairly judge, I think that many a Jewish prisoner begrudged the other Jews, who had at first successfully gone into hiding or enjoyed other privileges, the delay in their capture. He harboured the same feelings toward those Jews who by a successful attempt to flee abroad, or because of their marriage to a non-Jew, had managed to escape imprisonment in a concentration camp. And non-Jews he begrudged their "Aryanship" because of the advantages accruing therefrom. The Jewish prisoner would have liked to enjoy the same advantages to avoid the hell of the concentration camp, but they had been out of his reach. He was jealous of those who had had them; he despised, nay, he hated them.

Moreover, jealousy arose from repressed self-criticism, when, for example, the prisoner had been unable to muster sufficient courage to make an attempt at going into hiding or at flight; or when he had not been "shrewd" enough to bring off such an effort. This self-criticism, these self-reproaches—"I was a coward, I was stupid"—he would project on to the world outside of the concentration camps and on to the new arrival, as he may be still projecting them on to those who were never inside a concentration camp.

Jealousy of fellow prisoners, however, also occurred. The Jewish prisoner experienced in his own person that he, because he was a Jew, was made to suffer more than the "Aryan": he was never given a leading function; what he did get was the hardest labour groups and the worst treatment, he was arbitrarily refused admission to the H.K.B. He found that the "Aryan" had a better chance of survival than himself; he longed to be an "Aryan." Consequently one would expect that through projection the Jewish prisoner came to despise or hate the "Aryan." Curiously enough, this was far from being always the case, but it could be observed that in some of the prisoners projection was reversed and became directed towards the prisoner's own person and towards his own Jewish group.

This Jewish anti-Semitism, sometimes called "Jewish self-hatred," is already known in normal society. Because it is such a remarkable phenomenon, I will examine it in some detail.

Bernstein (16), viewing the anti-Semitism of non-Jews especially as a result of the circumstances that the Jews, as a group, constitute a minority within a non-Jewish environment,[35]

[35] The causes of anti-Semitism will not be gone into, as this would be going beyond the scope of this book. For the latest literature on this subject the reader is referred to Nos. 105 and 133 of the bibliography.

points to the great significance of emancipation [36] for the Jews. "Emancipation, . . . has shattered the belief of the Jews in themselves and in their mission and at the same time their will to be Jews" (16, p. 215). The result was: "For the Jew the standard and example in every domain of life has become everything non-Jewish, as presented by his environment of the moment" (ibid.), and "all that is typical of the non-Jewish majority of the moment is *passionately glorified* by the Jews concerned. An attempt is made to transform the whole of Jewish life in accordance with the picture of the ideal worshipped" (ibid.).

This last aspect, the attempt of the Jew to equate his life as much as possible with that of the non-Jew, is called assimilation.

Bernstein goes on: "Inevitably a *rejection* of all Jewish things must be the result of the glorification of everything non-Jewish. . . . This rejection is rooted in a collective consciousness of inferiority [37] which has been qualified here as perverse." (16, p. 216). Every Jew who aims at assimilation views himself as no longer a member of the body collective. He thinks that he does not look like a Jew, that he bears himself in a non-Jewish way, that by non-Jews he is regarded as one of them, etc., "but other Jews and everything Jewish he often looks upon as intellectually inferior, and always he *feels* them to be his inferiors, even when he does not realize the presence of this feeling, and would on occasion deny it with indignation. Actually he has adopted a great deal of the anti-Semitic attitude, of the disgust of everything that is typically Jewish; *and always he will even react to his own group in a characteristic group-psychological way, as to a hostile group of strangers"* (16, p. 216).

It must not be thought, however, that this "self-hatred" manifests itself in the Jew in the same way as in the non-Jew.

[36] Through emancipation the Jews came to be regarded as equals before the law with non-Jews, instead of second-rate citizens.

[37] Because the Jews live as a minority among another people, the best they can expect is a benevolent tolerance, which "is characterized by a more or less emphatic degree of subjection, a more or less thorough serfdom. As a result of serfdom that perverse hatred of many Jews towards their own group has arisen" (16, p. 213).

This particular manifestation may indeed occur, though only by way of exception. More often it is merely a being unpleasantly struck by Jews who look particularly "Jewish," or behave in a strikingly "Jewish" way—briefly, by those who reveal those characteristics which are attributed to Jews by anti-Semites. That the phenomenon of the assimilated Jew's irritation at another Jew is rooted in an unconscious hatred of the Jewish group seems to me self-evident (see also 106, pp. 30 ff.).

Loewenstein explains this thus: "Jewish anti-Semitism— outcome of the continual social and psychological pressures of their situation as a permanent minority group" (cf. 16, p. 157). The inevitable consequence of this situation has been what Anna Freud has called "identification with the aggressor," the aggressor in this case being the "gentile anti-Semite" (105, p. 144). In other words, the "Jewish self-hatred" comes into being through identification with the anti-Semite. But probably the fear that the behaviour of the Jew might tend to increase anti-Semitism also played an important part. Thus, to my mind, the fear of increasing anti-Semitism was responsible for the "critical" attitude of many Netherlands Jews towards the German Jews who entered the Netherlands between 1933 and 1940. The same phenomenon was observed when Polish Jews emigrated to Germany, and in our day it can again be perceived, now that many European Jews are emigrating to America. This fear is based on a fact of experience, that "every immigrating Jew carries anti-Semitism with him as an invisible part of his luggage." [38]

Jewish anti-Semitism is thus a result of the attempt at assimilation; and because the majority of Jews are in favour of assimilation—or at least used to be before the creation of the Jewish state of Israel—Jewish anti-Semitism must be of frequent occurrence. Even the Zionists, who thought they understood anti-Semitism and have given much thought to particular Jewish values, were not entirely free from it. In this respect I take issue with Melkman (see 106, pp. 30 ff.), whose opinion it is that Jewish anti-Semitism is not frequent. He has based his view on the fact that but few prominent Jews are known "who

[38] A well-known saying in Zionist circles.

were carried away by the thought that Jews are inferior" (106, p. 30), and on another fact, that during the religious disputes in the Middle Ages the number of Jews who acted as counsel for the prosecution of their former co-religionists was small. He also argues that in modern times "cases of Jews turning on other Jews and prosecuting or betraying them are very rare exceptions" (*ibid.*). By way of additional argument he mentions a research made by Lehrer among 43 Jewish children of five to twelve years. Of these only one denied being Jewish. "All the children accepted their Jewishness as a matter of course, and most of them said that they were glad to be Jews, despite the unpleasantness this might involve" (106, p. 31).

Finally Melkman records that Heine "in spite of his violent attacks on and criticisms of all kinds of Jews, always retained a close association with the Jewish people" (106, p. 32).

Still, the record of all these facts does not alter my view; I am also of the opinion that there have been few Jews who were consciously anti-Semites, but only because I believe that in the assimilated Jew anti-Semitism was repressed and therefore manifested itself not at all, feebly, or in a roundabout way. Also I think it is normal that Jewish children should have a positive association with the Jewish people, for no Jewish family can ever be so completely assimilated that "things Jewish" are entirely removed. And it is a matter of course that the outside world, which characterizes the Jewish family as Jewish, must be a factor of great importance.

In this connection I want to point once more to the interesting study of Jewish children by Lehrer, who tried to determine at what age the first signs of Jewishness appeared in Jewish children in the United States. He found that the children are "in their fourth year, acquainted with the national names of their residential neighbours, e.g., Italians, Jews, etc., but they have no emotional attitude towards them, not to speak of any attempt at a definition" (98, p. 200). In their fourth year, therefore, the children do not yet realize that they are Jews and have as yet no "positive attitude to the word 'Jewish'" (98, p. 207). However, Lehrer goes on, "This consciousness and the feelings connected with it do not appear gradually, but emerge suddenly . . . so that at the age of five they are distinct and pronounced" (98, p. 207). From their fifth year Jewish children, according to Lehrer, know to what group they belong. He stresses that he has studied only children in the United States, but I do not see why his conclusion should not obtain, for example, in the Netherlands.

Finally Lehrer remarks: ". . . no matter how divergent the various circles of the Jewish people in America, no difference is noticeable among their children in the positive and impulsive character of their national belonging. Apparently, the Jewish environment is so constructed that every circle leads to the same psychological state in early childhood" (98, p. 216).

To this I can subscribe without any reservation: almost every Jew has associations with the Jewish people, because he grows up in a milieu which in spite of everything is always somehow Jewish. Viewed in this light, Heine's association with the Jewish people need not be any occasion for surprise.

But we must not forget that according to Freud all human emotional ties are ambivalent, so that by the side of positive feelings, negative feelings are at the same time present. In showing the positive feelings, therefore, Melkman has also proved the negative. And these negative feelings, feelings of hate, are repressed as much as possible, but must as a matter of course be present in all these Jews.

Thus I trust I have proved the occurrence of Jewish anti-Semitism in very many Jews, even in normal times, although the Jews themselves might to a great extent not be conscious of them. And why should we be surprised that this unconscious affect did not remain unconscious in the camps?

Because the original superego had declined, the standards of the super-ego, which kept Jewish anti-Semitism in a state of repression, had entirely or almost entirely disappeared. In addition, Jewish feelings of inferiority were strengthened by their particularly bad treatment in the camp, as compared with that of the "Aryans." This again strengthened the individual's hatred of his own person and his own group. This Jewish self-hatred was quite obvious. In Auschwitz, for example, the Netherlands Jews would openly criticize those from Poland.

For the latter occupied a privileged position in this camp, since the majority of the prominents consisted of Polish "Aryans," with whom they could speak in their own language, while the Netherlands Jews could not.

Some examples of Jewish anti-Semitism may be quoted from Kautsky's [39] book: "Naturally among the bourgeois unpolitical Jews money played an important part: if the Jews were those who happened to suffer from the ever-spreading corruption, they had contributed not a little to the cause of this evil through their unscrupulous buying of every thinkable privilege from the 'Aryan' camp officials" (81, p. 157).

Kautsky's information on the Netherlands Jews is interesting: "Among them two groups could be sharply distinguished, on the one hand the vast majority from the dock quarter of Amsterdam, of whom even the Netherlanders said they had never known there was so much rabble among them, and on the other hand the minority, who resembled the non-Jewish Netherlanders in every essential. Curiously enough, the members of the latter group proved to be much tougher than those of the former" (81, p. 158).

These remarks will be left for what they are, as to my mind they speak for themselves.

The jealousy that I have discussed formed part of the *camp mentality*, which came into being in every prisoner. A particular mentality, however, does not only arise in a concentration camp. Vischer notices it, for example, among prisoners of war, and has termed it the "barbed-wire sickness." Of the symptoms of this psychoneurosis, recorded by Vischer, I mention: ". . . heightened irritability. People cannot bear the slightest contradiction. . . . In mutual intercourse they are extraordinarily small-minded and always aiming at their own advantage. . . . Their doings are somehow restless . . . a gray fundamental mood and a pessimistic view of everything that happens in their environment . . . suspicious . . ." (146, pp. 25 f.).

[39] Kautsky was a prisoner in various concentration camps from May 31, 1938, until April 11, 1945—five years as a Jew, and then he was "Aryanized" and registered as a Reich German.

As a probable cause of the "barbed-wire sickness" he regards the barbed wire, which is always there as tangible evidence for the prisoner that he is living in confinement. But, Vischer continues, "in view of this, we do not intend to state that the restraint, the barbed wire, is the most significant etiological factor responsible for this sickness . . . the uncertainty as to the length of confinement and the continuous and never varying presence of others is just as important" (146, p. 28).

Mrs. Pfister studies a totally different category of internees, those who had fled to Switzerland. She interrogated 305 refugees of either sex and of varying ages, about half of whom were Jews. These refugees were also confined behind barbed wire. The complex of symptoms that arose in their case she termed "internment psychosis," part of which, however, she herself has said "corresponds to the symptoms of the so-called 'barbed-wire sickness,' as Vischer has described for prisoners of war" (119, p. 109).

That these people were confined and lived in absolute idleness in the midst of a free, active, prosperous people explains, in her view, that "the mood of overflowing gratitude turned into hate and its ever-present companion, fear. Free psychic energy finds expression only in this one drive, man is mastered by his aggressiveness. . . . He projects his own aggressiveness onto his environment" (119, p. 109), in this case on his fellow refugees, the camp commander, Switzerland. Embitterment is infectious, and so "we experience veritable tempests of hate and fear" (119, p. 110).

According to Mrs. Pfister, this is the first phase of the "internment psychosis: the phase of aggressiveness"; this is followed by a stage in which the refugee has become "a passive object of care . . . , who, quiet and gray, sunk into himself, 'obediently' vegetates away and desires nothing but to remain *in statu quo*" (119, p. 110). And this is the second phase of the "internment psychosis: the phase of apathy."

In order to ascertain in what people this psychosis occurs most frequently, she makes two distinctions:

(a) The man who lives only for that which is related to his milieu, such as his family business, his physical security: man pledged to his milieu. Through his flight he has lost all this, and has become completely uprooted. This category is the most numerous. (b) The man who does not live only for his milieu, but even the "deepest roots of his being . . . lie in some intellectual, religious, or political idea" (119, p. 107). These people can never become entirely uprooted, "as their idea and their mission, which is not bound up in their milieu, remain with them always and everywhere" (*ibid.*). This category constitutes a small group.

It appears that "internment psychosis" occurs particularly in category (a): this group contains another subdivision: "the partially uprooted man. . . . People who come with their relations, who are therefore not alone, even in the camp, are more likely to remain free from camp sickness" (119, p. 111). In contrast to these there is category (b): "Refugees, whose being is rooted in an idea, are almost immune from internment psychosis, in particular when they are surrounded by congenial companions" (119, p. 111).

In how far does this apply to concentration camps? There too a camp mentality prevailed that manifested itself in irritability, egotistic behaviour, envy of others who were better off, extraordinary interest in food, lack of compassion, absence of the fear of death, decline or disappearance of sexual drives. In this enumeration, many of the symptoms of "barbed-wire sickness" will be recognized, so that this complex of symptoms may be considered as part of the camp mentality.

An entirely different case is the "internment psychosis" of Mrs. Pfister. This obtained in the concentration camp, in so far as she considers part of the symptoms as "barbed-wire sickness," but it certainly did not exist in the form of aggressiveness as the first and apathy as the second phase. The first phase in a concentration camp, as has been shown, runs a totally different course, namely as an apathetic and a depressive phase, in which, certainly in the beginning, there is no room for aggressiveness. It does indeed seem likely that during this phase aggressiveness comes into being and increases, for, as Kaas has remarked, "everywhere where people are oppressed aggressions will accumulate" (78, p. 416). These aggressions are evoked by the behaviour of the SS and the prominents. The as yet inexperienced prisoner may perhaps try to vent his aggressions on these people, and get himself into many difficulties; the old prisoner, on the contrary, will never do this. His behaviour can be compared to that of a child in whom, as Flugel states, aggressions arise "from the person's own anger and revolt against the frustrating parent figures" (44, p. 77). The child is not free to express this aggressiveness, because "the child is too weak to stand up to the opposition of the parents, and because at the same time it loves them and is dependent on them" (44, p. 77).

Because at an early age the child has few possibilities of repressing its aggression or venting it on others, it will direct the aggression against itself. Likewise the old prisoner: as the concentration camp has "taught him a lesson," he knows that it is no use for him to make the slightest attempt to assert himself with those who are the cause of his aggressiveness. Apart from repression (new arrivals to vent his aggression on are not always "available"), there is nothing for him but to direct his aggressiveness on to himself. Bettelheim has drawn the same conclusion: the old prisoners have learned "to direct a great amount of aggression against themselves so as not to get into too many conflicts with the Gestapo" (17, p. 443). The second reason mentioned by Flugel why the child directs its aggression against itself applies, as far as the prisoners are concerned, only to that small number of them who feel any affection for the SS and have completely identified themselves with the SS. This turning of the aggression toward the person himself would, I think, sufficiently account for the prisoner's irritability, his mental instability, and his inner uncertainty.

Another form of aggressiveness is caused by the total or partial identification of the prisoners with the SS, which will explain the aggression in word and act of the old prisoner against the others who are not prominents (see p. 178 of this book).

In this connection the fact that the old prisoner did not direct his aggressiveness against the SS may be once more considered. Apart from what has already been said about the prisoner having "learned his lesson" through concentration-camp experience, identification with the SS also played a part. Freud has pointed out that one of the effects of identification will be "a person limiting his aggressiveness towards those with whom he has identified himself, and in his sparing them and giving them help" (49a, p. 70). Since I trust I have shown that only very few prisoners escaped a measure of identification with the SS (pp. 177 ff. in this book), it is evident that the need for them to direct their aggression toward the SS decreased. This need disappeared entirely if the prisoner's identification with the SS became complete. Summarizing, then, I am of opinion that the "internment psychosis" as observed by Mrs. Pfister in Swiss camps is not the same thing as the camp sickness that prevailed in concentration camps. In the latter the first phase was apathetic-depressive and not aggressive (aggressiveness developed only after the prisoner had been there for a time). Nor did the second phase of the "internment psychosis" develop in the concentration camps. After what we have learned about concentration camps, everybody will understand that it was not possible for the prisoner to become an "object of passive care."

Another statement by Mrs. Pfister seems most appropriate, namely that "internment psychosis" was rare in those refugees who, free from their milieu, lived for a spiritual ideal. The strength these people derived from their ideal is strikingly similar to the great significance which I have attributed to the spiritual life of the prisoner in the concentration camp (see pp. 148 f. of this book).

Another remarkable aspect of the camp mentality of the old prisoner is *the absence of hatred* of the SS. Hottinger was struck by this lack of hate after the liberation. To quote: "It is remarkable how little hatred of their wardens is revealed in their stories" (73, p. 32). In line with his opinion on the occurrence of pity (this book, p. 143), Vrijhof says, "Hate also has this fundamental feature: the positive relationship with another person, the presence of congeniality. A man is hated because of his 'human' qualities, not his 'inhuman' ones. The 'beast' only inspires fear, abhorrence, or disgust" (150, p. 66).

This view of Vrijhof I endorse without any reservations. The behaviour of the SS often struck us as unreal, we could not understand it. We repeatedly asked, "How is it possible for a human being to be like that?" In addition to this, we often found the behaviour of the SS ridiculous. Their excitement at some petty offence struck us as exaggerated, unreal. Somehow we thought all their activity, however disastrous to ourselves, a mere waste of time. Because we were compelled to "live" with them we accepted their behaviour with the reflection, "They can't help themselves." Toward this attitude the factor of habituation contributed a great deal, so that in the end the behaviour of the SS came to lose for us its quality of strangeness (see also 150, pp. 65 f.): we had become familiar with the beast; and, finally, no prisoner could escape a certain measure of identification with the SS. Thus hate did not occur, and if it did, it was short-lived; what remained was the contempt we felt for the SS.

In the occupied Netherlands a different course of development was seen. The cause of this is found by Fortanier in the fact that the Netherlands is a democratic state which gives the individual full scope for his development. "In general terms, the greater individual freedom enabled the individual to choose for himself the most satisfactory way of life, so that . . . the ideal of power became less attractive and aggressiveness and hate did not figure prominently. . . . Aggressiveness and fear were repressed to such an extent that the primitive stage had been left so far behind that regression only appeared possible after many shattering events" (45, p. 140).

As Fortanier has said, there were inhibitions in the people of the Netherlands against aggressiveness that could be "traced partly to feelings of guilt, partly to the determining force of the fear of losing one's security in society" (45, p. 141).

As a result of the psychological blunders of the enemy, "it could be observed that, as terrorizing increased, hate gradually emerged, while it was strengthened by the feelings of hate released from individual repressions" (45, p. 142).

A remarkable difference, therefore, is perceptible between hate in the Netherlanders and hate in the prisoners. In the prisoners hate, if it had been felt at all toward the SS, tended to disappear during this imprisonment, whereas in the Netherlanders in occupied territory, it was during the occupation that hate developed through the influence of terrorization by the enemy, and these feelings gained in strength so as to terminate in active resistance.

Hate is a very important affect, as has been pointed out by Rümke: "Hate, like love, is a binding affect. Few ties are so strong as that of hate. The object of our hate haunts us, it is always present in our thoughts, and without realizing it ourselves, we begin to identify ourselves with the person whom we hate" (128, p. 457).

This identification is also stressed by Fortanier when he states that after the liberation the attitude and behaviour of many Netherlanders had become markedly fascist and "appear to have descended to the spiritual level of the enemy whom we have resisted for five years" (45, p. 144).

If we agree with Fortanier's observations, and I do not see any reason why we should not, we arrive at the following conclusion: Both the prisoners in the concentration camps and probably the majority of the Netherlanders at home have to a greater or lesser extent identified themselves with the German Nazis, although this identification was brought about by different mechanisms.

I hope that the identification by these Netherlanders may also have been, as I trust I have succeeded in demonstrating it was for most of the prisoners, only a partial one, and that they have remained free from identification with the standards of national socialism.

In the concentration camps only a small minority introjected both the methods and the standards of the SS. Only to them does the definition given by Bettelheim of the stage of resignation apply: "A prisoner had reached the final stage of adjustment to the camp situation when he had changed his personality so as to accept as his own the values of the Gestapo" (17, p. 447).

It would be wrong to say that this group comprised the

prominents. It was a group of prominents, but not all of them belonged to it; only those who had no spiritual life, called the "uncultured" by Vrijhof (150, p. 71) and defined by Kaas (78, p. 415) as that part of the camp aristocracy that was formed by the German criminals. The classic representative of this group is the Kapo, though it must be said that there have also been good and human Kapos; but these, alas, were the exception rather than the rule.

In order to avoid any misunderstanding it must be pointed out that generally there was a very great difference between the "green" and the "red" Kapos. In those camps in which the "reds," the political prisoners, held the leading functions, there was as a rule more justice and less corruption than in those where the "green" prisoners were in control. As Kautsky has stated in this connection: "If the concentration camp in itself was (already) hell, camps under the control of criminals were hell increased a thousand times" (120, p. 203).

Kaas (78, p. 415) has related that the criminals, when they were in control at Buchenwald, pursued a veritable rule of terror. One night more than one hundred criminals were massacred by the political prisoners; after this the latter were charged by the SS with the sub-management. And, Kaas goes on: "It must be said that afterward there was never any rule of terror, and also that many improvements were introduced into the existence of the non-privileged prisoners" (ibid.).

From my treatment of this question I therefore exclude the "red," the political prisoners, although also among them there were bad Kapos. When using the term Kapo, I exclusively refer to the "green," criminal, non-political prisoner.

The Kapo is that type of man who has completely adjusted himself to the camp, which he regards as his definitive life, and which he desires nothing more than to continue. Both outwardly and inwardly he has identified himself with the SS, as he reveals in his behaviour, his clothing, his bawling, his beatings, his treatment of the weak, his shameless "organizing," his cruelties on the pattern of the SS, his demand for discipline and obedience. Of these last two characteristics Kaas says, "Rigour and authoritative bearing are easily explained by his identification with the SS" (78, p. 413). As the Kapo was an extension of the SS, he wielded considerable power. He could make life unbearable for the prisoner, he could protect him, he could get him into a good labour group. As in many of the labour groups the Kapo distributed the lunch soup, he could give one prisoner a liberal portion and stint another.

The Kapo was rewarded with privileges in the way of accommodation, food, smoking, easier work. In the exercise of his authority he was often more rigorous than the SS: "Often the Gestapo would enforce nonsensical rules, originating in the whims of one of the guards. They were usually forgotten as soon as formulated, but there were always some old prisoners who would continue to follow these rules and try to enforce them on others long after the Gestapo had forgotten about them" (17, p. 450).

In order to keep the privileges granted him by the SS, the Kapo was capable of anything. He was prepared to act as a spy for the SS, even in the knowledge that if he was discovered by the others, his life would be at stake. The manner in which traitors in the camp were eliminated is taken by Bettelheim as evidence of the prisoners' identification with the SS: "That this was really a taking-over of Gestapo attitudes can be seen from the treatment of traitors. Self-protection asked for their elimination, but the way in which they were tortured for days and slowly killed was taken over from the Gestapo" (17, p. 448).

The Kapo was cruel, and his cruelty must to my mind be explained by his identification with the SS. Kaas disagrees with this view, for, as he argues, "then the question why the SS were so cruel would still have to be answered" (78, p. 413). In the following chapter I hope to explain the cruelty which was characteristic of the SS.

Miss Bluhm also holds the identification of the Kapo with the SS highly significant: "Identification with the aggressor represented the final stage of passive adaption. It was a means of defence of a rather paradoxical nature: survival through surrender; protection against the fear of the enemy—by becoming part of him; overcoming helplessness—by regressing to childish dependence" (20, p. 25).

The Kapo, as has been said, is a person of very little spiritual property, who makes everything subservient to his own interest. Such people, says Vrijhof, "live their lives in the instinctive, animal sphere. . . . Vital functions and needs are the dominating factors which determine their behaviour . . . Sentimental, lecherous, cunning, cruel and pitiless, cringing and flashy, these are the adjectives appropriate to this sphere" (150, p. 71).

I do not think that the Kapo could be more suitably characterized. As he has no values of his own, he has no inhibitions, and gives his egotism a free rein. But it is not only his egotism that can realize itself; actually all his drives can be fully satisfied, because in him there is no inhibition that keeps these unconscious drives repressed.[40] He recognizes only one restraining force, the authority of his superior. In society the Kapo would continually clash with his environment, hence it is not surprising that his type is especially found among the criminals. That the number of those with a Kapo mentality was small in comparison with the large number of prisoners is a gratifying reflection.

In the great majority of prisoners the weakened super-ego was apparently still sufficiently potent to prevent a man from sinking back to the lowest level of development, on which he is ruled only by his instincts. Vrijhof's assertion that "potentially the Kapo is present throughout society" (150, p. 75) may be true, but fortunately in normal circumstances the qualities of the super-ego save the individual from turning into a Kapo. In normal society the Kapo will as a rule be found either in jail or in a home for psychopaths. In spite of Herzberg's expressed view that "one can pick out everywhere, from boards and clubs, administrations, office staffs, factory workers, from officials, soldiers, welfare officers and organizers, those persons who would have become Kapos in a concentration camp, and those who would not" (66, p. 30), I am convinced that this view is a wrong one. Without any doubt some Kapo characteristic

[40] The unconscious drives are in the id and can in normal people not manifest themselves owing to repression; in the Kapo they can, because repression has ceased.

can be pointed out in many individuals, but between having one of these and having a Kapo mentality there is a wide gulf. On the contrary, it is gratifying to reflect that the Kapo mentality, which is a complex of almost exclusively bad qualities, was confined to a very small and moreover very definite group of people.

The Prisoner and Group Psychology

Before concluding this chapter I propose to devote some space to a study of the prisoner in the light of the theory of group psychology, propounded by Freud in *Group Psychology and the Analysis of the Ego* (49a). Though I do not intend to give a full-length exposition of this theory, a brief summary is indispensable for a proper understanding of the matter.

Freud has pointed out that there are various categories of groups: transient and permanent, homogeneous (composed of similar individuals) and unhomogeneous, natural and artificial,[41] primitive and non-primitive. According to Freud, it is remarkable that none of those writers who have dealt with the subject (he mentions the names of Le Bon and Sighele) should have drawn attention to one distinction which he thinks of great significance, that "between leaderless groups and those with leaders" (49a, p. 41). The leader may be a man of flesh and blood, but may also be an abstraction "to which religious groups, with their invisible head, form a transition stage" (49a, p. 53). A third possibility is that a leading idea, an ideal, takes on the function of leader; even "hatred against a particular person or institution might operate in just the same unifying way, and might call up the same kind of emotional ties as positive attachment" (*ibid.*).

Among other examples of an artificial group with a leader Freud gives that of an army. The great significance of an army leader is apparent from this: "The commander-in-chief is a

---

[41] "Artificial groups, that is, a certain external force is employed to prevent them from disintegrating and to check alterations in their structure. As a rule a person is not consulted, or is given no choice, as to whether he wants to enter such a group; any attempt at leaving it is usually met with persecution or with severe punishment, or has quite definite conditions attached to it" (49a, p. 42).

father who loves all his soldiers equally, and for that reason they are comrades among themselves" (49a, p. 43).

He concludes that "each individual is bound by libidinal ties on the one hand to the leader . . . and on the other hand to other members of the group" (49a, pp. 44 f.). Freud regards the libido [42] as the binding element in the group; he makes this probable by his conception of the occurrence of panic in an army.

Panic may occur through very great danger, for example an outbreak of fire in a theatre. As the essential characteristic of panic in an army, however, Freud considers the fact "that it bears no relation to the danger that threatens, and often breaks out upon the most trivial occasions" (49a, p. 46) whereas on occasions of great danger the same army will not panic. It is therefore not the greatness of the danger that is the cause of panic in an army, but the disappearance of ties. Panic means "the disintegration of a group; it involves the cessation of all the feelings of consideration which the members of the group otherwise show one another" (49a, p. 49). As a typical occasion for panic Freud mentions the case where the leader, through whatever cause, suddenly disappears: "The loss of the leader in some sense or other, the birth of misgivings about him, brings on the outbreak of panic, though the danger remains the same; the mutual ties between the members of the group disappear, as a rule, at the same time as the tie with their leader. The group vanishes in dust, like a Bologna flask when its top is broken off" (49a, p. 49).

That libido is the element that holds the group together is made clear by Freud in yet another way. In the emotional ties which exist between spouses, friends, parents and children, hostile emotions will in the long run also occur, which escape observation only by repression. "But the whole of this intolerance vanishes, temporarily or permanently, as the result of the formation of a group, and in a group. So long as a group formation persists or so far as it extends, individuals behave as though

---

[42] "Libido is an expression taken from the theory of the emotions. We call by that name the energy (regarded as a quantitative magnitude, though not at present actually mensurable) of those instincts which have to do with all that may be comprised under the word 'love' " (49a, p. 37).

they were uniform, tolerate other people's peculiarities, put themselves on an equal level with them, and have no feeling of aversion towards them. Such a limitation of narcissism [43] can, according to our theoretical views, only be produced by one factor, a libidinal tie with other people" (49a, p. 56).

What libidinal tie can be the cause of such a limitation of narcissism? First Freud tries to conceive it as *being in love.* Just as in people who are in love, one sees in group individuals an over-estimating of the object, a silencing of criticism, an increase of affectivity to the point of becoming uninhibited, a lack of initiative and independence, equality of reactions.

Being in love may be the result of uninhibited sexual drives, in which case it will vanish after sexual gratification has been attained; this form of being in love, usually called sensual love, is not further considered. But being in love can also consist in a combination of "uninhibited drives" and "drives inhibited in their aim." [44] In this case the phenomenon of sexual over-estimation occurs: the loved object is to a certain extent free from criticism, its qualities are valued more highly than those of other persons who are not loved, the object is idealized. We find that "the object is being treated in the same way as our own ego, so that when we are in love a considerable amount of narcissistic libido overflows on to the object" (49a, p. 74).

In extreme cases of being in love it may even happen that "the object has, so to speak, consumed the ego" (49a, p. 75). Simultaneously with this complete surrender of the ego to the object "the functions allotted to the ego ideal entirely cease to operate" (49a, p. 75).

This is evident from the absence of criticism (everything the object does is right). Also from the elimination of conscience with respect to the object: "In the blindness of love remorselessness is carried to the pitch of crime. The whole situation can be completely summarized in a formula: *The object has taken the place of the ego ideal*" (49a, p. 75).

[43] The hostile feelings of ambivalence, according to Freud, are "the expression of self-love—of narcissism" (49a, p. 55).

[44] These are drives which, although of sexual origin, have been diverted from their original aim. With these drives we see that "a certain advance has been permitted in the direction of satisfaction and then an inhibition or deflection has occurred" (49, p. 65). Instances of this are parent and child love.

Libidinal group ties must not, however, be equated with being in love, for the group does not aim at direct sexual gratification.[45] On the contrary, two lovers protest against the group feeling by withdrawing from the group, and as Freud puts it: "The rejection of the group's influence is manifested in the shape of a sense of shame" (49a, p. 121). Moreover, Freud points out, within the group there is no room for woman as a sexual object; "the love relation between men and women remains outside these organizations" [46] (49a, p. 122).

Then Freud tries to explain group libido by comparing it with hypnosis. Between hypnosis and being in love there are various points of resemblance: "There is the same humble subjection, the same compliance, the same absence of criticism, towards the hypnotist just as towards the loved object. There is the same absorption of one's own initiative; no one can doubt that the hypnotist has stepped into the place of the ego ideal" (49a, p. 77).

The difference between hypnotism and being in love is this —that in the former only drives inhibited in their aim play a part, and sexual gratification is therefore excluded, whereas in the latter this gratification is never definitely ruled out. The ties which find their origin in drives inhibited in their aim are more permanent than those in which uninhibited drives play a part, because the former can never be completely gratified, whereas the latter can, for example by the accomplishment of sexual gratification.

With respect to the question whether libido in the group is hypnosis, Freud says, "The hypnotic relation is (if the expression is permissible) a group formation with two members. Hypnosis is not a good object for comparison with a group formation, because it is truer to say that it is identical with it. Out of the complicated fabric of the group it isolates one element for us—the behaviour of the individual to the leader" (49a, p. 78).

---

[45] By the same token, libidinal ties of the group are not neurotic, for they are ties "that unite with their objects those love instincts which still pursue directly sexual aims" (49a, p. 58).

[46] By these are meant the two examples mentioned by Freud of an artificial group with a leader, namely the church and the army.

The hypnotic state is therefore in reality "a group" of two people which differs only in its number from the group. According to Freud, hypnosis might be taken as the explanation of the libidinal ties in the group, but then only of the relation leader–group individual; many aspects of the phenomenon of hypnosis itself still defy explanation (see this book, p. 206).

The formula of the libidinal constitution of a group with leader which Freud finally provides is this: "*A primary [47] group of this kind is a number of individuals who have substituted one and the same object for their ego ideal and have consequently identified themselves with one another in their ego*" (49a, p. 80).

The gist of the matter, therefore, is that "the individual gives up his ego ideal and substitutes for it the group ideal as embodied in the leader" (49a, p. 102).

In determining which of the characteristics of the group can be accounted for by the aforementioned libidinal tie, which, according to Freud, exists in the group, he concludes that it does explain "the lack of independence and initiative in their members, the similarity in the reactions of all of them, their reduction, so to speak, to the level of group individuals" (49a, p. 81).

But it does not explain "the weakness of intellectual ability, the lack of emotional restraint, the incapacity for moderation and delay, the inclination to exceed every limit in the expression of emotion and to work it off completely in the form of action" (49a, p. 81 f.).

This inclination, Freud holds, is a regression to "a primitive mental activity, of just such a sort as we should be inclined to ascribe to the primal horde" (49a, p. 91).[48]

A brief discussion of the hypothesis [49] of the primal horde as set up by Freud will be necessary. Freud assumes that the primal form of human society consisted in a horde whose un-

[47] A primary group is a group of people "that have a leader and have not been able by means of too much 'organization' to acquire secondarily the characteristics of an individual" (49a, p. 80).

[48] "A regression of this sort is in particular an essential characteristic of common groups, while . . . in organized and artificial groups it can to a large extent be checked" (49a, p. 82).

[49] The use of the term "hypothesis" should be noted.

limited ruler was one strong man: the primal father. All the females of the horde belonged to him, and he enforced sexual abstention on all his sons. This patriarchal system was brought to an end by "a rebellion of the sons, who united against the father, overpowered him and together consumed his body" (54, p. 206; see also 53, pp. 915 f.).

As a result of the murder of the tribal chief by his sons, the patriarchal horde was changed into a fraternal community, in which the leading part was no longer played by the male, but rather by the female. In the primal horde the individuals formed a unit, but the father of the primal horde was free. Viewed in this light regression would consist in the leader of a group being looked upon as the primal father, and the group still demanding domination by unlimited force. In Freud's formulation: "The primal father is the group ideal, which governs the ego in the place of the ego ideal" (49a, p. 100).

Similarly Freud finds an explanation for the enigmatic aspect of hypnosis—that is, the mysterious power attributed to the hypnotist. This power must be the same "that is looked upon by primitive people as the source of taboo, the same that emanates from kings and chieftains and makes it dangerous to approach them" (49a, p. 96). Further expatiation on this subject does not seem to be called for, as it would carry the subject outside the scope of this book.

Next we will consider the prisoners in the light of Freud's theory of group psychology. The prisoners constitute a complex of the most heterogeneous elements, brought and kept together by force. Their life is regulated, each of their actions is prescribed, while blind obedience is demanded of them. It is almost impossible for them to influence the conduct of affairs, or to voice criticism. This sort of community bears a close resemblance to an army, a resemblance which is heightened by the (graded) hierarchy of the leading prisoners. If the senior camp prisoner could also have been likened to a commander-in-chief, the similarity would be complete. In this vital issue, however, the resemblance ceases to hold good. The prisoner cannot possibly regard the senior camp prisoner as a figure who "loves" them all "equally," for he has too good a time, he is too much concerned with his self-interest, he protects and favours his own confederates too much. He is not as a father who loves his children equally. He is not the type before whom every form of criticism becomes silent, who inspires willing and unquestioning obedience; he is not the prisoner's ideal. But above all, he is not omnipotent. Not only can he be overthrown by the corruption among his confederates, but he "rules" merely by the authority of the SS, and so he is always in danger of losing his position overnight. Because he is not omnipotent he cannot symbolize the feared primal father, so that the prisoners also lack the feeling of being all-powerful. Hence the prisoners have to restrain themselves, and in consequence they lack the conviction of the group individual, for whom nothing is impossible. No man can be considered as the leader of the prisoners except the senior camp prisoner. However, as Freud has said, the leader need not be a human being; the leader can be an idea, and even a common hatred may function as leader. Theoretically a thought, an ideal common to all the prisoners, might unite them under its leadership, but this is made impossible by the heterogeneity of the prison community. Besides the political prisoners, who are united by their rejection of national socialism on considerations of principle, there are large groups of prisoners in the camps whose confinement is very far from being due to adherence to any ideal—the criminal and a-social elements. Neither can the Jews (apart from exceptions) be said to have belonged to the former category (that of political opponents), for they automatically became opponents to Nazism as a result of the Nazi attitude toward them. Hence the impossibility that in the concentration camp opposition based on principle should take the place of a human leader.

Nor could religious convictions provide the binding element, because many of the prisoners are either a-religious or anti-religious; even hatred of the SS could not unite them, because it does not exist (see this book, p. 198). Nevertheless there are some feelings common to all the prisoners: the contempt in which they hold the SS and the hope of leaving the concentration camp alive. In my opinion, however, these reflections are not sufficiently important to assume for the prisoners the significance of a leader. Also it should be kept in mind that these reflections were non-existent in an often very influential group: the leading criminals.

As has been shown, this group have completely identified themselves with the SS, whom they do not despise, nor have they any objection to spending the rest of their lives in a concentration camp. Even if those reflections were important, the prisoners would not, because of their diversity, have reacted as a totality.

Thus the conclusion is inevitable that the prisoners have no leader of any description and consequently do not constitute a "group," [50] so that they will not react in any way that is characteristic of a "group with a leader." The community of prisoners, therefore, cannot be styled a group; they are a crowd.

This will also make it clear that the prisoners' behaviour cannot but be individual; which should not be understood to mean that there are no ties at all among them. Of course there are, when, for example, men have the same nationality; and ties come into being when the prisoners have for a long time lived, worked, and dwelt together, and have experiences in common. These ties prove to have survived even the liberation and account for the sympathy of the ex-concentration-camp prisoner with his one-time fellow sufferers, even those unknown to him.

[50] Although I do not call the prisoners a group in the sense attached to this word by Freud, the Freudian theory of group psychology has been discussed in some detail; in the chapter on the SS it will be referred to again.

CHAPTER

FOUR

The Psychology of the SS

The Origin of the SS

THE letters SS were used as a designation of the "Schutzstaffel" (Protective Squad) of the NSDAP (National Socialist German Workers' Party). It came into being in 1923 as the "Stosztruppe (Shock Troop) Hitler," and was disbanded after the Munich coup on November 9, 1923, when the whole party was declared illegal. The ban on the party was removed in 1925, the SA (Sturmabteilung = Storm Troops) remaining illegal, so that meetings organized by the party were unprotected from attacks by political opponents. "Hence in the year 1925 the Fuehrer ordered a small mobile organization for the protection of these meetings to be built up: *the Schutz-Staffeln*" (142, Vol. XXX, p. 131). Each "Staffel" (squad) consisted of a leader and ten men. When in 1926 the ban on the SA was removed, the SS, which at that time numbered about 200, receded somewhat into the background. The year 1926, however, was a very important one for the SS, "when Adolf Hitler, at the party conference at Weimar, the second party conference of the NSDAP, placed in their faithful hands the most sacred symbol of the movement, the blood standard of November 9, 1923" (*ibid.*, p. 132).

On January 6, 1929, Himmler was appointed Reich leader of the SS by Hitler. The SS then numbered 280 and the instruction given to Himmler ran, "To form this organization into an élite troop of the Party, a troop dependable in every circumstance" (142, Vol. XXIX, p. 207).

211

The Organization of the SS

Originally the SS was part of the SA, and the Reich leader SS was subordinate to the chief of staff of the SA. On July 20, 1934, the SS was made into an independent organization by a decree from Hitler: "In consideration of the great meritorious service of the SS, especially in connection with the events of June 30, 1934,[1] I elevate it to the standing of an *independent organization* within the NSDAP" (142, Vol. IV, p. 184).

From this moment the Reich leader of the SS was responsible only to Hitler.

The SS was subdivided into the "Allgemeine SS" (General SS) and the "Waffen SS" (Armed SS).

The General SS was, as it were, the trunk from which the other SS units branched. Those who were members of the General SS carried out their normal occupational duties, but were obliged to attend the sports events regularly and to take the lessons in National Socialsim. As Best has stated, they had "as voluntary 'political soldiers' of the NSDAP, as in wartime, to stand guard over the values and visible manifestations of the National Socialist idea" (142, Vol. XXIX, p. 17).

It is Kogon's opinion that the demands made on the General SS should not be taken too seriously: "Things were made easy for the newly enrolled members: it was rare for the men on active duty to be called upon, they could regard themselves simply as the lords of creation, engaged in aristocratic sports (the Mounted SS!), the 'sponsoring members' were only expected to pay a monthly contribution for the privilege of wearing the black SS badge with the runic symbol of the SS. There was no sign of any hard theoretical or political indoctrination to prepare them for membership in the 'Order' " (87, p. 360).

Because most of them gained for themselves a position in the National Socialist state, Kogon thinks that "From 1936 on the General SS proved itself to be lacking in vitality" (87, p. 361).

[1] On this date the purge of the SA took place, and its chief of staff, Roehm, was murdered.

Himmler, on the other hand, stated that in the early part of 1937 the strength of the General SS was about 190,000 (142, Vol. XXIX, p. 211), while for the year 1939 Gunter d'Alquen mentions the number 240,000 (142, Vol. XXX, p. 137).

From the General SS arose the armed force of the SS, from 1938 on called *"Waffen SS"* (Armed SS). "The origin of the Waffen SS goes back to the decree of March 17, 1933 establishing the 'Stabswache' with the original strength of 120 men" (142, Vol. XXXI, p. 49).

This armed force was subdivided into (1) the "Verfuegungstruppen" (Special Service Troops), (2) the "Totenkopfverbaende" (Death-Head Units), (3) the "Sicherheitsdienst" (SD —Security Service), and (4) the "Rasse- und Siedlungswesen" (Race and Settlement Institute).

The Special Service Troops, "besides education to SS man, are given complete military training" (142, Vol. XXX, pp. 137 f.). The men of these Special Service Troops committed themselves to four years' service, which was considered equivalent to the performance of their normal military service. According to Best, they were "exclusively at the disposal of the Fuehrer for special duties in peace or war" (142, Vol. XXIX, p. 17); according to Himmler they were charged with "internal protection within the state" (142, Vol. XXIX, p. 224).

The Death-Head Units were formed in 1933 from volunteers of the General SS: "Their duty is, apart from the indoctrination of the armed political soldiers, to guard the enemies of the state confined in the concentration camps" (142, Vol. XXX, p. 138). The men of the Death-Head Units pledged themselves to twelve years' service. Most of them had already performed their military service in the "Wehrmacht." In this case the duration of their regular military service was counted towards their service in these units.

The Security Service arose from the intelligence service of the SS during the years of the struggle for power. It became important when the SS deemed it necessary for an adequate performance of their duty—"the personal protection of the Fuehrer and of leading personalities of the National Socialist movement" (142, Vol. XXX, p. 139)—to find out "what was going on in the adversary's camp, whether or not the Communists intended to hold up a meeting today, whether or not our people were to be attacked, and similar things" (142, Vol. XXIX, p. 222).

In 1931 the SD was made into a separate unit, so that it became independent of the SS. But the party, the NSDAP, had an intelligence service of its own; as this service was less thoroughly organized than the SD, confusion ensued. Therefore the deputy Fuehrer decreed on June 9, 1934, that "besides the security service of the RF-SS (Reichsfuehrer SS = Reich Leader SS), there must not be any Intelligence- or Defence Service of the Party" (142, Vol. XXX, p. 140).

In 1937 the duty of the SD was described by Himmler as follows: "The domains in which it operates are in the very first place Communism, Jewry, Freemasonry, Ultramontanism, political meddling by confessional groups, and reaction. . . . The Security Service is only interested in the great issues of philosophies of life" (142, Vol. XXIX, p. 223). In other words, it was the task of the SD to find out the opponents to National Socialism so as to make possible their elimination.

The Race and Settlement Institute dealt with the marriage requests of SS men, for as early as December 31, 1931, Himmler had by "SS Order A-Nr 65" announced his "marriage permit" decree. Some of the points it contained were:

2. In accordance with the National Socialist philosophy of life, and in recognition of the fact that the future of our people rests in the selection of racially and hereditarily sound, good blood, I institute as from January 1, 1932, for all unmarried members of the SS the "Heiratsgenehmigung" [marriage permit]. . . .

7. Expert examination of the marriage requests is the task of the "Rasseamt" [Race Office] of the SS. . . .

10. To the SS it is clear that with this order they have taken a step of great importance. Derision, scorn, and misunderstanding do not touch us; the future is ours (142, Vol. XXX, p. 134) .

In order to obtain the marriage permit "both [parties] are to produce their genealogical tables as far back as 1750, a testimony to the effect that they are hereditarily sound, and several police documents and other things" (142, Vol. XXIX, p. 225). The bride had to undergo a medical examination, and it was also required of her that she should be able to find securities vouching for her "philosophy of life and humanity" (*ibid.*); moreover, she had to state whether she was in debt or not.

The Race and Settlement Institute also regulated "the settlement of SS men as farmers, and moreover their complete indoctrination in the philosophy of life. The Race and Settlement Office is virtually also the scientific office in respect of excavations, of prehistory, with which we are thoroughly concerned" (*ibid.*).

The Ideology of the SS

Like the National Socialist ideology, that of the SS was Adolf Hitler's racial theory.

Hitler distinguished peoples into racially pure and racially impure ones. The racially pure he divided again into people on a high plane and those on a low plane. Interbreeding of races he regarded as "a sin against the will of the Eternal Creator" (70, p. 240). "Whoever"—thus Hitler—"ignores or despises the laws of race . . . places an obstacle in the victorious path of the superior race and, by so doing, he interferes with a pre-requisite condition of all human progress" (70, p. 242).

Further: "But the loss of racial purity will wreck inner happiness for ever. It degrades men for all time to come. And the physical and moral consequences can never be wiped out" (70, p. 275).

The "Aryans" belong to the most superior, the Jews to the most inferior race. The "Aryan" had nothing but good, the Jew nothing but bad, qualities.

The "Aryan" was regarded by Hitler as the "founder of culture," the Jew as its "destroyer." As by interbreeding the "Aryan" did not keep his blood pure, ancient culture was bound to perish. It was especially the Jew who had designs on the "good" blood: "The Jew uses every possible means to undermine the racial foundations of a subjugated people"

(70, p. 273). To check interbreeding was of great importance for the continuance of humanity, for, Hitler said: "In unnumerable cases wherein the pure race holds its ground the mongrel breaks down" (70, p. 335).

This racial theory is echoed in the objective of the SS. For, according to Himmler: "Should I succeed in selecting from the German people for the organization as many people as possible, the majority of whom possess this desired blood, and in teaching them military discipline and in time the understanding of the value of blood and the entire ideology resulting from it, then it would be possible actually to create such an élite organization as should successfully hold its own in every emergency" (142, Vol. XXII, p. 247).

Hitler's racial theory had its origin in his anti-Semitism; so that I think that the question must be posed: What caused Adolf Hitler to become such a thoroughgoing anti-Semite?

Miss Kurth has tried to provide the answer, though, as she states, she is aware of its hypothetical nature (92, pp. 263 ff.).

Adolf's father was an illegitimate child, and by the latter's third marriage to a woman twenty-three years younger than himself Adolf was born. For this marriage an episcopal dispensation was required because of the family relationship between Adolf's father and mother.[2]

According to Miss Kurth, Adolf's oedipal conflicts were not resolved and could therefore be reactivated when his father suddenly died in 1903 (Adolf was 13 years old): "The rival for his mother's love was eliminated, and Adolf was master of the field" (92, p. 272).

In Miss Kurth's view the death of Hitler senior was "a successful patricide," and similarly she accounts for Adolf's departure to Vienna in 1907 as "a frantic effort to break away from the unconscious fixation he had acted out for so long a

---

[2] Adolf's father, Alois Schicklgruber, was born in 1837 as the illegitimate child of Maria Anna Schicklgruber. In 1842 she married Johann Georg Hiedler. On June 6, 1876 Johann Georg Hiedler declared that he was the father of Alois Schicklgruber, after which the latter changed his name into Alois Hitler. On January 7, 1885, Alois married Klare Poelzl, the daughter of a cousin of his, and the third child of this marriage was Adolf (27, pp. 18 ff.).

time—an attempt to bribe his conscience at the last moment by saying in effect, 'See, I did not kill my father; nor do I want to take his place and thus to endanger my mother as he did' " (92, p. 274).

But also she views it as a partial identification with his father. For the latter, too, had left the parental home, intending to return when he had made a success of his life. It is Miss Kurth's opinion that "Adolf Hitler's oedipus complex had not only remained unresolved but that it had, through force of circumstances, acquired additional intensity and, with its attendant feelings of guilt, was exerting particular pressure at the period immediately preceding the outbreak of his anti-Semitism" (92, p. 274).

Throughout his life Hitler kept projecting his feelings of guilt; everything that went wrong in his life was the fault of "the bad world," of "that other man" or of "fate." [3] But why did he project his feelings of guilt especially onto the Jews?

Miss Kurth has pointed out that Adolf Hitler's first contact with a Jew was of extraordinary emotional significance. This Jew was the physician Eduard Bloch, who in 1908 treated Hitler's mother during her last illness, cancer of the breast. The Jewish physician became to Adolf a father image, and this in conjunction with the "successful patricide" "makes an intense revival of the oedipus, and its attendant feelings of guilt appear more than likely" (92, p. 273).

Miss Kurth attaches great significance to the probability that Adolf was aware of the blood relationship between his parents, and that this was an explanation likely to be accepted by the family for the death of three of the five children born of this marriage. From this Miss Kurth concludes: "That such associations may have been responsible for the equivalence of sexual intercourse to incest and 'blood poisoning' is quite likely" (92, p. 277).

On the grounds of the blood relationship between Adolf's parents, the unabated activity of the oedipus complex, the

[3] "It was always the other side who were to blame, and in turn he denounced the Communists, the Jews, the Republican Government, or the Czechs, the Poles, and the Bolsheviks for their 'intolerable' behaviour which forced him to take drastic action in self-defence" (27, p. 344).

treatment of his mother during her fatal illness by the Jewish physician, Miss Kurth arrives at the following conclusion: "The intimacy between the doctor and *Frau* Hitler was conducive to a 'confusion' of the doctor with his father in Adolf's psychopathology. Brutal assault, mutilation, was represented by the ablation of her breast. 'Poisoning' by 'injection' was represented, during the last months of her illness, by the doctor's almost daily hypodermics of morphine to alleviate the suffering woman's pain. While Hitler was consciously imbued with gratitude towards the kind doctor, unconsciously he made him the 'incestuous, poisoning murderer' of his mother, the incestuous, lascivious and aggressive father with whom he could not identify himself—and now in reality a Jew. . . . From intercourse between the parents, and the relation between the Jewish doctor and Frau Hitler, it finally came to mean nothing but intercourse between Jews and Germans" (92, p. 279 f.).

Gilbert [4] also tries to find an explanation for Hitler's anti-Semitism. In his function of prison psychologist he obtained data from the leaders of the NSDAP, *inter alios*, among which a 1000-page manuscript by the ex–Governor General of occupied Poland, Hans Frank. Taking his stand on testimony by Frank and on a description by Hitler in *Mein Kampf* of a labourer's family,[5] Gilbert states that Adolf's father was a drunkard who treated his son cruelly. "Although we need not subscribe to the universality of the Oedipal conflict, the evidence certainly points to it in Adolf Hitler's case. The scene of pure Nordic womanhood being attacked by a drunken sot of a labourer (father-son figure) was potent enough imagery for the projection of psychosexual conflicts into political symbols. It was probably before he wrote *Mein Kampf* that Hitler first became aware of (and repressed) the possibility that his own drunken father was a half-Jew. His

---

[4] See 61. It should be pointed out that the political, economic, and sociological factors also mentioned by Gilbert are left unconsidered.

[5] See 70, pp. 39 f.; Miss Kurath remarks in this connection, "Regarding the conception of sexual intercourse as a sadistic attack, we are on much firmer ground and need not rely on guesswork. The Fuehrer himself has disclosed a memory of his observation of the primal scene, though he has done so in such well-disguised form that hitherto it has escaped notice" (92, p. 277).

obsessive anxiety over the rape and pollution of Aryan womanhood, later in life, may well have originated in this repressed psychosexual conflict" (61, p. 21).

The suspicion that Adolf's unknown paternal grandfather was a Jew was founded on the fact that his unmarried grandmother had received an allowance from a Jew. What this meant to Hitler has been described by Gilbert: "Having already developed his ego-structure on the projection of his own inferiority and of all evil, to the Jews, and having staked his whole career on racial conflict, he could not tolerate such a possibility. To convince himself of the utter impossibility of such a threat to his entire ego-structure, Hitler had to fan his own hatred of all Jews—even unto the third generation, whether baptized or not—into a murderous fury" (61, p. 63).

Deriving his data from a publication by Greiner (63), Hitler's companion during his days in Vienna, Gilbert goes on to point out that Hitler's anti-Semitism was probably further inflamed by the frustration of his first love. The girl with whom Hitler fell in love was an artist's model posing for Greiner. She refused Hitler, but accepted a baptized half-Jew. Greiner has related that Hitler on learning this shouted: "A Jew! A Jew! . . . Jewish swine, that's what they all are, no matter whether they are baptized or not! Holy water and priestly hocus-pocus do not turn a Jew into an Aryan" (63, p. 62). All this, added to the anti-Semitism that was current in Vienna in those days and to the shabby vagabond life that Hitler led there, brings Gilbert to the conclusion that "it was in this Viennese school of daily frustrations that Adolf Hitler, a man of the masses, learned to displace his psychosexual aggressions, to project his feelings of inferiority on to the most popular scapegoat of the time, and to structuralize his political attitudes on these defence mechanisms" (61, p. 33).

Both Miss Kurth and Gilbert, as we have seen, insist on putting great emphasis on Adolf Hitler's oedipus complex; while Miss Kurth, moreover, seeks to account for Hitler's anti-Semitism by the treatment of Hitler's mother during her fatal illness by the Jewish physician Bloch, and Gilbert in this connection points to the possibility that the father of Hitler senior was a Jew, and to the fact that his first love did not accept him, but a half-Jew.

I will not set myself up as a judge of the views held by either concerning Hitler's anti-Semitism, but I will try to find an answer to a question posed neither by Miss Kurth nor by Gilbert: Why was it blood to which Hitler, to the exclusion of everything else, attached paramount importance? Why not rather, for example, the skin, language, or character?

According to Simmel, Hitler's blood theory is "nothing but a modern variation of the blood accusation." [6] Hitler's belief in an Aryan race which was united by blood "reflects his unconscious perception that it is untamed basic human hatred which drives people to devour one another, and in this way to become united 'in blood' by incorporation" (133, p. 63). But hatred must also be directed toward a common object outside the race. "For this reason, his message was a relief to the human instinct of destruction, when he re-instituted the totem animal by designating the Jew as 'the enemy of mankind.' The Hitler blood accusations against the Jew,—that he wants to defile Aryan blood by penetration—is nothing but the well-known projection of denying one's own devouring tendencies by accusing the Jew. In different form, it is a repetition of the accusation of the desecration of the holy wafer: the Jew causes the bleeding of the wafer which, to the anti-Semite, signifies the actual body of Christ" (133, p. 63).

Besides Simmel's explanation another possibility deserves consideration. In this respect what Freud has said about the neurotic is important: "A neurotic . . . invariably exhibits some degree of psychical infantilism. He has either failed to get free from the psycho-sexual conditions that prevailed in his childhood or he has returned to them—two possibilities which may be summed up as developmental inhibition and

---

[6] In 133, p. 62. The blood accusation was favourite device of anti-Semitism and the cause of many pogroms; it "includes the crime of piercing the holy wafers in churches so that they bleed, and the crime of the ritual murder at Easter; the Jews steal Christian children and slaughter them in order to use their blood for their ceremonial feasts" (133, p. 55).

regression. Thus incestuous fixations of libido continue to play (or begin once more to play) the principal part in his unconscious mental life. We have arrived at the point of regarding a child's relation to his parents, dominated as it is by incestuous longings, as the nuclear complex of neurosis" (53, p. 17).

This statement by Freud that psychic infantilism is a characteristic of neurosis I will make my starting point, in the sense that the neurotic may show the same reactions as can be observed in primitive man, with whom blood, for example, plays a magic role.

Thus, according to Freud, savages attach great significance to menstruation: "The countless taboo regulations to which the women in savage communities are subject during menstruation are said to be due to a superstitious horror of blood, and this is no doubt in fact one of their determinants. But it would be wrong to overlook the possibility that in this case the horror of blood also serves aesthetic and hygienic purposes, which are obliged in every case to cloak themselves behind magical motives" (53, p. 98).

But not only in their attitude toward a menstruating woman is the significance which savages attach to blood reflected. It is even more clearly so in the significance they attach to the sacrificial animal. With reference to a statement by Robertson Smith to this effect, Freud holds that "the sacrificial animal was treated as a member of the tribe; *the sacrificing community, the god and the sacrificial animal were of the same blood and members of one clan*" (53, p. 136).

Modern civilized man also assigns a certain influence to blood, as is shown in some religions. Several Jewish laws concerning food, for example, are founded in Genesis 9:4, which says, "But flesh with the life thereof, which is the blood thereof, shall ye not eat"; and at the Christian Holy Communion the faithful symbolically partake of the blood and the flesh of their God (see 54, p. 135). Even the language of daily intercourse shows the same trend; to indicate family ties we never speak of skin-, muscle-, or bone-, but of blood-relations. I believe it has now been made sufficiently clear that many people, especially savages, attach great, often mysterious, significance to blood; that the neurotic, too, should hold blood in mysterious regard appears to me a possibility.

In applying this opinion to Hitler, I concur with the aforementioned views of Miss Kurth and Gilbert, that Hitler had not resolved his oedipal tendencies, so that they remained active. According to Freud this makes the "central complex" of neurosis; Hitler, therefore, was a neurotic, with, as appears from a statement by Kelley, even compulsion-neurotic symptoms. As Kelley has related: "Hitler would seldom touch an animal unless he was wearing gloves. On those occasions when he caressed his dog without gloves, he would immediately go and wash his hands many times. . . . His daily routines were strict and were followed to the minutest degree. . . . At Berchtesgaden, Hitler had a small courtyard where he exercised, always taking precisely the same number of steps along the same path each time. . . . If at any time he got a spot on his collar, he would at once bathe and change all his clothing, including his underwear. He avoided everything he could of a soiling nature, cleaning his teeth immediately after eating anything and washing his hands many times each day" (82, pp. 178 f.).

Moreover, it is known that Hitler forbade people to smoke in his presence (141, p. 227) and that he refused to eat meat.[7]

As Hitler had markedly hysterical characteristics as well, Jung concludes that "a more precise diagnosis of Hitler's case might be *Pseudologia phantastica,* that it to say, that form of hysteria which is distinguished by the particular capacity for believing one's own lies" (77, p. 92).

[7] Gilbert has stated that Goering told him that a few days after the death of his niece Geli Raubal (September 18, 1931) ". . . Hitler suddenly refused to eat the ham which was served for breakfast. Hitler declared, '*It is like eating a corpse!*' and no power on earth could ever make him eat meat again. He had made such remarks previously, but this time (says Gilbert) the idea seemed to have traumatic significance. From that day forth he never did touch meat" (61, p. 62).

Greiner has related the following incident which took place the first time Hitler met the girl who, as we have seen, preferred a half-Jew to himself: "Before we set to work, we took our lunch, for which we had very nice succulent pork cracklings. As Hitler had no lunch with him, Gretl offered him a small paper bag of cracklings. But Hitler declined on the plea that he did not eat carcasses" (63, p. 55).

Summarizing, I hold the view that the fact of Hitler's attaching tremendous significance to blood allows of the explanation: as Hitler was a neurotic, he was to a certain degree infantile; this infantilism manifested itself, as it does in a savage, in the attributing of a magic significance to blood. Even in the last moments of his life, Hitler could not forget the blood theory. The conclusion of his political testament, drawn up in Berlin on April 29, 1945, at 4 P.M. reads: "Above all else I enjoin the leaders of the nation and their supporters to uphold the racial laws in all their severity, and mercilessly to resist the universal poisoner of all nations, international Jewry." [8]

Here the matter must be allowed to rest, because my objective is not so much to deal with the psychology of Hitler as with that of the SS. I thought it necessary, however, to examine Hitler's blood theory and anti-Semitism, as these were essential elements of National Socialism. Hitler the phenomenon I will consequently dismiss, after pointing out that the development of his personality and the power to which he attained should also be viewed as being conditioned by a definite milieu (Austria-Hungary in the beginning of the present century, and German society after the defeat in the First World War). A description of all this would be outside the scope of the present study.

Qualifications Required of the SS

In order to be admitted to the SS, candidates had to possess certain qualifications, the most important of which was the "good," the "Nordic," blood. Just like Hitler, Himmler was obsessed by the idea: "We are more valuable than the others, who outnumber us and will always outnumber us. We are more valuable, because our blood has fitted us to be more inventive than the others, to be better leaders of our people than the others, because it has fitted us to be better soldiers, better statesmen, to attain a higher culture, to be better characters". (142, Vol. XXIX, p. 230).

What standard was applied to ascertain whether a candidate

8 Photostat in 141, facing p. 198.

had the "good" blood? Fair hair and blue eyes were not sufficient. For a man's size also counted; a minimum height of 1.70
meters (5 feet 7 inches) was required, for, as Himmler said: "I
know that people whose height exceeds a certain number of
centimeters must somehow have the desired good blood" (142,
Vol. XXIX, p. 208). He was prepared to grant that this was
a probability, albeit a great probability, to which there might
be exceptions. He then went on to study a photo of the candidate, by which he tried to settle this question: "Are there in
this man's face obvious admixtures of alien blood, that is to say
too prominent cheekbones?" (142, Vol. XXIX, p. 208). Next
the candidate had to prove his ability to overcome difficulties.
The standard applied by Himmler was the amount of the sub-
scription the candidate could afford, and his willingness to
pay for the well-known black breeches and riding boots.
"Thus, gradually we came nearer to a picture envisaged and
desired by us" (142, Vol. XXIX, p. 209). But still Himmler
was not satisfied, for the ultimate requirement was for the
candidate to be accepted by the "Race Committee": "These
examination committees were composed of leaders of the SS,
of racial experts, and physicians" (ibid., p. 210). This examination was most important, as the decision whether or not the
candidate was to be admitted to the SS lay with this committee.
What points were particularly considered by this committee
appears from the following: "Therefore it is now of great importance how the young man bears himself before this committee, that he not only smartly puts his hands to his trouser
seams, but that, with all his discipline, he does not behave like
a serf, that, during an interview, when he is asked questions,
he is able to give really frank and decent answers, that his gait,
his hands, that all this really conforms to what we, after our
eight years' experience, wish as our ideal. These are the points
we examine, and which decide whether or not we accept the
man" (142, Vol. XXIX, p. 149).

On this "scientific" basis the decision was made whether a
man was allowed to join the SS, the élite corps. We are left in
no doubt as to whether the SS regarded themselves as such,

by a speech which Himmler made on October 4, 1943, on the occasion of the SS Major-Generals' meeting at Poznan. In this he proclaimed that after the war, which to his mind was identical with a German victory, the real work of the SS was to begin properly, for it was the task of the SS "to give the German people, the Germanic people, that superior ruling class that knits together and holds together this Germanic people and this Europe. . . ." (142, Vol. XXIX, pp. 110 f.).

In the same speech the qualities peculiar to the SS were stated to be:

(1) Loyalty; if anyone is disloyal toward Hitler or the state, he will be expelled from the SS and, to quote Himmler's own words, "we will see to it that he is expelled from life" (142, Vol. XXIX, p. 149).

(2) Obedience; this obedience is absolute. An order must be carried out not only to the letter but also in the spirit of the order. Objections to the order, if any, can be stated, though in most cases the answer will be, "All the same you will have to carry it out. . . . Orders must . . . be sacred" (142, Vol. XXIX, p. 151).

(3) Courage; this, according to Himmler, is a quality of every SS man. Faith in victory he regards as part of courage: "Faith gains battles and faith creates victory" (ibid., p. 153).

(4) Truthfulness; among SS men—thus Himmler—it should be unnecessary to put down any agreement in writing, but "the pledged word and the handshake mean that the compact stands" (ibid., p. 155). As characteristics of courage Himmler also classes justice and the bearing of responsibility.

(5) Honesty. He says, "We have become—that I am now saying this in a closed hall, is because it is intended for this small circle only—a very corrupt people" (ibid., p. 159). He promises that, especially after the war, he will take the severest measures against corruption.

(6) Comradeship.

(7) The joy of responsibility; though he has already mentioned responsibility before, he now means the joy one must feel when, unasked, one takes responsibility upon oneself.

(8) Industry; actually he means work. No one, he says, need be ashamed of any work whatsoever, if it is done for the sake of Germany.

(9) Abstention from alcohol; in order to fight the abuse of alcohol, he decrees: "Offences committed under the influence of alcohol will be punished twice as severely" (*ibid.*, p. 165).

As an illustration of what kind of conduct Himmler desired the SS to observe toward aliens, I give a lengthy quotation from his Poznan speech: "One fundamental rule must be absolutely observed by the SS man: we must be honest, decent, faithful, and friendly to those who are of our own blood and to nobody else. What happens to the Russians, what happens to the Czechs, is a matter of complete indifference to me. What the nations can offer in the way of good blood of our type we will take, if necessary by kidnapping their children and bringing them up among ourselves. Whether other nations live in prosperity or starve to death interests me only in so far as we need them as slaves for our culture; otherwise I am not interested. Whether 10,000 Russian women fall down from exhaustion while digging an anti-tank ditch interests me only in so far as the anti-tank ditch is finished for Germany. . . . We Germans, who are the only people in the world to adopt a decent attitude toward animals, will surely also adopt a decent attitude toward these human animals; but it is a crime against our own blood to worry about them and teach them ideals. . . . When somebody comes to me and says, 'I cannot dig the anti-tank ditch with children or women. That is inhuman, for they will die,' then I must say, 'You are a murderer of your own blood, for, if the anti-tank ditch is not dug, German soldiers will die, and they are the sons of German mothers. That is our blood.' This is what I would like to inoculate these SS with and—as I believe—have inoculated them with. . . . Our care, our duty, is our people and our blood. . . . We need not worry about anything else" (142, Vol. XXIX, p. 122 f.).

Carried to its ultimate conclusion, this "pure blood" theory resulted in genocide: the deliberate murder of people of "impure" blood; it is now sufficiently known for what wholesale massacre of, for example, European Jews this has been responsible.

The SS a Criminal Organization

The entire SS (with only the Mounted SS excepted) was pronounced a criminal organization, mainly with a view to legal procedure, by the International Military Tribunal at Nuremberg (144, p. 217). Before we go into this it must first be decided what is to be understood by a crime. No one is better fitted to supply the answer than the criminologist. According to Kempe,[9] a crime is an act which is considered as *harmful, improper*, and *intolerable* by the community of which the perpetrator is a member.

The term "harmful" implies, besides the material, also the psychical injury inflicted on the victim.

The qualification "improper" refers to those rules of conduct and intercourse that obtain in ordered society. The disregard of these arouses feelings of resentment among the members of such a society.

By "intolerable" is meant that the act committed is viewed as an infringement upon fundamental values. The consciousness of its intolerability creates the need for an unmistakable response to the act, which need is not always felt if the consciousness is simply that of the impropriety of the act. The conception of crime thus built on these three pillars does not merely include that which is legally forbidden; its implications are wider—in fact, it is determined by the degree of social consensus. With this statement I touch at the same time the substance of my subsequent argument: Viewed from *our* point of view there cannot be the slightest doubt that the acts of the SS were harmful, improper, and intolerable, and therefore criminal.

Proof of this is to be found in the "London Agreement" (143, Vol. I, pp. ix, x), which was signed in London by the representatives of the governments of the United States of Amer-

[9] Personal information received from Dr. G. T. Kempe, professor of criminology.

ica, the U.S.S.R., Great Britain, and France. To the "London Agreement" was added the "Charter of the International Military Tribunal" (*ibid.*, pp. xi through xv) (which will hereafter be called the "London Charter"). For it had become necessary for the Allies to set up an International Military Tribunal for the trial of those German war criminals whose crimes were not confined to territories limited by national boundaries. With respect to those who had committed crimes inside certain countries, it had been agreed in Moscow on November 1, 1943 (*ibid.*, p. viii), that they were to be tried in and by the countries concerned.

What is to be understood by crimes within this meaning has been clearly defined in Article 6 of the "London Charter":

The following acts, or any of them, are crimes coming within the jurisdiction of the Tribunal for which there shall be individual responsibility:

(a) *Crimes against peace:* namely, planning, preparation, initiation or waging of a war of aggression, or a war in violation of international treaties, agreements or assurances, or participation in a common plan or conspiracy for the accomplishment of any of the foregoing;

(b) *War Crimes:* namely, violations of the laws or customs of war. Such violations shall include, but not be limited to, murder, ill-treatment or deportation to slave labour or for any other purpose of civilian population of or in occupied territory, murder or ill-treatment of prisoners of war or persons on the seas, killing of hostages, plunder of public or private property, wanton destruction of cities, towns or villages, or devastation not justified by military necessity;

(c) *Crimes against humanity:* namely, murder, extermination, enslavement, deportation, and other inhumane acts committed against any civilian population, before or during the war; [10] or persecutions on political, racial or religious grounds in execution of or in connection with any crime within the jurisdiction of the Tribunal, whether or not in violation of the domestic law of the country where perpetrated (143, Vol. I, pp. xi f.).

[10] By protocol of October 6, 1945, in Berlin the semi-colon was changed to a comma (143, Vol. I, pp. xv f.).

There cannot be any question as to whether the world out-side Germany regarded the acts committed by the SS as "crimes against humanity"—that is, as crimes. The SS, however, did not regard their acts as crimes; they held the view that the ex-termination of Jews, far from being a crime, was a laudable and necessary act. This view is illustrated by the following in-stance taken from the testimony of the SS physician Gerstein (143, Vol. I, pp. 865 ff.; Gerstein was also an engineer):

With a party including Herr Pfannenstiel, professor of hygiene at Marburg (Lahn) University, Gerstein visited the extermination camps Belzec (August 18 and 19, 1942) and Tre-blinka (August 20, 1942). The object of these visits was, among other things, to find a more effective method for the gassing of human beings. Until then it had been done by means of the exhaust gases of an old diesel engine. On August 17, 1942, the party was welcomed at Lublin by SS Major-General Glo-bocnik, who told them that Hitler and Himmler had visited the same place on August 15, 1942. Dr. Herbert Linden of the Ministry of the Interior (see this book, p. 106), who accom-panied Hitler on this visit, had asked if it would not be a bet-ter plan to cremate the dead bodies instead of burying them, as "a future generation might think differently of these matters" (143, Vol. I, p. 866). Globocnik had replied: " 'But, gentlemen, if after us such a cowardly and rotten generation should arise that it does not understand our work which is so good and so necessary, then, gentlemen, all National Socialism will have been for nothing. On the contrary, bronze plaques should be put up with the inscription that it was we, we who had the courage to achieve this gigantic task.' And Hitler said: 'Yes, my good Globocnik, that is the word, that is my opinion, too' " (ibid. pp. 866 f.).

Gerstein further stated that not only Jews were being mur-dered, but also "the Poles and Czechs of category No. III, who did not deserve to live because they were unable to work" (ibid., p. 869). At Belzec (August 19, 1942) he witnessed the gassing of a transport from Lemberg. This transport consisted of 45 cars, containing altogether 6,700 persons, of whom 1,450 were already dead on arrival. The following day Treblinka was visited. After the inspection of the camp "a banquet was given in our 'honour,' attended by all the employees of the institution. The Obersturmbannführer, Professor Pfannenstiel, Hygiene Professor at the University of Marburg/Lahn, made a speech: 'Your task is a great duty, a duty useful and necessary.' To me alone he talked of this institution in terms of 'beauty of the task'; 'humane cause'; and speaking to all of them he said: 'Looking at the bodies of these Jews, one understands the greatness of your good work!' " (*ibid.*, p. 870).

Next the classification of criminal types as drawn up by Alexander and Staub (3) will be examined with a view to deciding whether it can be applied to the members of the SS, and if so, to what extent.

They distinguish three categories of habitual criminals.[11] The first category is that of the *neurotic criminals*. These persons are neurotics because their psychic life shows the neurotic conflict, namely the struggle between their social and a-social tendencies, in which struggle "despite the existence in their personality of a social faculty, the unadjusted tendencies of the id attain a substitute gratification" (3, pp. 33 f.). In contrast to neurotics in a narrower sense, they are not content that "an ego-alien demand of their drives achieves merely a substitute gratification in the shape of a symptom" (3, p. 69); for theirs is a neurotic character, the characteristic of which is "the great expansive force of the tendencies alien to the ego" (3, p. 72). They obtain gratification (this is in the first place determined by constitutional factors) in the active realization of the tendencies of the id, they "*act,* they realize their drives, including the a-social tendencies alien to the ego" (3, p. 69). As they (want to) convert their a-social impulses into deeds, they come into conflict with the penal law, and thus become criminals.

[11] Habitual criminals are those "who because of their personal (organic or psychic) predisposition tend toward crime" (3, p. 36). In contrast to these there are the normal individuals "who, under certain specific conditions become *acutely criminal.* . . . Not the idiosyncrasy of the individual, but the peculiarity of the situation, therefore, is characteristic of these acts" (3, p. 36).

Their social conscience, a function of the super-ego, disapproves of these acts but cannot prevent them from being carried into effect. This is a result of the elimination of the curbing influence of the super-ego, due to projection of guilt,[12] rationalization,[13] and a transformation of the meaning of the act.[14] These processes constitute a transition to the neuroses, particularly to compulsion neurosis.

The super-ego, which has not been harmoniously resolved into the personality, disapproves of the acts, and hence neurotic criminals can only partly identify themselves with their acts.

The second category is that of the *normal criminals*. These persons are psychologically normal, i.e. they have the same psychic structure as normal, non-criminal people, but they are distinguished from the latter by the content of their super-ego. Theirs is what Aichhorn has called "a criminal super-ego . . . , they are adjusted to their criminal environment and their criminal examples" (3, p. 35). The criminal super-ego has indeed a morality, which is, however, a "criminal's morality." Consequently they can identify themselves completely with their acts.

The third category comprises those criminals who commit crimes because of organic diseases. Criminals who act under the influence of intoxication are also classified in this category.

After this exposition the question will be considered: Can the SS be classed in one of these groups?

The super-ego, which, as we know, is the introjection of the

[12] Projection of guilt: "The creation of a state in which the active individual through a greater or lesser degree of distortion of reality gets himself to believe that his environment is responsible for his sufferings. . . . A false interpretation is put on the real situation, in such a way as if the culprit were the victim, the person attacked were guilty" (3, p. 62).

[13] Rationalization: "From the multitude of determinants only the motive accepted by the ego is acknowledged and observed by the consciousness. The unconscious tendencies that are alien to the ego can remain in the dark, as the act appears sufficiently justified by the motivations observed by the consciousness." (3, p. 63).

[14] Transformation of the meaning of the act: "That the act, in the same way as the neurotic symptom, appears in the conscious mind incomprehensibly, often senselessly, disguised. Such offences as are meant to replace unconsciously desired acts could be appropriately termed symptom acts or *symptom crimes*" (3, p. 64).

voices of parents, teachers, and society, acquired in the case
of the SS a criminal content. From 1933 on their super-ego was
taught by society (radio, films, newspapers, books), by teachers,
and in many cases by the parents as well that "the Jews are
our ruin," "the Jews must be exterminated," "the Russians
and the Poles are inferior creatures," etc. Thus the SS acquired
a criminal super-ego, and came to belong to the category of
normal criminals. Not to that of neurotic criminals, for their
social faculty did not disapprove of the acts they committed, so
that there arose no conflict between this faculty and their (to
our mind) a-social tendencies. The point that they were not
in the category of those who become criminals because of
organic disease need hardly be made. For the sake of completeness it will be mentioned that the two last categories mentioned were almost certainly represented among the SS; their
number, however, I take to have been small, so that they will
not be further considered. From what has been said it follows
that to my mind the SS may, in the system of Alexander and
Staub, be placed in the category of normal criminals and the
SS be branded as a criminal organization. This conclusion,
however, holds good only from *our* point of view, for the SS
did not regard themselves as criminals, as they only translated
into practice what they had been taught to look upon as right
by the standards of *their* society.

It was their super-ego that made it possible for them to behave as they did; in the case of those whose parents were Nazis,
and of those who had joined one of the organizations of the
NSDAP at an early age, this can be accepted as merely a
fact, but not in the case of those members of the SS whose
super-ego was already moulded before they joined the SS—that
is, in the case of adults. The behaviour of these people must, to
my way of thinking, be explained by a total or partial replacement of the old super-ego by a criminal super-ego. Alexander
is of the same opinion: "The religious-humane-cultural super-
ego common to all civilized peoples was replaced by an exclusively tribal super-ego. The psychiatrist stands in amazement
before the thoroughness and completeness with which this
perversion of essential super-ego values was accomplished in

adult people. Many of these had good intelligence, had the benefits of good family life and good religious and humane-cultural education throughout the decisive phases of their childhood, which are regarded as so important for the formation of super-ego ideals. Yet not only did they undergo a complete change of their super-ego ideals in their adult life, sometimes even their late adult life, but after committing crimes in accordance with these new super-ego notions, most of them remained completely free from guilt feelings" (6, p. 8).

All or nearly all SS men, to my mind, had a criminal super-ego. That it is not impossible for all the individuals who are members of a group to have a criminal super-ego is also apparent from what Flugel has said: "Submission to group prestige and the projection of the individual super-ego upon the group may lead to a great and tragic lowering of moral standards. All the individuals concerned may in fact acquire what, according to the standards of other times and other groups, might be called a criminal super-ego; they regard as right and praiseworthy what in the light of these other standards would be considered callous, treacherous, cruel, intolerant, or unjust. This is exhibited on the one hand by war, or in religious, political, or racial persecutions, when wholesale murder and destruction (to say nothing of mental torture) may be inflicted by one group on another, not only without guilt but with a supreme sense of moral rightness; and on the other by the changing standards of successive generations" (44, p. 211).

I trust that by virtue of psychological arguments I have made it clear that the SS men consisted of normal individuals (apart from exceptions), who because of their criminal super-ego had become normal criminals.

It must now be explained how it is possible for the super-ego with acknowledged non-criminal standards of adults or adolescents to be replaced by a criminal super-ego. The key to this problem has been provided by Freud in his theory of group psychology: "A primary group of this kind is a number of individuals who have substituted one and the same object for their ego ideal and have consequently identified themselves with one another in their ego" (49a, p. 80).

Hitler's theory took possession of the super-ego of each member of the SS; also, therefore, of the super-ego of those whose super-ego was already entirely or partially shaped, with the result, that in this case the normal (non-criminal) standards were replaced by criminal ones.

In order to keep the matter under discussion conveniently arranged I will not now go into the question of the group psychology of the SS, but will revert to it later (see this book, pp. 269 ff.).

The factors that favoured the psychological mechanism of replacement in the individual super-ego will first be considered:

(1) According to Alexander and Staub, if the super-ego is to maintain its normal content, it must be constantly strengthened by dosing with normal standards. As they put it: "A certain dependence of the super-ego on the examples of reality continues in most adults throughout life. With the dwindling of the confidence in the authorities the inner strength of the super-ego is also shaken. The man who remains righteous while the world is being ruined, while about him the whole of mankind breaks through the social restrictions, is surely the exception rather than the rule" (3, p. 32).

(2) Alexander stresses the weakness of the super-ego: "The only trouble with predominantly super-ego-determined guidance of the personality is that the super-ego, even at best, is the least deeply anchored part of the personality, therefore the least stable and reliable, unless continually reinforced by external social-moral forces, of which the most important are religion, law, and public opinion. The super-ego structure is therefore in peril whenever these established guiding forces weaken, or are being undermined, shifted, or perverted, and becomes itself open to undermining, shift, and perversion, even in adult life—a fact which is probably more important than we have been aware of heretofore" (6, p. 18).

It is a matter of course that the super-ego is the weakest part of the personality, as it is the last-formed psychic faculty.

(3) The intellect. In this respect it should be noted that of the 21 major criminals who were tried at Nuremberg, 17 had an intelligence quotient over 120 (60, p. 31). According to Van Der Heyden's classification, these 17 belong to the category of "bright people": "The class whose intelligence quotient lies between 130 and 120 may be regarded as bright people; they are suitable for secondary education" (69, p. 167). According to the same writer, of the total population of the Netherlands about 5 per cent have an I.Q. of 130 or more (69, p. 166); of the 21 leading Nazis there were 9 in this class, among whom was Seyss-Inquart (I.Q. 141). Hence I do not believe that lack of intellect was necessary in order to join the SS and to accept its ideology, although in a number of SS men this may have been an influencing factor.

(4) Disturbance in the maturity of the personality. Kelley has stated: "I became convinced that the country which had produced so many thousands of infantile young men was itself emotionally immature. . . . A frighteningly high percentage had an emotional-intellectual age of about ten years. . . ." (82, p. 201). It does not seem probable to me that Kelley's explanation applies to every German, not even to every SS man, but it certainly holds good for a number of SS men, who because of their immaturity accepted the SS standards the more readily.

Alexander places particular emphasis on a weak ego development, as a result of "a social and cultural moulding of the German personality in which somehow the ego part of the personality has been insufficiently developed or has been crushed by educational, social, or other forces. What we have left is a weak ego with a vastly over-developed but of necessity unstable super-ego which is superimposed over this weak ego and over a probably normal Id portion of the personality. The emptiness of the ego sphere is the most striking finding which differentiates members of the German cultural group from members of other cultural groups" (6, p. 20).

Through this weakness of the ego the super-ego acquires even greater import and becomes even more a determining force than is normally the case: ". . . when the super-ego ideals are good, . . . Then you have a personality, . . . more likely to become a saint than members of other cultural spheres. But when the super-ego ideals become undermined, shifted, or perverted, . . . then this same personality is more likely to become a devil than would a member of any other cultural group" (6, p. 20).

Summarizing, I think I may in the very first place hold the super-ego responsible for the behaviour of the SS men, in whom it developed into a criminal super-ego because Adolf Hitler's ideas took possession of it; this can be explained by Freud's group psychology. The process was furthered because the superego is the weakest part of the personality in some people, by reason of lack of intellect and a disturbance in the maturing of their personality.

In stamping the SS as a criminal organization I am not alone. Alexander also says: "The SS was a criminal organization not only because its members actually committed crimes, but also because the essential mode of its thinking and its group behaviour were those of all criminal organizations. If a member did anything which put his loyalty to the organization in a questionable light, he was either liquidated—killed—or he had to undertake a criminal act which definitely and irrevocably tied him to the organization. According to the age-old custom of criminal gangs, this act had to include murder. In the SS this process of reinforcement of group cohesion was called *Blutkitt* [15] (blood cement)" (5, p. 170).

As a very telling example of "Blutkitt" Alexander mentions the sulfanilamide experiments by Professor Gebhardt (this book, pp. 89 ff.). Alexander states that Professor Gebhardt had become suspect because of the charge of having given Heydrich inadequate sulfanilamide treatment, "and he was then expected to commit a crime which would dispel the suspicions against him and tie him more tightly into the SS criminal organization" (5, p. 170). This "Blutkitt" was the sulfanilamide

[15] From the German psychologist Wanda von Baeyer, Alexander learned that Hitler introduced this idea and this term, and that he had taken them from a book about Genghis Khan which he was supposed to have read in the prison at Landsberg, where Hitler was confined after the unsuccessful Munich coup in 1923 (7, p. 300).

experiments, in which a number of victims died in spite of treatment with sulfanilamide. In this way Professor Gebhardt proved that he was innocent of Heydrich's death. Gebhardt even went a step further and, according to Alexander, "involved the entire German medical profession in 'SS blood cement' by presenting his report before a national medical meeting where no objections were raised by the members" (5, p. 170).

It was particularly the super-ego which made it possible for the SS to murder Jews, Poles, Russians, etc. It can even be said that this was a necessity for the SS, for these people, according to Nazi ideology, were noxious creatures. To destroy them was as necessary for the SS as the extermination of Colorado potato beetles was for the Netherlands.

Bettelheim observed this in some interviews he had with SS men: "they really believed in a Jewish-capitalistic world conspiracy against the German people, and whoever opposed the Nazis participated in it and was therefore to be destroyed" (17, p. 447).

Because our super-ego is not so utterly deformed as that of the SS, their behaviour appears to us criminal and abnormal. The SS man looked upon himself as normal, and when he had finished his job he went home quietly, kissed his wife and children, played with his dog, called on his friends, etc. And whether this job consisted in gassing Jews, in shooting Poles, in taking roll call, in conducting a selection, in overseeing a labour group of prisoners, etc. made no difference, for it was his job and that had to be done.

A single example will serve to illustrate this point; it is taken from the diary of Professor Dr. Hans Hermann Kremer,[16] who had held a chair in the University of Münster (Westphalia) since July 30, 1929.[17] This man became a mem-

[16] Kremer also operated for a time in the Netherlands. One of the entries in his diary runs: "12-30.9.1926. Situation in the histological laboratory of Prof. Boeke at Utrecht (Holland)."

[17] Translator's note: For the English rendering of Kremer's diary I am indebted to 6, pp. 22–25. Only the entries under September 11 and September 25, 1942 are not to be found in Alexander's article. A four-line German ditty under September 6, 1942, has not been translated.

ber of the NSDAP (membership number 1265405) in 1932, and joined the armed SS on June 14, 1941; he was called up on August 18, 1941. On August 29, 1942, he was ordered to go to the concentration camp Auschwitz, to deputize for a physician who had fallen ill; he arrived in Auschwitz on August 30, 1942. I quote the following entries from his diary:

September 2, 1942. First time present at a Sonderaktion (special action) [18] at 3 hours in the morning. Compared with this the Inferno by Dante seems to me as a comedy. Auschwitz is not called for nothing the "camp of extermination." . . .

September 5, 1942. This afternoon present at a Sonderaktion (special action) from the female concentration camp [Muselmänner]: The most horrible of horrors. Hschf. Thilo, doctor of the troops, is right when he told me this morning that we are at *anus mundi.* In the evening at approximately 8.00 hours again present at a Sonderaktion from the Netherlands. Men all want to take part in these actions because of the special rations they get then, consisting of a fifth of a litre of schnapps, 5 cigarettes, 100 g. sausage and bread. Today and tomorrow on duty.

September 6, 1942. Today, Sunday, excellent lunch: tomato soup, half a hen with potatoes and red cabbage (20 g. fat), sweets and marvellous vanilla ice . . . in the evening at 8.00 hours outside for a Sonderaktion.

September 9, 1942. This morning I got the most pleasant news from my lawyer, Prof. Dr. Hallermann in Münster, that I got divorced from my wife on the first of this month (Note: I see colours again, a black curtain is drawn back from my life!). Later on, present as doctor at a corporal punishment of eight prisoners and an execution by shooting with small-calibre rifles. Got soap flakes and two pieces of soap. . . . In the evening present at a Sonderaktion, fourth time.

September 10, 1942. In the morning present at a Sonderaktion (5th time).

[18] "The most spectacular of the mass atrocities were called *Sonderaktionen* (special actions). One of these, which was practiced particularly in Auschwitz, was the burning of live prisoners, especially children, in pits measuring 20 by 40 to 50 meters, on piles of petrol-soaked wood. . . . Mr. Jerzy Bielski, a former prisoner who had been assigned as an electrician at the extermination plant in Auschwitz, . . . testified also that numerous SS men and German civilians, including 'visiting firemen' of officer's rank, came to witness these atrocities" (6, p. 21).

September 11, 1942. Today Obersturmbannführer Lolling in the camp. . . .

September 20, 1942. Listened to a concert of the prisoners' band this afternoon in bright sunshine. Bandmaster: conductor of the Warschauer Staatsoper. 80 musicians. For lunch we had pork, for dinner baked tench.

September 23, 1942. Last night present at the 6th and 7th Sonderaktion. In the morning Obergruppenführer Pohl arrived with his staff in the house of the Waffen SS. . . . In the evening at 20.00 hours, dinner with Obergruppenführer Pohl in the leader house, a real banquet. We had baked pike, as much as we wanted, good coffee, excellent ale and rolls.

September 25, 1942. Gruppenführer Grawitz in the hospital and the camp. During his visit he wants me to tell him what a physician prescribes in the very first place for infectious diseases. Really I do not know what to reply, as indeed with regard to this no general statement can be made. And what did he think? Listen and be amazed: a laxative! . . .

September 27, 1942. Sunday afternoon 16.00–20.00 hours, comradely meeting [Kameradschaftsabend] in the community house with dinner, free beer and cigarettes. The Commander Hoess made a speech; musical show and theatre.

September 30, 1942. Last night present at the 8th Sonderaktion.

October 3, 1942. Today we fixed living material of human liver, spleen and pancreas. . . .

October 7, 1942. Present at the 9th Sonderaktion (foreigners and emaciated females [Muselweiber]. Wirths came back. . . .

October 10, 1942. Taken out living material of liver, spleen and pancreas and fixed it. Heated my room first time. . . .

October 12, 1942. Inoculation against typhoid, after that, in the evening, fever. In spite of that, present at a Sonderaktion during the night (1600 persons from the Netherlands). Terrible scene outside the last bunker (*Hoessler!*). That was the 10th *Sonderaktion.*

October 13, 1942. Present at an infliction of punishment and the execution of seven Polish civilians.

October 15, 1942. Living, fresh material of liver, spleen, and pancreas taken out from an icteric. . . .

October 17, 1942. Present at an infliction of punishment and 11 executions. Taken out living, fresh material of liver, spleen, and pancreas after injection of pilocarpin.

October 18, 1942. In wet cold weather present at the 11th Sonderaktion (Netherlanders) on Sunday morning. Shocking scenes with three women, who beseech us for bare life.

October 24, 1942. Six women of the Budger rebellion "inoculated off" (Klebs).

November 1, 1942. At 13.00 hours left Auschwitz for Prague. . . .

November 6, 1942. . . . Duration of trip from Prague to Auschwitz more than 9 hours. Upon arrival I immediately went into the Fuehrerheim, where I had a really good meal again and ate myself full [wo ich mich mal wieder so richtig rundherum satt ass].

November 8, 1942. Took part in two Sonderaktionen last night in rainy weather (12th and 13th). In the morning I saw Hschaf. Kitt in the sick quarters, who is a pupil of mine from Essen. In the afternoon another Sonderaktion, which was the 14th I took part in. In the evening we had a nice time in the leaders' club (Fuehrerheim), invited by HStuf. Wirths. We had Bulgarian red wine and Croatian plum-schnapps.

November 13, 1942. Living, fresh material of liver, spleen, and pancreas taken from a Jewish prisoner of 18 years of age, who was very atrophic. First we took a photo of him. Liver and spleen fixed as usual in Carnoy and pancreas in Zenker (prisoner No. 68030).[19]

November 18, 1942. Left for Prague.

From this section of Professor Kremer's diary it is indeed obvious with what calm and tranquillity he carried out his assignment. Only on one or two occasions did he evince any response, which must, in my opinion, be regarded as due to some still active part of his former super-ego.

Alexander holds an ego disturbance responsible for Kremer's behaviour (6, p. 25 f.). I will not deny the contributory effect of such a disturbance, though in my opinion particular emphasis should be laid on the fact that Kremer's acts are a logical outcome of his "philosophy of life" [Weltanschauung], to which he had become a willing convert in 1932. His super-ego recognized the rightness of his behaviour, and, viewed in this

[19] The Netherlands Red Cross is in possession of a photostat of the administration of the prisoners' hospital Auschwitz. From this it appears that prisoner No. 68030 was one Hans de Jong, born February 18, 1924. An entry after his name shows that he actually died on November 13, 1942, in the Auschwitz camp hospital, while the same date of death is recorded after this prisoner's number in the Auschwitz "Death Book." (Information supplied by the Netherlands Red Cross.)

light, Kremer was a normal man. Also Hoess was himself convinced of his own normality, when he said, "I am entirely normal. Even while I was doing this extermination work, I led a normal family life, and so on" (60, p. 258).

The view that murdering people was a perfectly normal procedure was not, however, confined to the SS, but was, according to Padover, widespread in Nazi Germany. In his function of officer with the "psychological Warfare Division of the Army" he spoke to many Germans. During an interview with Wagemann, burgomaster of Kornelimuenster, he came to this conclusion: "It occurred to me that Gas Houses and Death Camps were possible not because Hitler ordered them but because the Wagemanns thought the orders right" (118, p. 27)—and Wagemann had been "good" (anti-Nazi) since 1933.

A German half-Jew told Padover that the Germans were not hostile, but merely indifferent. "All of them, he insisted, knew about the Nazi atrocities. (Later, when we got deeper into Germany, I had occasion to verify this startling fact)" (118, p. 40).

It is also Gilbert's view that the behaviour of the Germans was not rooted in hatred: "Most Germans had no active hatred of the Allies, no desire for war, and very little real hatred for the minority groups whose persecution they condoned. Even some of the top Nazi leaders assured the writer that they had always admired the French, or British, or Americans as people, and that some of their best friends were Jews. The irony of it was that it was true. Never in history have more people been killed with less real hatred than during World War II" (61, p. 314).

It was not hate, but the moral current in Nazi Germany that made the extermination of "inferior" races possible.

The super-ego of many Germans, therefore, had a very different content from that of, for example, the great majority of Netherlanders prior to 1940. This may also explain the unwillingness of the Jews to believe the wartime stories about gassing: they could not imagine such horrors; and for the same reason non-Jews after the war could hardly bring themselves to credit what they heard about concentration-camp atrocities. For the fact that the content of the average German's super-ego was different from ours, those who had moulded it were to blame—parents, youth leaders, teachers, society standards; in other words, the blame lay with the *education* to which the German (and in particular the German child) was subjected. This brings us to

German Education [20]

The moulding of personality begins in the family. In the German family an authoritarian spirit prevails, authority being vested in the parents, especially in the father. The father is "boss," and the mother as well as the children owes him unconditional obedience. It has been pointed out by Erikson (41, pp. 485 f.) that the behaviour of the mother in the father's presence is so markedly different that even a baby cannot but perceive it: "She hurries to fulfil the father's whims and to avoid angering him. The children hold their breath, for the father does not approve of 'nonsense,' that is, neither of mother's feminine moods nor of the children's playfulness" (41, p. 490).

Moreover, the father is the authority that imposes penalties, which in a German family often take the form of corporal punishment. The mother can decide whether or not she will bring the children's offences to the father's notice, and, as Erikson remarks: "The mother's betrayal, of course, does not improve the boy's opinion of women" (41, p. 490). But the son also knows that the all-powerful father is, in his turn, subordinate to *his* superiors and this knowledge does not tend to strengthen "the boy's belief in the dignity of man. All this is often amply balanced by respect and love." (*ibid.*).

This educational method gives rise to a powerful accumulation of aggressions in the child, which he is prevented from venting in a normal way by the dictatorship of the parents. The fear of the father together with its attendant aggression strengthens the fear which, according to Fortanier (45, p. 136),

---

[20] For some of the data worked into this section I am indebted to an address delivered on January 10, 1947, by Dr. A. J. W. Kaas to the Heerlen branch of the K.N.M.v.G. (Royal Netherlands Medical Association).

comes into being in every growing individual, because man feels weak and menaced for a long time and it takes many years for him to become an adult. Thus "the development of man proceeds in despite of a constant sense of fear, which occurs through the influence of the vaguely sensed possibility that he might be unable to overcome difficulties and be mentally or physically ruined or both" (45, pp. 136 f.).

According to Fortanier, man can respond to this fear in one of two ways—either individually or collectively. Individual man assumes more readily the responsibility for the struggle for life than he who is collectively bound. The latter conquers his sense of weakness by his voluntary incorporation in a mass.

A combination of the two might be supposed generally to occur, but Fortanier holds the view that "people are more apt to accept a leader who can suggest to them in their collective attachment a certain power and security, than to decide independently on their own leadership and responsibility for their attitude toward the problems of life" (45, p. 138).

If, therefore, normal fear, which exists in every growing individual, causes man to flee into the mass, how much more apt is this to happen in the German child through the strengthening of this normal fear by the powerful and severe father! These two factors together are responsible for the failure of any attempt at rebellion on the part of the majority of German adolescents against paternal or parental authority, and compel them to resignation in a subordinate position. That small minority of adolescents who refuse submission rebel overtly against parental authority and will sometimes even run away from home, as did Adolf Hitler's father and Hitler himself.

The schools proceed with authoritarian education. Here it is the teachers who wield the powers of dictatorship and even apply corporal chastisement. After the assumption of power by the NSDAP, schools became institutes for party education, where German youth was indoctrinated with party ideals. Education became "racial," and the authorities did not shrink from stooping to deliberate distortion of facts. A notorious example of this is the poem "Die Lorelei" by the Jewish poet

Heine, which in Nazi textbooks occurred with the note "by an unknown poet."

Among other things young people were also taught to become familiar with mass murders. Alexander (6, pp. 6 ff.) instances the book by A. Dorner *et al.*: "Mathematics in the Service of National-Political Education. A Handbook for Teachers" (38). According to Alexander, this book was "widely distributed and used, a new edition being printed annually" (6, p. 6). I quote only the following problems:

Problem 199. A 1000-Kg. poison gas bomb contains 70% of poison gas. How many bombs of this kind are needed for the gassing of an area of 2.2 square kilometres (town centre of Berlin) if for 1 square kilometre (a) 10,000 Kg. of mustard gas, (b) 20,000 Kg. of phosgene are necessary? How many planes would have to be in operation if every plane carried three bombs of this kind? At what intervals of time must the bombs be dropped if the planes have a speed of 50 metres per second and fly in single-file echelon? How great must the distance be between two neighbouring planes?

Solution: (a) 57; (b) 114 bombs; (a) 19; (b) 38 planes. $13\frac{1}{3}$ seconds; distance between planes about (a) 105, (b) 52 m.

Problem 200. According to statements of the Draeger Works in Luebeck in the gassing of a city only 50% of the evaporated poison gas is effective. The atmosphere must be poisoned up to a height of 20 metres in a concentration of 45 mg./m^3. How much phosgene is needed to poison a city of 50,000 inhabitants who live in an area of four square kilometres? How much phosgene would the population inhale with the air they breathe in ten minutes without protection against gas, if one person uses 30 litres of breathing air per minute? Compare this quantity with the quantity of the poison gas used.

Solution: 7.2 T.; 675 g.; 0.009% (6, pp. 6 f.).

Before the Nazi era the German child could find a vent for many of his pent-up aggressions in the youth movement by taking up sports and games, by consorting with youngsters of his own age, and finally by undertaking leadership himself. But in Nazi Germany every youth club was incorporated in the H.J., the "Hitler Youth," which of course followed the National Socialist party line. The Hitler Youth was taught that "the 'meaning of life' consists in carrying through the will of the 'Fuehrer' with *every* means, . . . that *death* in carrying through the 'idea,of the Fuehrer' is more glorious than *life*" (154, p. 8). Within the Hitler Youth the result was this: " 'With blind obedience' . . . they carried out unconditionally every command of their 'Fuehrer' " (154, p. 9).

In every domain of life, in the family, at school, and in the youth movement, and later in military service and in the labour service,authoritarianism was supreme. In NaziGermany the German was taught to obey, he was taught to follow out without thinking any instruction given by his superiors. This will sufficiently explain his conception of "command is command" ["Befehl ist Befehl"]; this attitude is common to the Germans and was to be found even before the Nazi era as in the "Kadaverdisziplin." It is the result of the fact that one of the sources from which the super-ego is fed,is the introjection of the moral ideas of parents and pedagogues. "By this process," says Van der Waals, "moral standards and conventions are transmitted from one generation to the next, which makes for a certain stability of standard and tradition" (151, p. 5). Jaspers, a German philosopher, though in a different connection, points also to the peculiar character of German education: "It is by political conditions that the Swiss and the Netherlanders are moulded,and that all of us in Germany have been reared during a long period, we to obedience, to the dynastic viewpoint, to indifference and irresponsibility toward political reality—and something of this we all have in us, even when we oppose these attitudes" (76, p. 54).

The authoritarian view of life, therefore, occurred in the German people as a living conception, even before Nazi rule; the dictatorial system of the Nazis was a worthy extension of it. Because in the schools, in the youth movement, in society, and in many cases in the family as well, the Nazi ideology was proclaimed as the only truth, we need not be surprised that through the Nazi poison the super-ego of the German had a content different from the super-ego which we regard as normal.

After this general exposition the behaviour of the SS inside the concentration camps will be subjected to a more detailed examination.

The Camp SS

Originally these were identical with the "Death-Head units" ["Totenkopfverbände"] (this book, p. 213); during the war however, SS men who were not members of these units also were appointed to concentration camps. Hoess mentioned this when he spoke about the guards: "Previously the guards were mostly young, voluntary, active men of the *Totenkopfverbände* . . . , but later they were older men of the *Allgemeine SS* . . . who were assigned for this purpose" (61, p. 244). Hence I include all of them in a new term: the camp SS.

We have already seen that the camp SS had to be proof against the spectacle of bestialities (this book, p. 9). The SS in general, but the camp SS in particular, had to be hard. In his speech at Poznan Himmler dwelt on this when he made mention of the extermination of the Jews: "Most of you know what it means when 100 corpses are lying side by side, or 500, or 1,000. To have stuck it out and at the same time—apart from exceptions caused by human weakness—to have remained decent fellows, that is what has made us hard" (142, vol. III, p. 501).

The concentration camp offered the best opportunity for training the SS in being hard. If an SS man proved unable to conquer (completely subdue) his normal human reactions as regards the prisoners, he was expelled from the camp SS.[21]

Thus a choice group of SS men was secured, who had few, if any, human feelings left as regards the prisoners. This behaviour was reinforced by the Nazi ideology, which pronounced the prisoners to be inferior creatures, a notion formulated by Himmler in 1937: For everybody "it is extraordinarily instructive to look about such a concentration camp on occasion. When you have seen it, you are convinced that none of those people are confined there unjustly; they are the scourings of the criminal world, of human failures. There is no clearer

[21] This rule applied only during the period that the camp SS was identical with the Death-Head units.

demonstration in favour of the laws of heredity and race, . . . than such a concentration camp. There are people with water on the brain, with squints, with deformities, half-Jews, an astonishing mob of racially inferior scum" (142, Vol. XXIX, p. 219).

For the SS it was possible to behave inside the concentration camp with even less control than outside. This opportunity for uncontrolled behaviour allowed the aggression impulse a wide scope.

Hitschmann (71, pp. 70–73) has pointed out that although Adler as early as 1908 drew attention to the aggression impulse (as Adler turned away from psychoanalysis, he never reverted to this), Freud did not describe it in full until 1930, in his book *Civilization and Its Discontents.*[22] Because of the important part played by the aggression impulse in the camp SS, I will go somewhat further into Freud's view on this subject. According to Freud, human beings are not content only to defend themselves when attacked, but are so constituted "that a powerful measure of desire for aggression has to be reckoned as part of their instinctual endowment. The result is that their neighbour is for them not only a possible helper or sexual object, but also a temptation to them to gratify their aggressiveness on him, to exploit his capacity for work without recompense, to use him sexually without his consent, to seize his possessions, to humiliate him, to cause him pain, to torture and to kill him. . . . This aggressive cruelty usually lies in wait for some provocation, or else it steps into the service of some other purpose, the aim of which might as well have been achieved by milder measures. In circumstances that favour it, when those forces in the mind which ordinarily inhibit it cease to operate, it also manifests itself spontaneously and reveals men as savage beasts to whom the thought of sparing their own kind is alien" (52, pp. 85–86).

In Freud's view (as in that of Reiwald too, among others—123, p. 104), "the tendency to aggression is an innate, inde-

---

[22] Freud's mentions of the aggression impulse in *Beyond the Pleasure Principle* (1916) and in *The Ego and the Id* (1923), as Hitschmann related, are not considered, because of their summarizing character.

pendent, instinctual disposition in man," [23] and this innate tendency leads "to aggression, destruction, and, in addition, cruelty" (52, p. 99).

The aggression impulse is non-erotic,[24] and hence is distinct from sadism, which is erotic and in which the play of tenderness is replaced by that of cruelty. In normal circumstances the aggression impulse is held in check by civilization. "Hence its system of methods by which mankind is to be driven to identifications and aim-inhibited love-relationships; hence the restrictions on sexual life; and hence, too, its ideal command to love one's neighbour as oneself, which is really justified by the fact that nothing is so completely at variance with original human nature as this. With all its striving, this endeavour of culture's has so far not achieved very much" (52, pp. 86–87). Civilization and aggression therefore are opposites. But still civilization cannot curb aggression. The main check on aggression has been described by Freud in the following passage: "The aggressiveness is introjected, 'internalized,'; in fact, it is sent back where it came from, i.e. directed against the ego. It is there taken over by a part of the ego that distinguishes itself from the rest as a super-ego, and now, in the form of 'conscience,' exercises the same propensity to harsh aggressiveness against the ego that the ego would have liked to enjoy against others. The tension between the strict super-ego and the subordinate ego we call the sense of guilt; it manifests itself as the need for punishment" (52, p. 105).

The sense of guilt which thus arises Freud wants "to represent . . . as the most important problem in the evolution of culture, and to convey that the price of progress in civilization is paid in forfeiting happiness through the heightening of the sense of guilt" (52, p. 123).

Freud (52, pp. 107–108) divides the sense of guilt attending aggressions into two stages. The first of these is the fear of los-

---

[23] 52, p. 102: Freud also says (ibid.): "This instinct of aggression is the derivative and main representative of the death instinct." This is left out of consideration, since the existence of the death impulse is still a moot question.
[24] "I can no longer understand how we could have overlooked the universality of non-erotic aggression and destruction, and could have omitted to give it its due significance in our interpretation of life" (52, p. 99).

ing· the affection of the external world: social fear. Man is dependent on this external world, for it protects him, but it can also punish him. Social fear compels man to forgo the gratification of those impulses which are not tolerated by the external world. If he does this no sense of guilt will arise. "Originally . . . renunciation is the consequence of a dread of external authority; one gives up pleasures so as not to lose its love. Having made this renunciation, one is quits with authority, so to speak; no feeling of guilt should remain" (52, pp. 111–112).

The other stage is the result of the introjection of the authority of the external world into the super-ego; there is no longer any difference between the doing and the wanting to do bad acts, for from the super-ego thoughts are not hidden. Actually—thus Freud—we cannot speak of a sense of guilt until the moment that it arises from the fear of the super-ego.

"Renunciation of gratification does not suffice here, for the wish persists and is not capable of being hidden from the super-ego. In spite of the renunciations made, feelings of guilt will be experienced. . . . Renunciation no longer has a completely absolving effect; virtuous restraint is no longer rewarded by the assurance of love; a threatened external unhappiness—loss of love and punishment meted out by external authority—has been exchanged for a lasting inner unhappiness, the tension of a sense of guilt" (52, p. 112).

No more than this brief survey of Freud's views will be given, as this is sufficient for my purpose: to find an explanation for the behaviour of the camp SS.

Killing a fellow man may be regarded as the strongest manifestation of the aggression impulse, particularly killing which is spontaneous and not a means of self-defence. That the prevention of homicide is one of the primary concerns of mankind is proved by one of the oldest ethical laws—namely, the sixth commandment: Thou shalt not kill. Normal society acknowledges the great value of this commandment and by the threat of severe penalties tries to prevent murders.

In Nazi Germany an entirely different viewpoint prevailed. Abel has pointed out that "a pattern of brutal treatment was developed early in the history of the Nazi movement and was continued and even augmented by virtue of the ferocity of the struggle for power in Germany itself. As a result, ruthlessness and disregard for human sentiments came to be regarded as a virtue and were not only condoned, but definitely encouraged" (1, p. 6).

As an instance Abel adduces the "Potempa case" of 1932, when four SS men were sentenced to death for murdering a political opponent. A violent campaign organized by Hitler by way of protest resulted in a commutation of the death penalty into life imprisonment. "When Hitler came into power, these men were not only immediately released, but were rewarded with high honours" (1, p. 6).

Similarly, in the case of the SS men of the camp at Hohenstein in 1934, "who were brought to Court and sentenced for 'the sadistic treatment of prisoners,' the Court decision was remanded by Hitler" (1, p. 6).

The instructions given to the camp SS were in accordance with this. As an instance of these I mention the "duty regulations for guards" issued by Eicke, commander of the concentration camp at Dachau, and dated October 1, 1933.[25]

In "No. 6, Guard regulation," it says, among other things, "If a prisoner tries to escape he must be *shot at without warning*. The guard who in the performance of his duty has shot an escaping prisoner will incur no penalty. If a guard is assaulted by a prisoner this assault must not be beaten off by means of corporal force, but by means of firearms. Any guard who disregards this order must expect to be dismissed without notice" (142, Vol. XXVI, p. 296).

By making every allowance it is still possible to regard a murder committed because of these regulations as a reactive aggression. This, however, is completely out of the question in the case which every prisoner has observed and which has been described by Kaas as follows: "In the beginning the guards made many victims everywhere because they forced the prisoners to cross a boundary line which they had marked before-

---

[25] "Reasons for punishment and kinds of punishment including the death penalty, to be meted out to prisoners of the Dachau concentration camp; duty regulations for the guards, issued 1 October 1933 by camp commander Eicke" (142, Vol. XXVI, p. 296).

hand and then shot them down. For this shooting down of 'fugitives' a bounty was offered, . . . It even happened that the guards received instructions as to the number of prisoners to be 'liquidated' in one day" (79, p. 614).

The only explanation I can offer for this conduct is that the SS were given an opportunity to realize their aggression impulse freely and were even stimulated to this realization by not being punished but offered bounties, and as an ultimate climax had it prescribed to them as a duty. Civilization (the dictates and interdictions of society), which, according to Freud, normally counteracts the aggression impulse, gave actual support to the aggression by the SS as far as the prisoners were concerned. As a result of the authoritarian education of the German individual (see this book, pp. 242 ff.) the SS man, like every German, was full of pent-up aggression and therefore we need not be surprised that these, now that the opportunity was there, were given a free rein. How this came about and to what unspeakable cruelties it led is now, I think, sufficiently known. Nor could any sense of guilt act as a curb on the SS, for the external world, proclaiming the doctrine of National Socialism, had taught them that in the concentration camps the scum of humanity was confined—that is to say, people who were so inferior that they no longer deserved the name of human beings. Toward these creatures, as *the* representative of whom the Jew was proclaimed, anything was permitted. The SS therefore did not need to refrain from gratifying their aggressive tendencies because of "social fear." They ran no risk of discovery, for the authority of the external world pronounced aggressiveness toward these people justified. And also the super-ego of the SS approved of their behaviour, for all they had been taught was that the prisoners were dangerous and inferior characters, whose annihilation was necessary for the good of mankind. Thus there was no tension between their ego and their super-ego, so that the sense of guilt which might have counteracted the aggression impulse was lacking.

Besides, by Freud's theory the various forms of behavior of the camp SS (and this certainly applies to some of them) can be explained by means of the hypothesis drawn up by

Dollard *et al.* to the effect that *"aggression is always a consequence of frustration.* More specifically the proposition is that the occurrence of aggressive behaviour always presupposes the existence of frustration and, contrariwise, that the existence of frustration always leads to some form of aggression" (37, p. 1).

As "frustration" they regard "that condition which exists when a goal-response suffers interference" (37, p. 8).

Interference may vary in strength and kind. "The interference may be slight, as when a mosquito hums near a person absorbed in thought, or great, as when an individual suffers the effects of kidney disease. It is, nevertheless, the same form of interference that induces the frustration" (37, p. 5).

The conception of frustration comprises many human feelings. As Ellenberger has stated, it includes "the sense of being injured, defrauded, neglected, wronged, etc. . . . but also conceptions such as disappointment, i.e. the nonfulfilment of an expectation that was felt as justified. Disappointed expectation on the one hand, and the sense of injustice suffered, on the other, both belong to frustration as a comprehensive idea" (120, p. 33).

Dollard *et al.* deny the existence of an aggression impulse and propose to regard every aggression as a result of frustration. The view held by Kunz shows a close resemblance to theirs, although he does not use the term "frustration." According to Kunz, "The essence of aggression lies in the contempt, the suppression, or the repudiation of the self-activity and characteristic of the objects that we encounter—including our fellow men— . . . it contradicts those opinions which view it as 'a primal drive' or at least a spontaneous complex of impulses originating in the same way as hunger and sexuality" (91, p. 21).

Kunz also, therefore, denies the existence of an aggression impulse and holds that all aggressions arise from reactions.

I am inclined, following Freud, to believe that we may assume the existence of an aggression impulse. This, however, does not alter the fact that I think it very likely that in some of the cases the aggressiveness of the camp SS was not a manifestation of the aggression impulse, but was an outcome of frustration. And because the formulation of the concept of frustration is very comprehensive, I think it very likely that the SS men were often frustrated. As a rule the aggression which resulted will not have been directed toward the individual who was the cause of this frustration—for example, because this person was a superior—and consequently this aggression in the concentration camp was vented on the prisoners.

In the view of Dollard *et al.*, "The strength of instigation to aggression varies directly with the amount of frustration" (37, p. 20).

As frustration began to be of greater import for the SS, their aggression became more violent and their cruelty greater. It is also of importance in this connection that "the strength of inhibition of any act of aggression varies positively with the amount of punishment anticipated to be a consequence of that act" (37, p. 24; italics omitted). This did not affect the SS because they had little or no reason to fear that they would be punished for cruelties inflicted on the prisoners.

To summarize, I propose to explain in part the cruelties inflicted by the camp SS on innumerable innocent people by the fact that their aggression impulse, strengthened by the pent-up aggressions of an authoritarian education, could manifest itself without any restraint on account of the absence of "psychical counterforces." Even, as it happened, the authority of the external world which normally provides these counterforces was the very factor that stimulated the aggression impulse in the camp SS men. The authority of their external world, National Socialism, found not only that, as regards the prisoners, anything was permissible, but even that the extermination of these people was a necessity. In the individuals concerned the unrestraint of the aggression impulse was also furthered by the factors mentioned before (this book, pp. 234 f.).

Occasionally the aggression impulse was provoked by the

prisoners (e.g., when they began to slack at their work as soon as the SS man moved away), but this, in my opinion, is a question of merely secondary importance.

Not all the cruelties inflicted by the camp SS men can, I think, be explained as manifestations of the aggression impulse. A part of them I prefer to view in the light of the hypothesis of Dollard *et al.*: "Aggression is always a consequence of frustration," namely in the sense that aggressions which arose in the camp SS men through frustration were vented on the prisoners.

A few words on the forms of *minor ill-treatment,* which term must be understood to include blows, kicks, or thrusts administered by the SS to a prisoner. In my opinion these should not be regarded as a manifestation of the aggression impulse, but may be explained by the hypothesis of Dollard *et al.* This behaviour on the part of the SS men may also be merely a "habitual" gesture, a result of their education, during which being beaten and kicked by a superior was a normal occurrence. Finally it might be rooted in the contempt which the SS felt toward the living wrecks which the prisoners often were and whose lord and master they were. This contempt has been described by Frankl. Once, when during his work in a blizzard he wanted to have a moment's rest, it struck him "that this guard did not even think it worth his while to *waste invective on* the decayed and ragged figure, . . . which I surely at that moment presented to his view. What he actually does is rather this: In a playful manner he picks up a stone and throws it at me. Thus, I was to experience, one draws the attention of some animal, thus a domestic animal is reminded of the job it has got to do, an animal for which one cares so little that one does not even punish it." (46, pp. 35 f.).

I want to emphasize, as Tas (138) and Kaas (78, p. 414) have emphasized, that I do not consider the camp SS as sadists, in whom the aggression impulse is tied up in the sexual impulse. As the concentration camp was an exquisite opportunity for the gratification of this perversion it seems probable to me that among the camp SS men there were sadists, but the latter did not put their seal on the camp SS. This is apparent from what Hoess told Gilbert: "You can be sure that it was not always a pleasure to see those mountains of corpses and smell the continual burning" (60, p. 260). It looks as if Hoess meant to say: "Don't run away with the idea that I did it because I liked it." I further call attention to the fact that there were also SS men who themselves did not take the initiative to ill-treat the prisoners. But this no more prevented these SS men from obeying every order given, nor from, as a rule, taking good care not to be kind to the prisoners if other SS men were present. In the total behaviour of the SS these "good" SS men remained inconspicuous, and consequently they have been left out of consideration.

A few figures of the camp SS will now be discussed in some detail. In the first place, Rudolf Hoess.[26] I have chosen him for the following reasons: Hoess was a follower of the SS ideology, but not its inventor or designer. His political importance was not such that he can be regarded as a major Nazi personality. He spoke of himself as "a minor cog in the wheels of Himmler's organizational machinery" (61, p. 240). Then he had been one of the camp SS for years and as commander of the concentration camp Auschwitz he played a major part for a long period in the extermination of the Jews. But my choice has been mainly effected by the fact that Hoess fell into Allied hands alive. Thanks to this fact we have at our disposal authentic reports of his actions and need not rely on information by witnesses.

Hoess, as he told Gilbert, was born into a very strict Roman Catholic family. He gave the following description of his father: "My father was really a bigot. He was very strict and fanatic. I learned that my father took a religious oath at the time of the birth of my youngest sister, dedicating me to God and the priesthood, and after that leading a Joseph married life (celibacy).—He directed my entire youthful education toward the goal of making me a priest. I had to pray and go to church endlessly; do penance over the slightest misdeed—

[26] I have drawn on the following publications: 60, 61, 97, 142, Vol. XI, pp. 396–422; *ibid.*, Vol. XXXIII, Document PS-3868 (see bibliography).

praying as punishment for any little unkindness to my sister, or something like that" (61, p. 241). He was never beaten, but by way of punishment he was always made to pray. The fact that he was of a very retiring disposition and that he had never made any friends, he thought he could explain because his father was to him a kind of superior being, in with whom any form of intimacy was ruled out: "I feel that this bigoted upbringing is responsible for my becoming so withdrawn. My mother also lived in the shadow of this fanatic piety" (61. p. 241). Gradually he drifted away from Catholicism, and after breaking with the Catholic Church in 1922, he joined the NSDAP. Nazi ideology took the place of his religion and he accepted this ideology, to quote his own words, "just as a Catholic believes in his church dogma" (61, p. 256). In 1923 he was sentenced to ten years' imprisonment for participation in a murder. The first five years of this term he spent in solitary confinement. "Hoess stated that he felt no guilt for this murder because it was a political murder for the protection of the Fatherland and not just an ordinary criminal murder. His five years of solitary confinement only served to broaden the gulf between society and his 'withdrawn nature' " (61, p. 243).

He was released in 1928 and took up work on a farm. He married in 1929. Hoess described this marriage as sexually normal, but owing to lack of spiritual contact with his wife he again felt alone.

From 1934 on, his only activities as a member of the SS Death-Head units were concerned with concentration camps: from 1934 to 1938 at Dachau, from 1938 until May 1, 1940, at Sachsenhausen, and from May 1, 1940, until December 1, 1943, at Auschwitz. After that, until the defeat of the German armies, he was the chief of "Office I" of the office group D of the Economic and Administrative Main Office. In this function he was responsible for the co-ordination of the concentration camps and of office group D of the Economic and Administrative Main Office.

On account of his activities in the concentration camp Auschwitz he was promoted from SS captain to SS lieutenant colonel and decorated with the "Kriegsverdienstkreuz I mit Schwertern" (War Service Cross I with swords). Because of the crimes he committed against Russians, Poles, and Jews, he was sentenced to death in 1947 by the Supreme National Tribunal of Poland.

As has already been stated, during the time that Hoess was commander at Auschwitz at least 2,500,000 Jews were gassed (this book, p. 30); at least another half million died, of illness and starvation.

During the Hoess rule, therefore, at least 3 million people lost their lives in the concentration camp Auschwitz. At his own estimate these 3 millions constituted from 70 to 80 per cent of the total number of prisoners that were sent to Auschwitz. He stated further that in the summer months of 1944 about 400,000 Hungarian Jews had been murdered in Auschwitz.

These and many other statements he made both to Gilbert and to the International Military Tribunal at Nuremberg "in a quiet, apathetic, matter-of-fact tone of voice" (60, p. 250). We know that Hoess received the order for the "final solution" of the Jewish problem from Himmler in the form of a "Führerbefehl" (see this book, p. 16). Gilbert asked him if he could not have raised any objections and if he could not have refused to carry out the command. From his answer it will be seen that the SS training to obedience had been completely successful in the case of Hoess. He replied: "I had nothing to say; I could only say *jawohl!* . . . We could only execute orders without any further consideration" (60, p. 250). It was even, Hoess said, exceptional for Himmler to have given him an explanation, he could simply have let a mere order suffice. Gilbert, who was not easily satisfied, discussed with Hoess the problem of whether the Jews whom he had caused to be murdered had deserved such a fate. Hoess calmly made it clear that these considerations had never occurred to him: "Don't you see, we SS men were not supposed to think about these things; it never even occurred to us. . . . We were all so trained to obey orders without even thinking that the thought of disobeying an order would simply never have occurred to anybody and somebody else would have done just as well if I hadn't . . ." (60, pp. 259 f.).

That indeed other SS men held similar views is proved, for example, by the testimony given by Ohlendorf before the International Military Tribunal at Nuremberg. This man was the leader of "Special Task Unit D," which under his direction murdered 90,000 Jews. He described in detail how he had the male Jews shot and had their wives and children liquidated in gas vans. "It was all directly ordered by Himmler on behalf of the Fuehrer, so he had to obey" (60, p. 101). The same view was voiced by Field Marshal Keitel: *"I had absolutely no command function!"* (60, p. 108).

Another instance of this attitude was that afforded by Joseph Kramer, who gassed about 80 Jewish prisoners for the "scientific" researches of Professor Hirt. To the question what he would have done if the first attempt at gassing these people had failed, Kramer replied: "I would have tried once again to suffocate them with gas, throwing another dose of gas into the chamber. I had no feelings in carrying out these things, because I had received an order to kill the eighty inmates in the way I already told you. That, by the way, was the way I was trained" (109, p. 86).

The same attitude toward "command is command" is also revealed by the leading Nazi figures. As Goering stated: "We had a *Fuehrerstaat* . . . . we had orders to obey from the head of the State" (60, p. 106). This point of uncritical compliance with an order was also discussed during an interview that Alexander had with Karl Wolff (SS "Obergruppenfuehrer" and general of the Armed SS), who from 1933 until 1943 was the chief of Himmler's personal staff. In connection with the fact that Ohlendorf, after twice refusing, had, when ordered for the third time, obeyed the command to become the commanding officer of a Special Task Unit, Alexander asked what would have happened if Ohlendorf had stuck to his refusal. "Wolff replied: 'He would have been silenced. He (Himmler) would not have let him live. He would have liquidated him in some illegal way. Himmler would have done so from his conviction that someone must do it if it is necessary for the welfare of 85 million Germans. Then one must sacrifice the salvation of one's soul, or one must give up one's life.' Wolff added that the view which an SS member had to take in this matter was like this: 'I must do it. In order to clear this new living space I must sacrifice myself, the salvation of my soul, and my honour, or else give up my life' " (7, p. 321).

It is clear what an extreme of obedience was demanded of the SS men. If the former values of his super-ego could have been upheld beside the new, then they would not have been allowed to manifest themselves, for "command is command."

To return to Hoess. Because of the authoritarian education he had had, he took it as a matter of course that he must obey an order received. He agreed with the extermination of the Jews, as it was his conviction that the Jews were guilty. This he had been taught during his training in the SS and by the speeches and articles of Hitler, Goebbels, Rosenberg, and the rest. Of any sense of guilt there was no sign, for the only thing he knew was that he had done what was right. The same was observed by Van der Heyden during a psychological examination of F., the former chief of the "Judenreferat" in one of the biggest cities of the Netherlands. This man, too, had not the slightest consciousness of guilt; even the idea that he had committed a punishable offence was entirely alien to him (69, p. 239).

The thought that he would ever be called to account for his outrages had never occurred to Hoess, for, as he said, everyone in Nazi Germany was convinced that "the man who gave the orders was responsible" (60, p. 251). For this reason he felt himself betrayed by the suicide of Himmler, for the latter had not been loyal to the device of the SS: "My honour means loyalty."

What kind of personality was Hoess? Gilbert, who had several talks with him, writes, among other things: "There was nothing about this apathetic little man to suggest that he was the greatest murderer who had ever lived. The only clue to the nature of the personality that had lent itself so readily to such a thing was that apathy, the hallmark of the schizoid personality. . . . [He] responded to all questions in a mechanical, matter-of-fact way. There was no indication of emotional reaction of any sort as he calmly related how he had received and executed Himmler's orders to exterminate Jewish families by the trainload. Only a certain air of remoteness in his expression, the cold eyes gazing out into space when he looked at you, gave outward evidence of a personality that was not entirely of this world" (61, p. 250).

But Gilbert himself observes that the schizoid character of Hoess explains little, for schizoid characters exist throughout the world "without getting involved in human extermination. The functional gap between the detached human and the inhuman being can be filled only by complex social interaction . . . we must bring into play the dual forces . . . the progenitors of the Nazi police state: (a) militaristic authoritarianism and (b) racial ideology" (61, p. 254).

Gilbert's final conclusion is: "It was that combination of absolute authoritarianism and hostile racial ideology that had crystallized a new set of social norms in the police state of Nazi Germany and had produced a new species of schizoid murderous robots, like Colonel Hoess of Auschwitz" (61, p. 261).

I am prepared to accept Gilbert's view that Hoess had a schizoid character, but in my opinion this is not necessary to explain his apathy. Just as Gilbert does, I attach great importance to the moral standards which prevailed in Nazi Germany, particularly because these, as a result of the German education (see this book, pp. 242 ff.), of which the training to unconditional obedience is an essential part, were blindly accepted. The principal aim of Hoess' education had been to teach him that criticism of his superiors was not permissible and that it was his duty to obey them. Therefore he could be expected to speak calmly about these mass murders, *for he only did his duty!* [27] Our failure to understand this lies within

[27] Cf. the following quotation by Jaspers from Hannah Arendt: "The rule of terror resulted in the amazing phenomenon that the German people were made to participate in the crimes of the Fuehrer. The oppressed became accomplices. Only, it is true, to a limited degree, but all the same to such an ex-

ourselves, because our super-ego differs from that of Hoess. We surely do not get excited when we take dogs to a gas chamber, or if a house is fumigated because there are bugs in it? To Hoess' way of thinking the gassing of Jews was on the same plane. If Hoess had not been able to fulfil this particular duty, he would have been expelled from the SS Death-Head units before he came to Auschwitz. It may be true that his behaviour was supported by his schizoid character, but that was all. I at least am not under the impression that Professor Kremer, for example, who, as we know, carried out some fourteen first selections, was a case of schizoid character. And does it not speak volumes that, as Professor Kremer stated, men elbowed each other aside for the privilege of participating in "special actions" for a little gin, a few cigarettes, and a slice of bread and sausage? [28] I therefore stick to my opinion that Hoess' behaviour can be explained primarily by the content of his super-ego. This criminal super-ego accepted his acts as right, and any possible doubt was cancelled out by his education (command is command).

One person whose behaviour, especially in view of his profession, intrigues me, is the SS camp physician. It is known that he excelled in the neglect of the medical and hygienic care of the prisoners, which resulted in a vastly increased mortality rate among the latter. Desoille has stated in this connection: "The Nazis—including the Nazi physicians—pursued but one aim: *extermination*. The whole medical apparatus was nothing but a *décor*, nothing but a lie intended to disguise the massacre" (101, p. 69). Any physician who refused his co-operation was ineligible for the function of camp physician. Kogon gives an example of this: SS Captain Hofter temporarily held

---

tent that people of whom one would never have thought it possible, fathers of families, diligent citizens, who dutifully pursue any occupation, murdered with equal dutifulness and, when ordered to do so, committed the other misdeeds in the concentration camps" (76, p. 61).

[28] Hoess' statement forms a contrast to this: "Of course none of the SS men who participated in this work cared for it, especially since most of them, like myself, were married and had children. But later one became desensitized even in this cruel activity" (61, p. 245). But perhaps this statement by Hoess must be interpreted as indicating that he continued to screen his men, in contrast to Himmler's behaviour toward himself.

the function of camp physician at Buchenwald. Shortly after he had entered upon this duty he said to SS Colonel Dr. Lolling, chief physician of all concentration camps: "I am prepared to look after the camp as first camp physician, and assure you that the number of dead will be reduced to a minimum, as it has already begun to be." Lolling's reply to this was: "That is why you will not become first camp physician" (87, p. 154). Hofer then requested to be sent to the front, which he was a few days later.

One of the most important duties of the camp physician was the selection of prisoners. In Auschwitz the aim of these was, as we have seen, to send aged people, mothers with their children, semi-invalids and invalids, those who looked delicate, and the sick to the gas chambers. To remove any doubt as to this, I cite a statement by Hoess: "The way we selected our victims was as follows: We had two SS doctors on duty at Auschwitz to examine the incoming transports of prisoners. The prisoners would be marched by one of the doctors who would make spot decisions as they walked by. Those who were fit for work were sent into the camp. Others were sent immediately to the extermination plants. Children of tender years were invariably exterminated since by reason of their youth they were unable to work" (142, Vol. XI, p. 417). This was also confirmed by one of the ex–camp physicians of Auschwitz, one Klein, during a trial for which he was committed at Lüneburg, where he was condemned to death by hanging. He stated that his chief had instructed him to divide an arriving prisoner transport into batches, one of those who were fit, the other of those who were unfit to work. The latter category comprised "the aged, the weak, the unhealthy, children up to the age of 13, 14, or 15 years, and pregnant women. The selection was done exclusively by doctors, but it was not a proper medical examination. The doctors simply looked at the prisoners, who were dressed, and asked them a few questions if they looked ill. Dr. Klein said that he heard that some of the unfit went to the gas chamber" (96, p. 41).

The descriptions by Hoess and Klein refer to the first selections. The conduct of the SS physician on these occasions has been described by Lettich, among others. He has stated that "they filed past the German doctor, who, unmoved, with a cigarette in his mouth, always made a sign with his hand: left, right" (101, p. 27; italics omitted. Cf. my quotation from Frankl on page 37 of this book).

The German "Aryan" prisoners' physician, Mrs. Lingens-Reiner, has related a few particulàrs about some camp physicians who had to select the transports: "Of our various camp doctors, Dr. König repeatedly declared that this duty at the railway track was a torture for him, and he had to drink a lot of alcohol to stick it out. Dr. Mengele, on the other hand, whistled and pointed his thumb to one or the other group" (102, p. 74).

Apparently something of Dr. König's former super-ego had remained alive, which he còuld silence by means of alcohol. In Auschwitz-Stammlager I have seen the camp physicians Klein and Rode conduct many a selection in the prisoners' hospital. On these occasions I was able to observe the quiet, or rather the indifference, with which these physicians sent Jews who were no longer fit for work to their death.

During my stay in Auschwitz this fate was only allotted to the Jewish prisoners. In other camps, the non-Jewish prisoners also were not spared. Desoille (101, p. 65) has described how in the concentration camp Gusen the camp physician Vetter had the patients who suffered from pulmonary tuberculosis march past him. Working on temperature curves and X-rays, which, because they had been made with a bad apparatus, were almost illegible, Dr. Vetter decided which patients were to receive further treatment—"but the majority were classed in what was called group III, in other words were doomed to death" (101, p. 65). This group III was sent to Block 31, where the senior block prisoner killed them by means of "an intra-cardial injection, as I saw with my own eyes" (101, p. 66). This can still be regarded as euthanasia, but on this subject enough has been said.

In various concentration camps selections among the prisoners took place which served the purpose of picking out the victims who were to be the subjects of medical experimentation. In these experiments the camp SS physicians took an active part. Among these I include, besides the "Lageraerzte" (camp physicians) and other SS physicians, those medical men who, without being members of the SS, performed researches in the concentration camps. The following considerations therefore are not confined to the camp physicians.

Although in the discussion of the medical experiments a few words were said on the subject of their scant scientific value, some additional space will be allotted to this aspect in the present connection. Desoille and Laffite have stated that "in the majority of cases *their total lack of real scientific value is established*" (36, p. 4). Also in his Opening Statement on the "Medical Case" Taylor denies these experiments any scientific value. To quote part of his statement: "The Nazi methods of investigation were inefficient and unscientific, and their techniques of research were unsystematic. These experiments revealed nothing which civilized medicine can use. It was, indeed, ascertained that phenol or gasoline injected intravenously will kill a man inexpensively and within 60 seconds. . . . There is no doubt that a number of these new methods may be useful to criminals everywhere and there is no doubt that they may be useful to a criminal state. Certain advance in destructive methodology we cannot deny. . . . Apart from these deadly fruits, the experiments were not only criminal but a scientific failure" (143, Vol. I, p. 73).

Professor Rose, a defendant in the "Medical Case," was, as to typhus fever, of a different opinion. He declared:

"The Buchenwald experiments (with typhus vaccine) had four main results:

(1) . . . that belief in the protective effect of the Weigl vaccine was a mistake, . . .

(2) . . . that the useful vaccines did not protect against infections, but almost certainly prevented death, under the conditions of the Buchenwald experiments;

(3) . . . that the objections of the biological experts to the vitelline membrane vaccines and to the louse vaccines were unjustified and that membrane, rabbit lungs, and louse intestines

were of equal value. . . . This left the way open to mass production of typhus vaccines.

(4) The Buchenwald experiments showed in time that several vaccines were useless. First the process according to Otto and Wohlrab, the process according to Cox, . . . the vaccines of the Behring Works, which were produced according to the Otto process, . . . finally the Ipsen vaccines. . . . Without these experiments the vaccines, which were recognized as useless, would have been produced in large quantities. . . . In any case, one thing is certain, that the victims of this Buchenwald typhus test did not suffer in vain and did not die in vain . . . (143, Vol. II, p. 69 f.) .

I mention these findings and refrain from comment, as I would not care to set myself up as qualified to pronounce a well-founded scientific opinion on this matter. But even if these experiments had yielded the most important results, they should never have been carried out in the circumstances under which they were conducted. This conclusion I rest on the "medical ten commandments," which, according to Military Tribunal I, have to be observed if anyone wishes to conduct medical experiments on human beings. A condensed rendering of them runs:

(1) The voluntary consent of the human subject is absolutely essential. . . .

(2) The experiment should be such as to yield fruitful results for the good of society, unprocurable by other methods or means of study, and not random and unnecessary in nature.

(3) The experiment should be so designed . . . that the anticipated results will justify the performance of the experiment.

(4) The experiment should be so conducted as to avoid all unnecessary physical and mental suffering and injury.

(5) No experiment should be conducted where there is an *ex priori* reason to believe that death or disabling injury will occur; except, perhaps, in those experiments where the experimental physicians also serve as subjects.

(6) The degree of risk to be taken should never exceed that determined by the humanitarian importance of the problem to be solved by the experiment.

(7) Proper preparations should be made and adequate facilities provided to protect the experimental subject against even remote possibilities of injury, disability, or death.

(8) The experiment should be conducted only by scientifically qualified persons. . . .

(9) During the course of the experiment the human subject should be at liberty to bring the experiment to an end. . . .

(10) During the course of the experiment the scientist in charge must be prepared to terminate the experiment at any stage, if he has probably cause to believe, . . . that a continuation of the experiment is likely to result in injury, disability, or death to the experimental subject" (143, Vol. II, pp. 181 f.).

If the camp SS physicians had known and observed these "medical ten commandments," the experiments as described in this book would never have been carried out. But the German and therefore also the camp SS physician was instructed during the Nazi era in matters of an entirely different nature. The director of the Department of Public Health in the Ministry of the Interior, Dr. Arthur Gütt, published in 1935 a book, *The Structure of Public Health in the Third Reich*,[29] in which he proclaimed among other doctrines that love of one's fellow men had to disappear, especially in regard to inferior and a-social elements, and that it was the supreme duty of a state to allow life and sustenance only to that part of the nation which was sound and free from hereditary taint, in order to secure the continuance of a racially pure people free from hereditary taint for all eternity.

The Nazis ordered the physicians in state service to attend a reconditioning course, at the same time forcing them to join the party. Young physicians often had to attend for several months every year the "Fuehrerschule für Germanische Aerzte" (Fuehrer's School for German Physicians) in Mecklenburg, where they were indoctrinated in National Socialism.

Medical students also had to comply with special requirements. They had to be "Aryans" and members of the "National Socialist Student's League." Any student who at his examination proved to be insufficiently grounded in German racial theory and the notorious Nuremberg Laws failed to pass.

[29] I have been unable to secure this book. The data have been taken from 143, Vol. I, pp. 58 ff.

Thus the German physician was imbued with the Nazi doctrine, and he suffered himself to be thus imbued, for it must not be forgotten that the German medical man is also a German, who is subjected to the same influences as every German, for example to German education. And that the Nazi doctrine aroused in the camp SS physicians a boundless contempt of political opponents, Russians, Poles, and Jews, has been proved by, among other things, the medical experiments that have been mentioned.

Taylor has stated in connection with the physicians in question: "The 20 physicians in the dock range from leaders of German scientific medicine, with excellent international reputations, down to the dregs of the German medical profession. All of them have in common a callous lack of consideration and human regard for, and an unprincipled willingness to abuse their power over, the poor, unfortunate, defenseless creatures who had been deprived of their rights by a ruthless and criminal government" (143, Vol. I, p. 68).

These physicians, however, were merely strikingly illustrative individuals of this group. The behaviour of nearly all was bad. Lettich has given the following description of his experiences (which are the same as mine) of the SS camp physicians: "After Auschwitz we went to other camps: Gross-Rosen, Hersbrück, and Dachau, and in each camp we found the attitude of the German physicians to be similar to that of the medical men at Auschwitz" (101, p. 58).

Even the "Arbeitsgemeinschaft der Westdeutschen Aerztekammern," in a statement of March, 1949, condemns the acts of the camp SS physicians: "After the termination of the Nuremberg trials and most other similar trials the German medical profession is in a position to state that only an infinitesimal part of the members of our profession has violated the laws of humanity and of medical morality. These few persons were either SS physicians and high state officials or M.O.'s, who obeyed the dictates of political leadership rather than the medical conscience and the ethics of their profession and of science. Of about 90,000 physicians practicing in Germany, some 350 have committed medical crimes. The majority of the experiments were only made possible by the special position occupied by the SS in the concentration camps and their powers of authority. German physicians as a whole performed their duties under the dictatorship of National Socialism in accordance with the requirements of the Hippocratic Oath, and knew nothing of what occurred nor had any concern with it" (110, p. V).

For me to pass a verdict on the attitude of the German physicians during the Hitler rule would be going outside the scope of this study.[30] It is, however, beyond dispute that the tribute paid by Alexander to the resistance by the Netherlands

[30] I only want to call attention to the following:

(1) The freezing experiments of the work group Holzloehner-Rascher-Finke were presented by Holzloehner to a conference on "Medical Questions in Marine and Winter Emergencies," held at Nuremberg on October 26 and 27, 1942 (see this book, p. 86), which was attended by 95 physicians (see 110, pp. 45 and 48). One of the participants in this congress, giving evidence for the defense of Professor Weltz, defendant in the "Medical Case," said ". . . that Weltz with his animal experiments had accomplished more than Rascher with his experiments on prisoners" (110, p. 49). According to a statement by Professor Hippke, "Air Force Hygiene Inspector," "No formal protest was made by any of the participants against the experiments on prisoners" (110, p. 51).

The same address was delivered by Professor Holzloehner on December, 1942, in Berlin "at a conference of consulting physicians of the army" (ibid.).

(2) The sulfanilamide experiments of Professor Gebhardt and Dr. Fischer were announced by the latter after an introductory address by Professor Gebhardt at the "Third Conference East of Consulting Specialists from May 24 to 26, 1943, in the Academy of Military Medicine in Berlin." The number of participants amounted to over 200, none of whom, according to Fischer, publicly voiced any criticism (see this book, p. 91), although one stated on June 18, 1947: "It is now my honest opinion that it would have been the duty of every one of those present (over 200) to protest against the experiments" (110, p. 145).

(3) At the "Third Conference East of Consulting Physicians of the Army in the Section Hygiene in May, 1943" Dr. Ding-Schuler gave an address "On the Results of Experiments with Several Typhus Vaccines against Classical Typhus" (110, p. 89). With reference to this address Professor Rose lifted his voice in protest against this kind of experiments on human beings. He was interrupted by Conference Leader Professor Schreiber: "He (Schrieber) must protest against the criticism voiced by me (Rose); if the gentleman wanted to discuss questions of ethical principles, we could do that during the interval" (110, p. 89).

Seven months later an experiment was conducted at Buchenwald at the instigation of Professor Rose, which cost the lives of six prisoners (110, p. 89).

(4) Mitscherlich and Mielke, as members of the "Aerzte-Kommission der Westdeutschen Aerztekammern," were allowed to attend the "Medical Case" and to examine all the documents relative to this case. They declare: "Though before a human, whether national or international, court of justice, a collective guilt cannot be imputed to us, yet in our conscience when it comes before the tribunal of history we are all sufficiently laden with guilt" (110, p. 6).

All this is not sufficient to warrant my passing judgment on the German physicians during the Nazi rule, but it certainly provides food for reflection.

physicians (148) cannot be given to the German medical world. Alexander points out that the German physicians were taking a first step on the downward slope when they failed to oppose the propaganda for murdering incurable patients, who were no longer of any use. The Germans made similar propaganda, albeit with great caution, in the occupied territories. But, he goes on to say: "It is to the everlasting honour of the medical profession of Holland that they recognized the earliest and most subtle phases of this attempt and rejected it" (4, p. 18).

As I am not of the opinion that the behaviour of the camp SS physicians differs from that of the other camp SS men, I refer for an explanation of this behaviour to what has been stated before.

The SS and Group Psychology

At the end of the previous chapter after a short summary of Freud's group psychology (to repeat which will be now superfluous) the conclusion was reached that the concentration-camp prisoners, viewed according to Freud, constituted not a group, but a crowd. I will now examine the question whether the group concept can be applied to the SS.

The SS can be compared to an army, which was taken by Freud as an example of a group with a leader. In this connection, as we know, it is very important that to the commander-in-chief—for the SS this was their Fuehrer, Adolf Hitler —all are equal and that therefore he "loves" them all equally. That all SS men were equal was stated by Himmler himself. Discussing the process by which a man becomes an SS man, Himmler said: "He then becomes on 9 November . . . an SS man in the sense in which each of us is an SS man. The Reichleader of the SS is an SS man in the sense of the Order of the SS, in exactly the same way as the simple man at the front" (142, Vol. XXIX, p. 213).

As to Adolf Hitler's being the leader of the SS, there cannot be any doubt. We need only listen to the end of Himmler's speech at Poznan: "Now our thoughts are with the Fuehrer, with our Fuehrer Adolf Hitler, who will create the Germanic Reich and who will show us the way into the Germanic future.

Our Fuehrer Adolf Hitler, Sieg Heil, Sieg Heil, Sieg Heil!"
(142, Vol. XXIX, p. 173).

Obedience and devotion to Hitler were almost beyond belief. Kersten, who as Himmler's masseur had regular contact
with him for years, mentions as the latter's most striking characteristic "his blind veneration of Hitler, to whom he was
devoted with slavish attachment" (83, p. 36). Once when
Kersten asked Himmler if he thought the Fuehrer was infallible, Himmler replied, "Providence has sent the *Fuehrer*
and it is almost amazing that he is never mistaken" (83, p. 37).

But it was not only the SS who submitted completely to
Hitler's authority. Within the party, the NSDAP, some of the
"commands of the Nationalist Socialist" that were in force
were: "The Fuehrer is always right! Never violate discipline!
. . . Let the party programme be your dogma; it demands of
you utter devotion to the movement! . . . If you act in accordance with these commands, then you are a true fighter
of your Fuehrer" (142, Vol. XXIX, p. 85).

And further, when the Fuehrer is mentioned, we read: "The
will of the Fuehrer is the supreme law in the party" (*ibid.*,
p. 92).

By way of illustration I mention the murder of Roehm and
many others on June 30, 1934. According to Gilbert, Frank,
who at the time was Minister of Justice in Bavaria, received
the order to have more than 100 people executed. Ringing up
Hitler, he asked him by what paragraph of German law these
people were to be executed: "Hitler snapped back that he had
ordered the executions to protect the safety of the Reich, and
that was law enough" (61, p. 75). When Goebbels announced
this massacre to the German people, he had to change "according to law" to "by order of the Fuehrer." Gilbert adds:
"There was to be no misunderstanding about who was the
law, who wielded the power of life and death in Germany
from now on" (61, p. 75). Thus the complete submission of
every German to Hitler was fostered so that he obtained unlimited power over the people and certainly over the SS, who
considered themselves "chosen."

As we have shown, Freud defines a group with a leader as

a group of which each individual is tied to the leader and to the other individuals of the group. The SS appears to conform completely to this. In connection with this definition which Freud gives of a group, there remains one difficulty to be solved before we can with justification call the SS a group.

Let us once more consider this definition closely. It runs: "A primary group of this kind is a number of individuals who have substituted one and the same object for their ego ideal and have consequently identified themselves with one another in their ego" (49a, p. 80).

I think I may rightly assert that every SS man substituted the same object—in this case Adolf Hitler—for the ego ideal (super-ego) (see this book, pp. 233 f.), and that consequently all the SS men identified themselves with one another. But—and this is the issue to be decided—was the SS a "primary" group, that is, a group which had not secondarily acquired the characteristics of an individual? At first glance this would not seem to be the case. They were well organized, well dressed, they had an expert leadership, they went in for "culture," and in order to be admitted as a member, the candidate had to comply with very definite requirements.

All the same I think the SS may indeed be regarded as a primary group, for the aim of the SS was stated by Himmler in a speech of September 7, 1940,[31] as follows: "The collective aim is for me, . . . : to create an Order of good blood, . . . to create an Order which thus spreads this idea of the Nordic blood, . . ." (142, Vol. XXIX, pp. 109).

The requirements which had to be complied with for this candidate to be admitted to this "Order" were primitive. Certificates were not important, but physical development was, and so was the knowledge of "the philosophy of life," which was identical with the Nazi ideology. Mulock Houwer in a treatise on the problem of youthful political offenders points out that "in the German army and in German civil society

[31] In this speech (142, Vol. XXIX, pp. 98–110) Himmler also said, ". . . in Poland . . . , where we had to deport thousands and tens of thousands and hundred of thousands, where we had to be so hard as—you will hear this and you will also immediately forget this again—to shoot thousands of prominent Poles" (ibid., p. 104).

attention was only paid to character and the display of courage" (113, p. 5).

All standards had been changed. The realization of the individual's instincts, particularly the sexual instinct, was encouraged. As an instance of this I refer to the "Lebensborn" (life source) founded by decree of Himmler on December 12, 1935. The "Ausbildungsbrief Nr. 3" [32] (letter of instruction) of May 31, 1937, which mentions a practical assistance for "the care of mothers who are valuable for their racial or hereditary biological qualities," reads in part: "The present position, particularly of the unmarried future mother, renders a special *legal protection*, a special guarantee of her legal interests necessary. . . . In order once and for all to bring relief, the Reich Leader SS has decided to undertake himself the guardianship through the institution 'Lebensborn' of all illegitimate children in so far as appears necessary. . . . In special cases the Reich Leader SS can guarantee complete secrecy as to the actual delivery as well as the name of the child's father."

Instead of, as is customary in a normal society, restricting the number of illegitimate children, Himmler even granted extra facilities for illegitimate birth.

Aggressiveness toward "inferior elements" was tolerated, even encouraged. This point has already been discussed in connection with the Camp SS, (this book, p. 247) but it applied not only to them, but rather to all Nazis. In the present connection it will suffice to mention only the organized "spontaneous" outrages inflicted by the Nazis on the German Jews on November 8, 1938.

The fact that the SS were given an opportunity to realize all their drives and that they were even encouraged to do so, I can only regard as a regression. Through this the SS was degraded to a group which to a great extent was primitive.

By the foregoing I trust to have proved that the objection against looking upon the SS as a group with a leader in the sense of Freud has been removed. But though the SS can be

[32] The following data have been taken from Document N.O.-3325: "Ausbildungsbrief Nr. 3 des SS Sanitätsamtes." This document is on file in the Netherlands State Institute of War Documentation.

considered the most typical manifestation, the NSDAP constituted a very similar group. And it does not seem impossible to me to conceive of the whole or nearly the whole of Nazi Germany as a group, so that my considerations are likely to obtain for (almost) every German. For Lowenstein this is not even a matter of doubt. He writes: "Freud took the army and the church as examples to illustrate the psychological structure of organized masses. But a far more striking example would have been Nazi Germany" (105, p. 48).

If we regard the SS as a group with a leader, much of the behaviour of the SS men can be explained. The super-ego of the SS men knew no other value than Hitler's words; hence every SS man lacked independence and only carried out Hitler's orders. For them Hitler was the embodiment of all existing authority, as parents, teachers, the laws of society were all pervaded by the same spirit. Hitler's theories controlled the super-ego of the SS man; for him Hitler was "the great man." Automatically the question presents itself: How was this possible? In order to find an answer to this, I take counsel with Freud to learn what he says as to "the great man." Freud states "that the great man influences his contemporaries in two ways: through his personality and through the idea for which he stands. This idea may lay stress on an old group of wishes in the masses, or point to a new aim for their wishes, or again lure the masses by other means. Sometimes—and this is surely the more primitive effect—the personality alone exerts its influence and the idea plays a decidedly subordinate part. Why the great man should rise to significance at all we have no doubt whatever. We know that the great majority of people have a strong need for authority which it can admire, to which it can submit, and which dominates and sometimes even ill-treats it. We have learned from the psychology of the individual whence comes this need of the masses. It is the longing for the father that lives in each of us from his childhood days, for the same father whom the hero of legend boasts of having overcome. And now it begins to dawn on us that all the features with which we furnish the great man are traits of the father, that in this similarity lies the essence—which so far has eluded us—of the great man. The decisiveness of thought, the strength of will, the forcefulness of his deeds, belong to the picture of the father; above all other things, however, the self-reliance and independence of the great man: his divine conviction of doing the right thing, which may pass into ruthlessness. He must be admired, he may be trusted, but one cannot help being also afraid of him" (54, p. 173 f.).

This view of Freud will now be applied to Hitler. That Hitler was an imposing personality appears beyond dispute. Speer, who held the office of Minister of Armament and War Industry, said, "Hitler was one of those inexplicable phenomena which emerge at rare intervals among mankind. His person determined the fate of the nation. . . . The nation was spellbound by him as a people has rarely been in the whole of history" (141, p. 46).

According to Trevor-Roper (146, p. 80), Hitler had a hypnotist's eyes, and even his physicians are said to have acknowledged that a fascinating influence emanated from them. Freud, as we have seen, said, "The great man influences his contemporaries in two ways: through his personality and through the idea for which he stands."

In my opinion Hitler fulfilled the condition of exercising influence on people through his personality. What kind of personality he was will not be considered; the main point is that he was one. And what about "the idea for which he stood?" This idea is Nazi ideology. By this Hitler proclaimed the German to be a superior being, to be one of the "Herrenvolk" through his good "Nordic" blood; he proclaimed other peoples to be inferior and to be the serfs of Germany. He proclaimed Germany not to have lost World War I, but to have been defeated by the knife-thrust in the back; he proclaimed the Jew, who is the cause of all evil in the world, to be guilty; he proclaimed the German to be the appointed ruler of the world, and the German people to have a mission in it, to need "Lebensraum"; etc.

Of course this Nazi ideology would not have struck a responsive chord in the German people if there had not been a certain preparedness to receive it. For in other countries as well, say England or the Netherlands, the National Socialists had ample opportunity to propagate their ideology, without, however, achieving success. What this readiness consisted in, I do not intend to discuss in detail, as it would lead me too far. I will be content to quote an opinion by Jaspers: "To the fact that in the spiritual conditions of German life there lay the possibility for such a régime to come into being we are all of us accessories. This, however, by no means implies that we are to acknowledge that 'the German world of ideas,' 'the German way of thoughts in the past,' is simply the origin of the evil deeds of National Socialism. But it does imply that in our national tradition there is something, powerful and menacing, that is our moral ruin" (76, pp. 56 f.).

As Hitler was a personality and as he inspired an old wish complex of the majority of Germans with new life, he must in accordance with Freud's view be regarded as "the great man." Hence, for almost all Germans (those who refused fled abroad or were "re-educated" in concentration camps) he became the father, and in Freud's hypothesis of the primal horde even the primal father. The primal father will not be considered, but as a father image he controlled the super-ego of his followers and particularly of the SS, who were his "elite sons." And it is perfectly clear that Hitler's closest collaborators, i.e. the German government, only thought and acted in accordance with his views. The result of this has been characterized by Röling, one-time Netherlands judge in the International Military Tribunal for the Far East at Tokio, as follows: "The aspect of the Japanese war crimes shows an essential difference from that of the German crimes. The Germans obeyed the orders given by 'the highest authority' to the effect of exterminating populations, a criminality of government that one would have supposed to be impossible in any European country" (124, p. 16).

I have already called attention to my view that it is of the greatest importance that more research should be undertaken by those qualified to do so, on this subject. This should be done in order to obtain a perfect insight into the essence of the SS. An enormous amount of material is at the disposal of any researcher. He need not be limited to evidence by witnesses, who are apt to become confused through memory distortions, as he has at his disposal an almost inexhaustible source of original documents.

One warning, however, must be given. Anyone who has no personal experience of the SS will be overwhelmed by the facts. He will gaze into an abyss of bestialities which he had not thought possible. He will end by being filled with loathing and he might even come to doubt the authenticity of the documents.

The misery which the SS inflicted on their victims defies description; the cool, calculating manner in which it was inflicted is atrocious. To look back on this piece of human history fills us with horror. Of course I must not assert that such crimes as were committed by the SS have never occurred before in the past of mankind, but I do hold that the SS were the first to perform them in such a way and to make such a number of victims.

I fervently hope that through the co-operation of many researchers the course of this evil may be completely exposed, so that mankind may be spared a recurrence.

CHAPTER

FIVE

Conclusions

IN THE preceding chapters I trust I have achieved the aims I set before myself. It will be remembered that these were to find an explanation for the behaviour of the prisoners and an answer to the question of how the SS came to be capable of the crimes they committed. I will end with a review of what conclusions might be of general interest.

In the first place, this: The human power of adaptation, both physical and mental, is very great, at least much greater than I would have thought possible. To give one instance: I would never have thought that a man who was given very inadequate nourishment, who was insufficiently clothed, who slept little, who lived in the worst possible hygienic circumstances and moreover was exposed to all conditions of the weather, would still be able to perform heavy physical labour; and certainly I would have thought it impossible that he would go on living and not collapse before long.

Or to give another example: I would not have believed that I could bear the hardships of the death march by the end of January, 1945. I did bear them, and not only did I survive, but I did not even fall ill. Once more: I would have pronounced this incredible if I had not experienced it in my own person. I do not believe that this can be explained as the "survival of the fittest," for the greater part of our transport survived. In my opinion the only explanation is that the powers of adaptation and endurance of the human body are so great that this body is capable of efforts which are held to be impossible in normal life.

The same applies to the faculties of the mind. Who could have imagined that a man on learning that all those who were dear to him had been basely gassed, or on beholding and suffering the atrocities of a concentration camp, would "merely" respond in the way described in these pages? Would not everyone have expected that a man would have either become acutely psychotic or been driven to suicide?

We know, indeed, that many broke down and perished, but the miracle is that, considering the horrible conditions of the concentration camps, there are still survivors. Hence my opinion that, although much can be explained, one is faced in the last analysis by a mystery, and one must be content with this bald statement: *The physical and mental powers of adaptation and endurance of man are much greater than they are believed to be.*

My next conclusion is this: The super-ego, which is, as we know, among other things the introjection of the voices of parents, teachers, and society, *is no unchangeable quantity.* Therefore we must rid ourselves of the idea that the super-ego after being moulded remains constant during the remainder of an individual's life. This is most clearly seen in older people. We may surely assume that the super-ego of, say, Professor Kremer, and of the camp physician Klein, originally had a content different from that which it had when they conducted the selections in the concentration camp Auschwitz. And as to the prisoners, it has been shown that the super-ego, that is the standards of the individual, may, as it were, wither away and be replaced by other hitherto unknown or unaccepted standards. In connection with this I propose to consider a very important question: Would any persons, other than German, have been capable of similar crimes? Or were these a monopoly of the German people?

I think it has been proved that the Germans were capable of these misdeeds especially through their authoritarian education, for which German family life, schools, and society were responsible; this gave the Germans a specific character structure. This structure delegated the responsibility for the acts committed by the Germans, from each individual to the persons in command: " 'It is a command!'—this meant and still means emotionally for many people the expression of their supreme duty. But this word implied at the same time a shedding of responsibility, when it allowed a man to accept with a shrug everything that was evil and foolish. This behaviour under the inner compulsion of obedience became altogether sinful in the moral sense, this instinctive behaviour which pretended to itself to listen to the voice of conscience, whereas in fact it had entirely done with listening to this voice" (76, pp. 43 f.). This would explain the casualness with which the SS carried out their criminal acts and also why the German people tolerated these. It is not my opinion, therefore, that the Germans because of inherited qualities or an innate temperament were predisposed to behave as they did.

Everybody will understand that I do not in the least feel called upon to act as counsel for the defence for the German people, but this does not alter my conviction that if in Netherlands society the same educational system should obtain as in Germany, the same excesses might be committed by Netherlanders. My opinion is strengthened by a remark which I heard from Jews as well as from non-Jews to the effect that, although the percentage of Jews in the Netherlands after the war is a mere fraction of the total population, anti-Semitism is supposed to be much greater than before the Second World War. As no public-opinion poll has been taken, this is of course not proved. But if it is true, then it might be partly explained by the "education" of the Netherlanders to this end over a period of five years. If Netherlanders and Germans were reared from their birth in the same social atmosphere (family, school, youth clubs included), then I believe the differences which are now noticeable between the two people would cease to be so. In my view it is not the German as such, but the German individual *malformed* through his German education, that is the determining factor in the behaviour of the German people. This does not in my opinion relieve the Germans of their guilt towards the millions of innocent victims murdered by the SS, nor towards the victims of the Nazi system who are to a greater or lesser degree broken for life, nor towards those who are still mourning the ones who did not survive the hell of Nazism; it does, however, explain *why* many Germans even now fail to realize that they are guilty (a phenomenon which since the war everyone has been able to perceive again and again), or what appears even more significant, that many perhaps still hold the view that they behaved rightly.[1]

It seems, therefore, no use trying to improve the moral standard of the German people by measures from outside, for it is no mere accident that authoritarian education does obtain in Germany and not, for example, in the Netherlands; for this education is entirely suited to the authoritarian view of life which is peculiar to the German in general (see this book, p. 245). As long as German education retains its authoritarian character (as I am afraid it will for some time to come), so long will there be danger that the German people may relapse into the same excesses as it committed and tolerated in the Nazi era.

The crux of the problem, why the Germans rather than any other people should have acquired such a psychological structure, still remains to be solved. As this would require an entirely separate study, I will refrain from any suggestion.

We have observed that when a man is starving everything is made subordinate to the gratification of the hunger drive. Every bodily function (including sexual function) which is not essential for survival disappears. The organism helps, by working very economically, and reduces its efforts to the smallest possible proportions, thus restricting itself to keeping up its vital organs.

In the struggle for existence on its lowest level, as it is fought in the jungle, there is for most human beings (and I am only referring to this majority) only one object: to obtain food. However, they do not try to achieve this regardless of everything, but take into account any circumstances that might

---

[1] Another note is struck by Jaspers: "It cannot be doubted that every German in some way or other is guilty, if what we have stated is not completely unfounded" (76, p. 50).

possibly endanger their lives. This, the "reality principle," is the only restraining influence, but if this last safeguard ceases to be operative, then they have become creatures merely possessed by the hunger drive. And then this hunger drive sheds every psychic disguise, then all that we call civilization succumbs to the hunger drive; then we see these people behaving like animals, in their spiritual nakedness: cowardly, hard, cruel, selfish, and egocentric. Any protection of rank, social position, or occupation is of no avail. Probably only character (see this book, p. 139, note) may remain as a restraining influence, in that it causes the ultimate limit of human behaviour to be reached later in one man than in another. Knowledge, wealth, or cultural accomplishments are not the slightest guarantee that the individual who has acquired them is at the same time a man of high character. It is disappointing to see that even prominent figures from normal society not seldom failed to live up to their standing in the concentration camps. Because one had expected better of these people, one was often struck by the fact that the "ordinary" man in this respect formed a favourable contrast to them.

In the stage in which the hunger drive is supreme (a stage which not everyone is equally quick to reach) there is as a rule no room for feelings of morality and ethics. "Erst kommt das Fressen und dan kommt die Moral" (food first and after that morality). During this stage all other drives, including the sexual drive, are silenced. Only the hunger drive continues to speak; hence I am persuaded that the hunger drive is the most vital of all drives of man.

The fact that several diseases which are frequently diagnosed in normal medical practice were hardly if ever observed in the concentration camps, is important enough for me to consider it in some detail. I will only deal with the neuroses in the narrower sense (see 128, p. 151) and with the psychosomatic diseases, such as gastric and duodenal ulcers and bronchial asthma.

A characteristic of these neuroses is that the ego represses the drives and tendencies of which it disapproves from the conscious, or refuses to admit them into the conscious. For any genuine neurotic symptom to come into being is conditional upon the attitude of the ego (formulation by Rümke, 128, p. 153).

A struggle between the ego and the id does not imply that a man is neurotic (see 128, p. 154, etc.). The cure of the neurosis is not effected by giving up this struggle, by allowing the forces of the id free play, by realizing oneself in life, but in the removal of the pathological repression and its transmission into a conscious control of the id (formulation by Rümke; see 128, pp. 154 f.). Whether or not a man is neurotic is therefore conditional upon the ego. If the struggle between the ego and the id continues, a normal man does not become neurotic and a neurotic man will recover from his neurosis, because the ego does not repress the drives from the id but controls them.

I will go on to apply this view to the concentration camps. Probably all prisoners, including therefore the neurotics among them, soon came to realize the relative insignificance of what once they had thought to be important. The ego which used to get excited about certain tendencies emerging from the id ceased to do so. As the ego began to realize that inside the concentration camp entirely different concerns mattered to it, the ego became more sensible and could control the tendencies of the id with little or no difficulty, so that there was no need for these to be repressed. On the other hand, we must not forget that circumstances were making things easy for the ego. To mention one instance: If a man had become a neurotic as a result of repressing the desire to be unfaithful to his wife as the ego would not acknowledge this desire, then in the concentration camp this would cease to be a circumstance of serious import. Even if the tendency arose, there was no possibility of realizing it, as there were no women in the camp. Moreover, the tendency was very likely not to arise at all, as the prisoner would idealize everything in his former life and therefore also his wife.

Another possibility was that neuroses in the concentration camps disappeared because to the prisoners their confinement assumed the significance of a punishment for their guilt feelings.

It also seems probable that the ego, because it had to spend all its attention on the problems which were part and parcel of confinement in the concentration camps, did not even perceive the tendencies arising from the id.

And finally, I believe that because of the real danger in the external world, within the individual a shift took place in the energy cathexis tied to certain conflicts.

Thus I hope to have provided sufficient explanation why neuroses in the narrower sense did not occur in the concentration camps and why neurotics recovered there.

A similar phenomenon may have influenced the rare occurrence of psychosomatic diseases. Besides the fact that the emotional conflicts specific to these diseases, as indicated by Groen (see this book, p. 65), did not occur in the concentration camps, another fact seems worthy of consideration, namely that the individual directed his attention almost exclusively to his survival, so that these conflicts—if they occurred at all—were considered as of no importance or remained unnoticed. In this condition men walked about with spiritual blinkers, so that other impulses were not perceived.

The disappearance of diseases is not particular to concentration camps; I have often observed it also in normal society. It struck me that during and for a considerable period after the German invasion of the Netherlands the number of sick people in my medical practice showed a sharp decline; this happened again during the tension caused by the war in Korea in 1950.

In conclusion, I believe that the diseases in question are found almost exclusively in normal society, because in this normal society no external tensions, or too few, are felt for the attention of people to be completely absorbed by them. It is also likely to be of importance for people to realize that the blame for these tensions does not rest with them. I do not think it impossible that these factors apply not only to neuroses in the narrower sense and to psychosomatic diseases, but also to the frequency of diseases in general.

One would wish that the attention of people could often and for long periods be occupied by events which are of great moment to all. Perhaps they would take less interest then in being ill, with the possible result that the percentage of sick people would be smaller than it now is. It is deplorable that, to all appearances, this desirable state of affairs should be restricted to tensions inherent in war and the danger of war.

Bibliography

1. Abel, T. The sociology of concentration camps. Lecture given in Section IV b, "Concentration Camps and Persecution of Jews," of the congress "The Second World War in the West." The congress took place in Amsterdam, September 5–9, 1950, under the auspices of the National Institute for War Documents at Amsterdam. The complete text may be found at this institute.

2. Adelsberger, L. Psychologische Beobachtungen im Konzentrationslager Auschwitz. Schweizerische Zeitschrift für Psychologie and ihre Anwendungen. Band VI, 1947.

3. Alexander, F., and Staub, H. Der Verbrecher und seine Richter. Vienna, 1929.

4. Alexander, L. Medical science under dictatorship. New England Journal of Medicine, 241: 39–47 (July 14), 1949.

5. Alexander, L. War crimes. Their social-psychological aspects. American Journal of Psychiatry. Volume 105, No. 3, September 1948.

6. Alexander, L. The molding of personality under dictatorship. Journal of Criminal Law and Criminology of Northwestern University. Volume 40, No. 1, May–June 1949.

7. Alexander, L. War crimes and their motivation. Journal of Criminal Law and Criminology of Northwestern University. Volume 39, No. 3, September–October 1948.

8. Alexander, L. Destructive and self-destructive trends in criminalized society. Journal of Criminal Law and Criminology of Northwestern University. Volume 39, No. 5, January–February 1949.

9. Apfelbaum, E., Chain, J., Guzik, D., Kenigstein, M., Plockier, L., Sack, J., Turkow, J., and Zweibaum, J. Maladie de famine. Recherches cliniques sur la famine exécutées dans le Ghetto

de Varsovie en 1942. American Joint Distribution Committee. Warsaw, 1946.

10. Arntzen, F. I. Psychological observations of prisoners of war. American Journal of Psychiatry. Volume 104, No. 7, 1948.

11. Auschwitz, Deel I: Het Dodenboek van Auschwitz. Headquarters of the Netherlands Red Cross. The Hague, 1947.

12. Auschwitz, Deel II. De deportatietransporten van 15 Juli 1942 tot en met 24 Augustus 1942. Headquarters of the Netherlands Red Cross. The Hague, 1948.

13. Auschwitz, Deel III: De deportatietransporten in de z.g. Coselperiode (28 Augustus tot en met 12 December 1942). Headquarters of the Netherlands Red Cross. The Hague, 1952.

14. Bakels, F. B. Verbeelding als wapen. Haarlem, 1947.

15. Bayle, F. Croix gammée contre caducee. Les expériences humaines en Allemagne pendant la deuxième guerre mondiale. Dépot légal, quatrième trimestre, 1950.

16. Bernstein, F. Der Antisemitismus als Gruppenerscheinung. Berlin, 1926.

17. Bettelheim, B. Individual and mass behavior in extreme situations. Journal of Abnormal and Social Psychology. Volume 38, No. 4, October 1943.

18. Billig, J. L'Allemagne et le génocide. Paris, 1950.

19. Bloch, H. A. The personality of inmates of concentration camps. American Journal of Sociology. Volume LII, 1946/1947.

20. Blu
m, H. O. How did they survive? American Journal of Psychotherapy. Volume II, No. 1, 1948.

21. Boerema, I., et al. Medische ervaringen in Nederland tijdens de bezetting 1940–1945. Groningen/Batavia, 1947.

22. Bok, J. De kliniek der hongerziekte. Dissertatie. Leiden, 1949.

23. Bondy, C. Problems of internment camps. Journal of Abnormal and Social Psychology. Volume 38, No. 4, October 1943.

24. Borst, J. G. G. De betekenis van het dieet en van de bestrijding van infecties bij de behandeling van uraemie. Nederlands Tijdschrift voor Geneeskunde, 1947.

25. Borst, J. G. G. Hongeroedeem twee en een half jaar na de bevrijding. Nederlands Tijdschrift voor Geneeskunde, 1949.

26. Brozek, J., Chapman, C. B., and Keys, A. Drastic food restriction. Journal of the American Medical Association. Volume 137, No. 18, 1948.

27. Bullock, A. Hitler. A study in tyranny. London, 1952.

28. Carp, E. A. D. E. Psychopathologische opsporingen. Amsterdam, 1951.

29. Carp, E. A. D. E., Fortanier, A. H., Plokker, J. H., and Bok, J. C. M. Patho-psychologische bijdragen tot de kennis van het moordprobleem. Lochem, 1948.

30. Cavan, R. S. Suicide. Chicago, 1928.

31. Cayrol, J. Les rêves concentrationnaires. Les Temps Modernes. Paris, Sepember 1948.

32. Central Commission for Investigation of German Crimes in Poland. German crimes in Poland. Warsaw, 1946.

33. Colaço Belmonte, A. Ervaringen uit gevangenkampen op Java en in Japan. Nederlands Tijdschrift voor Geneeskunde, 1945.

34. Coultre, R. le. Het ziektebeeld van de chronische depersonalisatie. Psychiatrische en Neurologische Bladen. Vol. 45.

35. Coultre, R. le. De doodsdrift.

36. Desoille, H., and Lafitte, M. M. Psychologie criminelle des Hitlériens. Paris, 1947.

37. Dollard, J., Miller, N. E., Doob, L. W., Mowrer, O. H., and Sears, R. R. Frustration and Aggression. New Haven, 1939.

38. Dorner, A. Mathematik im Dienste der Nationalpolitischen Erziehung mit Anwendungsbeispielen aus Volkswissenschaft, Geländekunde und Naturwissenschaft. Ein Handbuch für Lehrer. Published by order of the Reichsverband Deutscher mathematischer Gesellschaften und Vereine. Frankfort, 1936, third edition.

39. Dostoievski, F. M. Aus einem Totenhause. Part II, Vol. 18. Munich, 1916.

40. Duncan, G. G., et al. Diseases of metabolism. Philadelphia, 1947.

41. Erikson, E. H. Hitler's imagery and German youth. In C. Kluckhohn and H. A. Murray, Personality in nature, society, and culture. New York, 1949.

42. Federn, E. Essai sur la psychologie de la terreur. Synthèses, No. 7 and No. 8. Brussels, 1946.

43. Federn, E. The terror as a system: The concentration camp. Psychiatric Quarterly. Supplement. Vol. 22, 1948, Part I.

44. Flugel, J. C. Man, Morals and Society. London, 1948.

45. Fortanier, A. H. Over de haat. Nederlands Tijdschrift voor de psychologie en haar grensgebieden. Nieuwe reeks. Deel III, 1948.

46. Frankl, V. E. Ein Psycholog erlebt das K. Z. Vienna, 1947.

47. Freud, A. The ego and the mechanisms of defence. New York, 1946.

48. Freud, A. Introduction to psychoanalysis for teachers. London, 1949.

49. Freud, S. The ego and the id. London, 1927.

49a. Freud, S. Group psychology and the analysis of the ego. London, 1945.

49b. Freud, S. Instincts and their vicissitudes. Collected Papers, Volume IV. London, 1925.

49c. Freud, S. Mourning and melancholia. Collected Papers, Volume IV. London, 1925.

50. Freud, S. Certain neurotic mechanisms in jealousy, paranoia and homosexuality. Collected Papers, Volume II. London, 1924.

51. Freud, S. Introductory lectures on psychoanalysis. London, 1949.

52. Freud, S. Civilization and its discontents. London, 1930.

53. Freud, S. Totem and taboo. New York, 1952.

54. Freud, S. Moses and monotheism. London, 1951.

55. Friedman, F. This was Oswiecim. London, 1946.

56. Friedman, P. Some aspects of concentration camp psychology. American Journal of Psychiatry. Volume 105, No. 8, February 1949.

57. Friedman, P. The road back for the D.P.'s. Commentary. Volume 6, No. 6. December 1948.

58. Gagern, F. von. Der Retter von Mauthausen. Vienna, 1948.

59. Gebhardt, H. Grundrisz der Pharmakologie, Toxikologie (Wehrtoxikologie) und Arznei-Verordnungslehre. Munich, 1940.

60. Gilbert, G. M. Nuremberg Diary. New York, 1947.

61. Gilbert, G. M. The psychology of dictatorship. New York, 1950.

62. Gollwitzer, H. Und Führen wohin du nicht willst. Munich, 1952.

63. Greiner, J. Das Ende des Hitler-Mythos. Vienna, 1947.

64. Groen, J. De Psychopathogenese van het ulcus ventriculi et duodeni; karakterstructuren en emotionele belevenissen en hun betekenis voor aetiologie en therapie. Amsterdam, 1947.

65. Groen, J., Horst, L. van der, Bastiaans, J., Valk, J. M. van der, and Vles, S. J. Organisatie, werkterrein en enkele uitkomsten van de werkgroep voor psychosomatisch onderzoek in het Wilhelmina-Gasthuis te Amsterdam. Nederlands Tijdschrift voor Geneeskunde, 1950.

65a. Per Helweg-Larsen, et al. Famine diseases in German concentration camps. Complications and sequels. Acta Medica Scandinavica. Supplement CCLXXIV (274). Copenhagen, 1952.

66. Herzberg, A. J. Amor Fati. Amsterdam, 1946.

67. Herzberg, A. J. Tweestromenland. Arnhem, 1950.

68. Herzberg, A. J. Kroniek der Jodenvervolging. "Onderdrukking en Verzet." Arnhem/Amsterdam. Parts 23–26, inclusive.

69. Heyden, P. M. van der. Nazi-mentaliteit en geestelijke volksgezondheid. Groningen/Batavia, 1949.

70. Hitler, A. Mein Kampf. Translated and annotated by James Murphy. London, 1936.

71. Hitschmann, E. The history of the aggression-impulse. The Yearbook of Psychoanalysis. Volume 4. London, 1948.

72. Hoop, J. H. van der. Nieuwe richtingen in de zielkunde. Arnhem, 1948.

73. Hottinger, A., Gsell, O., Uehlinger, E., Salzmann, C., Labhart, A. Hungerkrankheit, Hungerödem, Hungertuberkulose. Basel, 1948.

74. Houwink, R. H. Enkele beschouwingen over Freudiaanse ethnologie, in het bijzonder over Freud's theorie betreffende het Totemisme. Mens en Maatschappij. Jaargang 26, No. 1.

75. Hunsche, J. F. PDA; waarin: Kort verslag van het verblijf van 85 Amsterdamse gijzelaars in het "Polizeiliches Durchgangslager Amersfoort." Amsterdam, 30 January–20 April, 1942.

76. Jaspers, K. Die Schuldfrage. Zurich, 1946.

77. Jung, C. G. Aufsätze zur Zeitgeschichte. Zurich, 1946.

78. Kaas, A. J. W. Over de psychologie der politieke gevangenen in het concentratiekamp. De nieuwe stem. Jaargang I, Aflevering 6, 1946.

79. Kaas, A. J. W. De Duitse concentratiekampen. "Onderdrukking en Verzet." Arnhem/Amsterdam. Aflevering 10.

80. Kars, H. J. Enige beschouwingen en gegevens, naar aanleiding van de uit Duitsland gerepatrieerde inwoners van 's-Gravenhage, welke tot 1 Januari 1946 op het consultatiebureau ter bestrijding ter tuberculose aldaar, bekend werden. Nederlands Tijdschrift voor Geneeskunde, 1946.

81. Kautsky, B. Teufel und Verdammte. Zurich, 1946.

82. Kelley, D. M. 22 cells in Nuremberg. London, 1947.

83. Kersten, F. Klerk en Beul. Amsterdam, 1948.

84. Keys, A., Brozek, J., Henschel, A., Mickelsen, O., and Taylor, H. L. Experimental starvation in man. Laboratory of Physiological Hygiene, University of Minnesota, 15 October, 1945.

85. Keys, A., Brozek, J., Henschel, A., Michelsen, O., and Taylor, H. L. Rehabilitation following experimental starvation in man. Laboratory of Physiological Hygiene, University of Minnesota. 15 January, 1946.

86. K. L. Bu. Bericht des internationalen Lagerkomitees Buchenwald. Weimar.

87. Kogon, E. Der SS-Staat. Stockholm, 1947.

88. Kolff, W. J. De Dieetbehandeling van uraemie. Geneeskundige Gids, 1949.

89. Kouwenaar, W., et al. Geneeskundige waarnemingen in de interneringskampen op Noord-Sumatra, 1942–1945. Geneeskundige Bladen uit Kliniek en Laboratorium voor de praktijk. 42e reeks. No. I/II.

90. Kremer, H. H. Dagboek. A photocopy of this may be found at the National Institute for War Documents at Amsterdam.

91. Kunz, H. Die Aggressivität und die Zärtlichkeit. Berne, 1946.

92. Kurth, G. M. The Jew and Adolf Hitler. The Yearbook of Psychoanalysis. Volume 4, 1948.

93. Langen, C. D. de. De lage Basaalstofwisseling, haar kliniek en behandeling. Geneeskundige Bladen uit Kliniek en Laboratorium voor de praktijk, 43e reeks, XII.

94. Langen, C. D. de. Verdwenen hypertensies. Nederlands Tijdschrift voor Geneeskunde, 1947.

95. Langen, C. D. de. De dagelijkse calorieenbehoefte van de mens. Nederlands Tijdschrift voor Geneeskunde, 1949.

96. Law Reports of Trials of War Criminals: Selected and prepared by the United Nations War Crimes Commission. English Edition. Volume II. The Belsen Trial. London, 1947.

97. Ibid. Volume VII. London, 1948.

98. Lehrer, L. The Jewish elements in the psychology of the Jewish child in America. Yivo Annual of Jewish Social Science, Volume I. New York, 1946.

99. Lengyel, O. Five chimneys. Chicago/New York, 1947.

100. Letheby Tidy, H., and Browne Kutschbach, J. M. Inter-allied conferences on war medicine 1942–1945. New York, 1947.

101. Lettich, A. A. D. Trente-quatre mois dans les camps de concentration. Temoignage sur les crimes "scientifiques" commis par les médecins allemands. Thèse Faculté de médecine de Paris, 1946.

102. Lingens-Reiner, E. Prisoners of fear. London, 1948.

103. Loghem, J. J. van. Nederlandse statistische gegevens over de eerste helft van het jaar 1940. Nederlands Tijdschrift voor Geneeskunde, 1940.

104. Losekoot, A. Document uit Dachau: De Stem der Lage Landen; orgaan der Nederlanders in Dachau (van 2 Mei tot 25 Mei 1945). Edited by E. Hoornik, N. Rost, M. van Hasselt, J. Vis. Amsterdam.

105. Löwenstein, R. M. Christians and Jews. New York, 1951.

106. Melkman, J. Israel. Amsterdam/Brussels, 1949.

107. Meyler, L. De behandeling van thyreotoxicoses. Nederlands Tijdschrift voor Geneeskunde, 1937.

108. Minkowski, E. Les conséquences psychologiques et psychopathologiques de la guerre et du nazisme. Archives Suisse de Neurologie et de Psychiatrie. Volume LXI, 1948.

109. Mitscherlich, A., and Mielke, F. Doctors of infamy, translated by Heinz Norden. New York, 1949.

110. Mitscherlich, A. and Mielke, F. Wissenschaft ohne Menschlichkeit. Heidelberg, 1949.

111. Mollison, P. L. Observations on cases of starvation at Belsen (an abstract of a report to DMS 21 Army Group). British Medical Journal, 1946.

112. Monneray, H. La persécution des Juifs dans les Pays de l'Est présentée à Nuremberg. Paris, 1949.

113. Mulock Houwer, D. Q. R. Enige aspecten betreffende het probleem der jeugdige politieke delinquenten. Psychiatrisch-Juridisch Gezelschap, No. 28.

114. Musaph, H. Doodsdrift, castratiecomplex en depressie. Dissertatie. Amsterdam, 1948.

115. Nederland in Oorlogstijd: Orgaan van het Rijksinstituut voor Oorlogsdocumentatie te Amsterdam. February, 1947.

116. Ibid. March 1950.

117. Nyiszli, M. S.S. Obersturmführer Docteur Mengele. Les Temps Modernes. Paris, March/April 1951.

118. Padover, S. K. Experiment in Germany. New York, 1946.

119. Pfister, M. Vorläufige Mitteilung über psychologische Untersuchungen an Flüchtlingen. Bulletin der Schweizerischen Akademie der medizinischen Wissenschaften. Volume 2, 1946/1947.

120. Pfister-Ammende, M., et al. Die Psychohygiene. In P. Federn and H. Meng, Bücher des Werdenden. Volume II, Berne, 1949.

121. Poliakov, L. Breviaire de la haine. Paris, 1951.

122. Rapport van de commissie van onderzoek in zake het verstrekken van pakketten door het Rode Kruis en andere instanties aan Nederlandse politieke gevangenen in het buitenland gedurende de bezettingstijd alsmede inzake het evacueren van Nederlandse gevangenen kort voor en na het einde van de oorlog. Published by the Netherlands Red Cross. The Hague, 1947.

122a. Reitlinger, G. The final solution. The attempt to exterminate the Jews of Europe 1939–1945. Valentine, Mitchell. London, 1953.

123. Reiwald, P. Zur Psychologie der Massenaggression. Schweizerische Zeitschrift fur Psychologie und ihre Anwendungen. Volume IV, No. 1, 1945.

124. Röling, B. V. A. Over psychologische aspecten van het proces tegen de Japanse "Major War Criminals," te Tokyo. Psychiatrisch-Juridisch Gezelschap, No. 32.

125. Rosencher, H. Medicine in Dachau. British Medical Journal, 1946.

126. Rose, N. Goethe in Dachau. Amsterdam, 1946.

127. Rousset, D. L'univers concentrationnaire. Paris, 1946.

128. Rümke, H. C. Studies en voordrachten over psychiatrie. Amsterdam, 1948.

129. Sauvage Nolting, W. J. J. de. Gedachten over honger- en liefdedrift. Nederlands Tijdschrift voor de psychologie en haar grensgebieden. Nieuwe reeks, Deel III, 1948. Aflevering 6.

130. Schwarz, F. Probleme des Selbstmordes. Berne, 1946.

131. S.H.A.E.F. The German Police, April, 1945.

132. Sherif, M. An outline of social psychology. New York, 1948.

133. Simmel, E., et al. Anti-semitism. A social disease. New York, 1946.

134. Sobibor. Publication of the Headquarters of the Netherlands Red Cross. The Hague, 1947.

135. Soviet Government Statements on Nazi Atrocities. London.

136. Speyer, N. Bijdrage tot de kennis van de energetisch-psychologische gronds-lagen van de zelfmoord. Dissertatie. Rotterdam, 1935.

137. Spritzer, J. Ich war nr. 10291. Zurich.

138. Tas, J. Het raadsel van Bergen Belsen. Vrij Nederland. 3 November 1945.

139. Tas, J. Psychical disorders among inmates of concentration camps and repatriates. The Psychiatric Quarterly. Vol. 25, No. 4, October, 1951.

140. Taylor, T. Final report to the Secretary of the Army on the Nuremberg War Crimes Trials under Control Council Law No. 10. U. S. Government Printing Office, Washington. 15 August, 1949.

141. Trevor-Roper, H. R. The last days of Hitler. New York, 1951.

142. Trial of the Major War Criminals before the International Military Tribunal. Official text in the English language. Published at Nuremberg, 1947.

143. Trials of War Criminals before the Nürnberg Military Tribunals under Control Council Law No. 10. U. S. Government Printing Office. Washington. Volumes I, II (pp. 1–353), "The Medical Case."

144. Ibid. Volume IV, to p. 597: "The Einsatzgruppen Case."

144a. Ibid. Volume V, pp. 193 ff. "The Pohl Case."

145. Utitz, E. Psychologie des Lebens im Konzentrationslager Theresienstadt. Vienna, 1948.

146. Vischer, A. L. Die Stacheldraht-Krankheit. Zurich, 1918.

147. Vogel, L. Dagboek uit een kamp. The Hague, 1946.

148. Vries, P. de. Geschiedenis van het verzet der artsen in Nederland. Haarlem, 1949.

149. Vroom, M. G. Schrik, angst en vrees. Dissertatie. Den Helder, 1942.

150. Vrijhof, P. H. Psychologische beschouwingen over concentra-

tiekampen. Nederlands Tijdschrift voor de psychologie en haar grensgebieden. Nieuwe reeks, Deel III, 1948. Aflevering 1.

151. Waals, H. G. van der. Verwikkelingen door schuldgevoel. Nederland Tijdschrift voor de psychologie en haar grensgebieden. Nieuwe reeks, Deel III, 1948. Aflevering 1.

152. Weyel, J. A. De vernietiging der Joden in Polen. Haarlem/ Barendrecht.

153. Wielek, H. De oorlog die Hitler won. Amsterdam, 1947.

154. Wilde, H. Sozialpsychologische Erfahrungen aus dem Lagerleben. Zurich, 1946.

155. Wind, E. de. Eindstation . . . Auschwitz. Amsterdam, 1946.

156. Wind, E. de. Confrontatie met de dood. Overgedrukt uit "Folia Psychiatrica, Neurologica et Neurochirurgica Neerlandica," Jaargang 1949, No. 6.

157. Wulfften-Palthe, P. M. van. Neuro-psychiatric experiences in Japanese internment camps in Java. Documenta Neerlandica et Indonesica de Morbis Tropicis. Volume II, No. 2, June 1950.

This new edition of
Human Behaviour in the Concentration Camp
was finished in October 1988.

The new material was commissioned,
edited and copy-edited by Ann Scott,
and produced by Martin Klopstock and Selina O'Grady
for Free Association Books.

It was printed on a Miller TP41 onto
80g/m² vol 17.5 New Edition Cream Antique Wove.